About the author

Nabil Shaban was born in 1953 in Amman, Jordan and arri[illegible] for treatment for his osteogenesis imperfecta (brittle-[illegible] Tomlinson founded **Graeae** (pronounced Grey Eye) [illegible] performers. A writer and performer with many film [illegible] known to television viewers for his role as ruthless [illegible] Who stories **Vengeance on Varos**, and **Trial of** [illegible] **Mission to Magnus** (Big Finish Audio, 2009). On sta[illegible], and Jesus in **Godspell**, Haille Sellassie in **The Emperor** [illegible] Iranian **Nights**, the storyteller Rashid in the Royal National Thea[illegible] Salman Rushdie's **Haroun and the Sea of Stories** (1998), Mack the Knife [illegible] Workshop's production of Brecht's **Threepenny Opera**.....for which he was nomina[illegible] Critics' Best Actor in Scottish Theatre (2004-2005). He played Hamm in Becket's **Endgame** (2007/8) and Marquis de Sade in Peter Weiss **Marat/ Sade**. He played Siegfried in his own play, **The First To Go**, about disabled people in Nazi Germany, which toured Scotland in 2008. He played Emperor Constantius in Ibsen's "Emperor and Galilean" (Royal National Theatre, 2011). He has performed in such movies as **City of Joy** (d. Roland Joffe, 1991), **Wittgenstein** (d. Derek Jarman, 1992) and **Born of Fire** (d. Jamil Dehlavi, 1988), and on television in **Walter** (d. Stephen Frears 1982) and **Deptford Graffiti** (d. Phil Davis 1991). More recently, he appeared in **Children of Men** (2006), **Trouble Sleeping** (d. Robert Rae 2007) and **Morticia** (d. Nabil Shaban 2009).

Nabil Shaban is a political actor and has worked in plays about Palestine (**The Little Lamp**, 1999 and **Jasmine Road**, 2003), and about the State murder of Northern Ireland lawyer, Rosemary Nelson (**Portadown Blues**, 2000). Also **D.A.R.E.** (disabled terrorists opposed to genetic cleansing of disabled people) (1997-2004). Shaban has written and presented several documentaries on themes of disability, including the Emmy award winning **Skin Horse** (Channel 4, 1983), about disability and sexuality, the **Fifth Gospel** (BBC, 1990), exploring the relationship between the Christian gospels and disability. He also instigated and presented the Without Walls documentary: **Supercrips and Rejects** (Channel 4, 1996), about Hollywood's representation of disabled people. Also in a Secret History documentary **The Strangest Viking** (Channel 4, 2003), he argued the case that Ivarr the Boneless was a disabled viking leader.

Shaban's radio work includes writing and presenting a six part series on the life of **Gandhi** (BBC World Service 1984). Playing Benn Gunn in BBC Radio 4; **Treasure Island** (1994) and Jaturi the vulture in BBC Radio 2; **The Ramayan** (1994).

Shaban's voice was used in English version of Werner Herzog's movie **Cobra Verde**. In 1995, he founded **Sirius Pictures** to make video arts documentary **Another World**. This was followed in 1997 by the award-winning **The Alien Who Lived in Sheds** (BBC, 1997) which he wrote, directed and starred in. He produced, wrote and directed a music film, **Crip Triptych** (2006). He also produced, wrote and directed a short drama film, **Morticia** (2009), about a little girl who wants to be a vampire.

Shaban's written plays include **The First To Go** (about disabled people in Germany's Third Reich) and **I am the Walrus** (about a schizophrenic who believes he made Mark Chapman assassinate John Lennon). Shaban has worked as dramaturg for Theatre Workshop's commission of Ghazi Hussein's play **One Hour to Sun Rise** (2005), as well as contracted as assistant director for the rehearsed reading and Theatre Workshop's production of Robert Rae's 2005 Christmas Show **A Christmas Tale of Hans Christian Andersen**. Nabil Shaban, who has a degree in Psychology and Philosophy, was awarded an honorary doctorate from the University of Sorry for the achievements of his career and his work to change public perceptions of disabled people. In 2005 Nabil Shaban published his first book, **Dreams My Father Sold Me**, an anthology of thirty years of his artwork and poetry, with a foreword by Lord Richard Attenborough. Other books published include **The First To Go** (2007), and a crime novel, **The Ripper Code** (2008).

Also by Nabil Shaban
DREAMS MY FATHER SOLD ME
THE FIRST TO GO
THE RIPPER CODE

D.A.R.E.
a play about the Disabled Anarchist Revolutionary Enclave
(written with Daryl Beeton, John Hollywood, Jim McSharry, Robert Rae)

Nabil Shaban
Diary of the Absurd

Sirius Book Works publishing

First published in United Kingdom in 2012
by Sirius Book Works publishing

ISBN 9780954829438

Printed and bound in Ireland by Hudson Killeen

Sirius Book Works publishing

6 Vaucluse Place
Jackson Street
Penicuik, EH26 9BF
SCOTLAND

Nabil Shaban

Diary of the Absurd

Note from the Editor

It is 353 years since "Diary of the Absurd" was written, and still all that is known about its author, Shiram Labif, is what can be gleaned from the diary's pages. Sorry.

Diary of the Absurd

PERSONAL NOTES

Name...... *Shiram Labif*

Address...
53 Karma Close, Wellingtonia, England, Dis-United Kingdom, EU

Telephone: *Obsolete – use telepathy*
Mobile: *Brain fried*
Fax: *There are no facts, only perceptions.*
Email: *Hacked + virus-fucked by CIA, MI5, Freemasons, Mafia and ET*

Business Address: *none of your fucking business*
Business Telephone: *Forget it. Only automated voices left to speak to. Never a human being at the other end. Just menu choices.*

Bank Telephone: *Banks are legal thieves. Keep away from them.*
Credit Card: *Credit cards are for morons who like to be robbed.*

National Identity Card No. *EL/07/28/53 X*
National Insurance No. *Abolished. The State has absolved itself of all health and welfare responsibilities*
Passport No. *National borders control obsolete (I wish)*
Okay, I'll tell you - ELX 1075364928
Driving Licence No. *EL/07/28/53 X*
Car Registration No. *N353 WEL*

IN CASE OF EMERGENCY PLEASE CONTACT:
Name: *whichever God (or Goddess) you believe in*
Address: *Everywhere and nowhere...but probably within you*
Home Telephone: *888*
Business Telephone: *666*
Mobile: *Very*
Doctor: *Who?*
Known Allergies..... *Capitalism, Religion, USA, Conservatives, junk food, Hollywood, popular television, Sky channel, FOX, Extra-terrestrials*

January
1 Friday

"She's gone without me!" I cried. And I cried. And I cried. Two years without end. Laura has gone without me. Where? How? Why? Did she die? It has remained, to this day, a mystery.

And why did the alarm go off at 7:53 this morning? I didn't set it for 7:53. I had set it for 8. I know I did. Weird. Bloody weird.

Jesus, that was a close shave. Heard on the news - China has backed down from starting WW3 because USA have developed a new nuclear missile which upon exploding, sprouts an extra war head and flies low level to the next target.
And each time a warhead explodes, a new one takes its place.

A sort of Hydra-gen bomb.

HAPPY NEW YEAR. Will I live to see the end of it?

January
2 Saturday

A terrible, evil blackness. Thicker than glue, started to envelope me. There was something tempting about it. Seductive in a sensual way. But I knew that that way would lead to madness, chaos, the abyss. As I pulled back from the brink. I began to suffocate. Suddenly, a shining sword appeared in my hand, a black-hilted masonic sword, named "Don Alda Light" and I thrust upwards, shouting in defiant triumph "I am for Christ!". With that, the darkness was split asunder and light came.

How embarrassing!
Why did I proclaim such nonsensical words.
How ridiculous.
Absurd.
Because everyone knows I gave up being Christian years ago.

January
3 Sunday

Heard today that my old boss, Rocks Handy was killed on Saturday by a Chinamen. Had his head smashed in with a paper weight.

Funny that...because it was on Friday, at the New Year Eve party, Ferdinand and Delilah were telling me of their plans to visit China.

I was yet again having problems driving my invalid carriage. The bloody "Crip Machine" was picking up speed whenever I tried to bring it to a halt. Eventually I managed to park my "Blue Dalek" beside a lamp post and switched off the ignition. I look at the mile-ometer. It reads 66,653 miles. (53 again). I got out and waited for rescue by the Automobile Association.

After sitting around for quite awhile, someone came up behind me, and started to longingly caress me. I turned and saw this rather sad, lonely and yet still attractive woman. She seemed very nervous about touching me. I smiled at her, and she immediately relaxed. It was then that I recognized her. It was Laura, my ex-lover.

"Thank you" she said, grateful of my spontaneously benign response to her reaching out to me. At last, I had stopped giving her the steel blue eye treatment (for dumping me) as if she was a total stranger. She also thanked me for the postcard I had sent her from Russia.

The night sky. I see the stars on a clear cloudless night. My eye catches a red light. Is it a planet? Mars? I'm tempted to think it is a UFO but I refuse to. It is now moving. Too fast for a planet. Wrong colour for a meteorite or shooting star. Besides, it's moving upwards. A plane? But no flashing - just a constant red light. Common sense forces me to deny it UFO status. I move on with the question unresolved as usual.

January
4 Monday

Postman trying to push letter through the keyhole. The police arrive to help him, using their combined weight to force the mail through the tiny aperture. It looks like they will break the door down with the amount of violent exertion they are throwing into the effort. Eventually the letter passes through and lands on the floor. The postman sticks his head through the cat flap to check that the item has been successfully delivered.

It's a letter warning me that there's a warrant for my arrest, and that an enforcement officer will be coming in the next few days to take me into custody.
I decide to do nothing. It's probably a wind-up.

January
5 Tuesday

My theatre group, CYCLOPS, went to the mental hospital to give a performance of "Freaks". I may have started out as a visiting actor but quickly became a member of staff. Why? Because the staff had seriously upset the patients. As a result, the patients had turned into rampaging and irrational beasts. They were going to tear us all apart. There were too many of them, and too few of us. We were doomed. We hid behind tables in a locked room, the staff room, but we knew they could easily break in, and there would be no escape for us. We waited shaking with fear. When they get in, there will be a short struggle and maybe some of them will die but in the end we will all perish. Some of the more gung-ho staff suggested guns, but I said "No". I had pity on the Mob outside (I mean, it wasn't so long ago that I was one of them). I argued there has to be a peaceful way out for all of us. I suggested that I go out and face the Mob alone and try to reason with them. "We can't just sit in idleness and helplessness behind this pathetic protection of these upturned tables. Let's face it, you have nothing to lose by letting me go and meet the Mob." Finally everyone agreed with my suggestion, and so I ventured out into the ward to chance my luck. The lunatics were surprised by my approach and were soon persuaded that we meant them no harm. I was soon playing games with them and eventually the besieged staff tentatively emerged from their shelters. I was congratulated by all. Eventually we did the show, which was a great success.

Later at about 10:30 pm I was travelling back from the hospital in the mini-bus with Kyles and others from the cast. I was seated at the back of the bus, and saw behind some tall buildings, a moving red light, low in the sky. Not high from skyscrapers, left to right (anti-clockwise?) below the red light, a cluster of white lights in quarter circle slowly revolve around it. In the bank of lights I had the impression that a word or words were inscribed but could not make them out. (May have been "Wake Up"). It was a beautiful spectacle, reminding me of a fabulous flying multi-tiered chandelier, a hovering diamond encrusted tiara. Or better still, how I imagined the Holy Grail must have appeared to King Arthur and his knights of the Round Table. The craft circled the buildings and was crossing over the road behind us. Then we drove out of sight.

I pointed it out to the others but only Kyles saw it. He was frightened and told me it was like the one he had seen two nights previous from the bus. "It looks like the Holy Grail," I said, "It is said that if you see the Holy Grail, then you have become too pure for this world and must shortly die." This scared Kyles even more. He had also dreamed about them when we were touring the USA. To him, it signified the End of the World. In his dream, first there was one and then the sky was full, which brought Peace upon him because he knew it was the Second Coming.

Kyles is a Born Again Christian.

January
6 Wednesday

Today I went with my best mate, Igor, on a sort of "Holy Grail" Quest, and we journeyed across a desert. Later we parted company and Igor goes off to build an oasis, and then a great city which he called Waters of the Moon. I continued the Quest in my own way. I didn't understand what the goal was but it had something to do with becoming a camel! At the end of the path, approaching twilight I saw a split-screen, as seen in films, of a desert horizon. The sky was red and the sand grey. On the horizon on the lower picture was the silhouette of a long camel train. I looked up at the upper picture and saw the same horizon except that there were only two camels going from left to right. Looking on from the outside (I must have been having an OOBE, "out of body experience") I surmised that the two camels were Igor and me.

Did we fulfil the Quest?

I think we had since both the train of camels and the pair were shrouded in a blue aura.

Later.

On page 53 of "Kabbalistic Aphorisms" by James Sturzaker, I found a possible meaning of why Igor and I had become camels for a short time. It seems we were on the Thirteenth Path of the Kabbalah which is GIMEL.
CAMEL in Hebrew is GIMEL, which is the 3rd letter of the Hebrew alphabet… and is the 3rd card in the Tarot pack - represented by the High Priestess.
The Camel carries the Waters of Wisdom.
"It is easier for a Camel to pass through the eye of a needle…." Blah blah….It also said that Blue is the ray of Love and Wisdom.

The book says a lot more about the significance of being a camel but I can't be arsed to write it all down here. We were camels for only a couple of minutes, anyway.

January
7 Thursday

The Man (someone like the fictional Dr Hannibal Lecter – the notorious Cannibal) was in the cavernous lecture theatre.

And I was alone....

Later in Chipping Norton, I saw a flying saucer. It was daylight, and the UFO was flying from the right to the left. It was dark in colour.

Why did I notice that the movie “One flew over the cuckoo’s nest” is 2hours 53mins long?
There’s that “53” again?

First I dreamed of her life, but I don’t know her. Then I awoke and watched her live the life I had dreamed. I saw how she could not avoid doing exactly the course that had been predetermined…but by whom? Fate? Her Karma? Me? But when I watched her live her life for the second time, there was a slight difference. Before it was like watching a movie. I was simply an objective observer. However, witnessing her re-enactment or replay of her life, I experienced her thought processes, and saw the illusory nature of her decision-making. She believed she had a choice, imagined that she was choosing but it wasn’t so, because I had already seen the film of her life, I knew she was never independent, that she was never acting out of her own free will.

January
8 Friday

The old answer machine comes to life.
What answer machine? I don't have one anymore.
Clunk-click-whirr.....
"Uncle Shiram, it's, eh....." ("Oh its shit...") or ("Unger-nitzu-rum...") or (Uxmal, Chichen Itza)
or (Jacinta Groser? But I'm not her uncle. She's old enough to be my aunt)
.....The ("Polly"?) parrot cuts in...
"Pieces of Eight"
Silence

I ponder upon this strange message and see that it's 8:53 in the morning.

Igor and I go to the cinema to see a Western, starring Clint Eastwood and Paul Newman. They were a pair of adventurers. Paul was going on a train journey across the Rocky Mountains. I and the girl (Igor's sister, Zinaidi) decide to see him off. Igor (I will call him Clint) also went with us, but only I saw Clint (let us call him Igor) get on the train with Paul. She was looking the other way. He had to go. The need was great and there was no dissuading him, even though I knew disaster would await him. The girl said goodbye and we went back home.
Then it started to go dark. I could hear the approaching rumble and drone as the train's rattle disappeared into the distance. I could see and hear.... and knew.
The dog, Leonie, she knew.... her howling got louder and merged with the drone.
Soon the girl became aware of the impending doom. Paul had been killed but only the dog and I knew that Clint (aka Igor) went with him. I saw the obituary on the back of a record sleeve. And as I read the scant lines I heard my thoughts cry out to the girl, Zinaidi.... "IGOR/SHIRAM WENT WITH HIM!"

January
9 Saturday

Driving along in my Spaz-Wagon, an old black car cuts in front of me, nearly causing me to swerve off the road. The registration number was X753 UPC.

That's interesting. The number 53 in the driver's number. Why do I keep seeing 53? Every time I look at the time, it's always the 53rd minute past the hour…or cars with 53 on their licence plates keep forcing their way into my consciousness…or the book I'm reading has the most important point on page 53 (or 253 or 353 etc.). What's going on? What is the meaning of "53"? Is it trying to tell me something?

Later that evening. We were all in church and we had all been there for some time. Our theatre workshop formed the congregation. Samuel Soap, the workshop leader, gave me a hymn to sing solo . I couldn't find the hymn that he wanted me to sing. So I tried to interest him in another one but he orders me to keep searching. Eventually I find it but I didn't know how to sing it. In the end he relents and said I could sing the song I first wanted to sing, but then, to my horror, I was unable to find that one either. Everyone else was made to stay until I found it. But I just couldn't locate the damn song. Samuel kept nagging me, so I was getting flustered and sweaty. The congregation got restless and threatening. We waited hours but no matter how many times I leafed through the hymn book, I still failed to find it. And all the while, Samuel was making it worse for me by letting forth an incessant stream of sarcastic comments. Eventually at 11:53pm, he backs down and suggests that the congregation may depart if they wish. But no one got up, they were all reluctant. They had great difficulty in making themselves go. Finally some do. Samuel then asks the others why they refused to follow. At first, there's no reply, just a hostile and menacing atmosphere. Just when it looked particularly grim for Samuel and me, one of their number came forward and spoke. "We would have all walked out, if religion had not been brought into it," he grumbled.

January
10 Sunday

Got a letter from unknown disabled girl. Seems to be slightly backward. She was asking me to marry her. Out of pity (PC?) for her I agree. Immediately, her overjoyed family organize the wedding arrangements. They want me to marry her tomorrow …before I change my mind.
And yes, already I've started to get cold feet.
However, my honour won't allow me to back out.

Zinaidi rang me. As I expected, the time was 53 minutes past something. (9:53am) Wanted to know if I had had any word from her brother, Igor. Had to say "no".

Found a coin in the toilet. Silver shilling it was. "Must be 1953". It bloody well was. Jesus, this is getting weird. The last electric bill was 53 pounds exactly.

Bringing up an Alsatian puppy in my flat is not easy.. it kept shitting on the carpet. I didn't want to hurt it to teach it a lesson and I endeavoured to be gentle with it. But, nonetheless, I found it dead on the floor. As I wept over its corpse, confused as to how it could have died. I heard the U.S. President on TV being interviewed. She was giving assurances that in her determined attempts to release the hostages she would not resort to military actions as she had no wish to precipitate a third world war. This came as a surprise to us all since she'd once been in favour of nuking Karachi. That was her election campaign promise.

Phone rang at 9.53pm. Must be Igor, I thought. It was. He's back.

The Four Horrors.
What are they?
Igor said they have something to do with the occult.
Are "the four horrors" the Four Horsemen of the Apocalypse?

Checked my Passport and noticed the Yank visa number has a "53" in it.
- US visa no. 124530. Hmm.

January
11 Monday

Igor rang at 8.53 this morning. His sister, Zinaidi, has tried to commit suicide by taking an overdose of heroine…heroin…heron. She and her boyfriend, Spitz, were tripping on acid and decided to engage in a mutual suicide pact. Igor found them both, locked in their bedroom, puking green slime with hypos stuck in their arms. Zinaidi is now in hospital.
"Her ward number is 153A, if you want to visit her," said Igor.

Midday
Flying high over a mountain range in eastern Turkey, I see five peaks all flattened and circular, like extinct volcanoes but suggestive of landing pads or heliports. I realise these table top mountains are for UFOs to land.

The silver cord pulls me back home and I watch the cop movie "Sweeney 2"; they were searching for a particular villain, went to his old school to dig into his files. I thought to myself, "I bet he was born in 1953. The Sweeny Todd will bring out the box labelled "53" I was initially disappointed when, instead, the box marked "52" was brought out. "Nah", said John Thaw, "Wrong year", and they brought him "53". YES.

More 53s

- Igor's Dad was 53 when he died and I met his Mum when she was 53
- drivers licence no. P853/4
- council reference number is 530085023
- Air Canada flight no. vr 0153 es

Nocturnal Attack by Succubi. I was lying on my back paralysed - with Ulrike, the dwarf girl, sitting on my chest and my baby sister, Fay, on my left chewing my fingers. They were both evil. Ulrike was pressing her fingers on my wind-pipe. I tried to tell her to stop but she just pressed even harder and with such glee. I was terrified. Then I realised they weren't really Ulrike and Fay, but demons or aliens in disguise (they both had dark rings around their eyes). At which point, they vanished.

January
12 Tuesday

I went out (to go to the hospital to visit Zinaidi) and saw three babies of different ages, waddling along the street. Innocent and oblivious to possible dangers and reckless drivers. Some people pass them by unsurprised. I stopped to listen to the people's conversations as the babies chatted among themselves. The babies' names were SHADRACH, MESHACH and ABEDNEGO. I crept up behind the smallest (MESHACH) and popped it into my mouth. Within seconds I had crushed it to death in my jaws. I was so surprised and ashamed of my infanticide I wanted to spit out the remains in disgust but the other people were there. I don't think they had seen me gobble the baby up but they soon became aware that one was missing, and started calling blue murder and sent out a search party. With my mouth tightly clenched not daring to utter an opinion on the disappearance, I guiltily gulped the masticated body down into my belly, knowing that I could never be found out. Eventually the Lynch mob found a pair of scapegoats, with circumstantial incriminating evidence on them. Apparently, the couple had wanted to wreak revenge on the babies' parents. I kept quiet whilst the police went through the items to be used in evidence against the couple. Some of the items were mine and could have indicted me, but everyone assumed that the scapegoats had nicked them from me. The scapegoats were released on bail but had nowhere to stay. They had been dispossessed of everything. I offered them my flat for the night. The lady-suspect immediately agreed. I could see she was lusting after me. She demanded my bed whilst her husband sadly volunteered to sleep on the sofa. As the woman sneered and smeared her body on my bed sheets, I told her I was sleeping in my bed and if she was sharing it with me, she would have to accept the consequences. "I'd hoped you would say that," she replied. That was when I knew she knew I was the baby killer. And she was going to compound my sins by allowing me to fuck her in front of her husband. He may be sent to the gallows tomorrow and will be cuckolded tonight before his very eyes - but God will preserve his innocence. And my guilt, when I die, will torment me for all eternity.

January
13 Wednesday

Message left on my phantom answer machine - "Hello my name is Wolf Light from 'White Witches Against Cruel Sports'. Did you know that beagle pups are trained on baby hares? We're organising a hunt sabotage on Saturday. Yvonne gave me your name. Ring this number if you are interested in coming along. - 315355"
....Maybe I'll go, coz there's a 53
...and I like her name, "Wolf Light"
.....I'm mad about wolves.

It was supposed to be my wedding to the disabled girl today (I don't know why I have to say "disabled girl" when I'm also a cripple. What am I? Some closet "Body Fascist"?), but I got called away to Paris. However, I did book a return flight that would get to me to the church on time. But whilst in Paris, the snows began and my plane was grounded. So I wasn't able to attend my own wedding. The girl is going to be bitterly disappointed. She'll think I rejected her. I thought of sending the family a telegram, explaining the hold up, and apologize to her for the wedding cock up. Visions of a humiliated bride and empty reception haunt my conscience.
Eventually I did get a later flight but I'd forgotten to send the telegram. I curse my insensitivity. When I arrived back home in the middle of the night, I found Sam Soap, my boss, and Laura, my ex-girlfriend, sleeping in my bed. Naturally, they were surprised and embarrassed by my arrival. However, I was still too disturbed by my absence at my own wedding. That poor little cripple girl (Stop it, Labif, you patronising hypocritical wanker) must be heart broken.

Restless night, I am still indecisive about this jilted girl problem. I get up and drive to London, to discuss with Caffeine Corky about how the situation can be a rectified. We didn't come up with any solutions.

January
14 Thursday

My teeth are falling out.

I was swimming in the thick, gooey airless fear, the darkness was suffocatingly black and getting heavier and heavier and I cried out. The pain came back in echoes.

I don't believe in God, so how can I believe in the Devil? Surely, you can't have one without the other. Yet, I feel the atmosphere has turned Evil and His Almighty Goat Head (Goat? Gott? God?) presence is slowly poisoning me.
I try to incant decant recant descant the Lord's Prayer... but I can't remember the words which were always paper thin. Nothing comes out of my mouth that makes any sense. Finally, as I panic and drown in the foul-smelling treacle, I remember the "Exorcist" movie and quietly whisper the pure and simple words "HELP ME".

Suddenly I am filled with warmth and comforting sweetness, and a soft breeze of light blow away the clinging sticky cobwebs of fear.

Five pound note in my wage packet with telephone number 07842 44534 written on it.
...53 strikes again.

A five pound note in my wage packet? A blast from the past. Five pound notes are as dead as a ten bob note.

January
15 Friday

The New Falklands War is still raging. The Argentinians re-took the Malvinas while we continued to war in the Middle East. Britain's new Prime Minister is yet another Thatcher clone. I thought the International Rainbow Anarchists had bombed the last Yank factory that was manufacturing them.

You froze. You phoney.
Euphonious.
UFOs were banging or hurtling themselves against a brick wall.
Junk-Jung believes UFOs (You folks) are portents of disaster.
I think the "warnings" feel that they are being ignored.

On page 53 of "UFOs from Behind the Iron Curtain" (Ion Hobana + Julian Weverbergh), is an account of a UFO flying around the village of Robozero in Russia in 1663 - 53 years after the mass UFO mass sighting in Chipping Norton on the 10th of July, 1610. Is there a connection between UFOs and 53? Are UFOs trying to draw my attention to the number 53? If so, Why? Is it more than just a number?

As I read the book, I hear something fall to the ground. There is nothing on the floor. I realise if I look at the clock I will probably see that it is 53 past the hour. I try not to look but my eyes are dragged to the clock face, and reluctantly I see the time is 14:53.

My National Identity Card number is EL/07/28/53 X. Why?

A rare event. A pure white wolf has been found. Is this event as spiritual as the birth of the sacred White Buffalo the Native Americans are eagerly anticipating? The wolf, I'm told, is not albino. I am given a Digital Visual Disc copy of The White Wolf. They say if I am patient, it may turn into the real thing.

January
16 Saturday

I was trying to contact God. And there's this new way of doing it. Even agnostics and atheists were trying it. But is it really a new way? I was with a group of the non-believers. Of course I'm one, and we are going to the chapel to pray and sing the praises. The service was in a hospital and we were escorted there by the nurses. None of us were ill or indeed patients but we have become part of the hospital's system and routine. We were placed at the back of the chapel, a glass partition separated us from the main body of the congregation. The service is coming to us through the PA system, though we could nonetheless observe everything that was going on. I suppose, in a kind of sound proof room. We could hear them but they couldn't hear us. We took advantage of this fact and spent most of the service, laughing and joking amongst ourselves. We even poked fun at the minister and his congregation for being so stupidly naïve for believing in God. The medical orderly - cum-church wardens standing at the doors watching over us were visibly annoyed and frowning but they didn't do anything to interfere with our rowdiness. It occurred to me that whilst it may be an advantage that the people beyond the glass partition couldn't hear us, neither can we join in, even if we wanted to. We couldn't take part in the service. Was that the price we pay for choosing to be non-believers and irreligious?

Before the service came to an end, nurses arrived to escort us away from the chapel. "But the service hasn't finished yet" I objected as they started to round us up.

"I'm sorry but it's the rules. Those people behind the partition… i.e. you people… because they… i.e. you people… are blocking the gangway, and those taking part in the service must leave immediately it is over. Now, they are not going to be able to, are they, if you are in their way? You are in the way of the door and they, poor lambs, are not going to be able to open it, so we have to clear you all beforehand. There's only two of us on a duty and we're under-staffed as it is, and we are under obligation to see that every man Jack of you are all individually escorted off the premises. And that takes time, doesn't it? So we have to start removing you 15 minutes before the end. So please, don't to be uncooperative and come along quietly. It's for the best."

"But that's ridiculous," I protested, "I've a right to stay to the end.. No one has the right to deprive me of that right. Who says I have to leave before the others? I might miss something. Something which may

convince me that God exists. You can't deprive me of that possibility."
"I'm afraid it can't be helped, sir. It's the rules. Now we've already wasted five minutes arguing. Let's get a move on, otherwise we'll all be in trouble, and where will that get us? Honestly sir, I can tell you it's more than my job's worth to go listening to you. We were warned that you were a trouble maker. You may not be sick, but we do have jurisdiction over you. So, no more fuss or we shall have to report you. And what good will that do you? None. It's not in your best interests to contradict us or contravene the Hell- Fire regulations."
"But if I stayed to the end, I might learn something that's in my best interests." I screamed. "Besides, look at the Believers. Even they have a glass partition between them and the priest!"
"Ah but they are connected by telephone. They have only to dial to make contact."
"But what if the line is a broken," I gibbered in desperation, "what if they're disconnected for failing to pay their bills? What if there isn't any one on the other end ? Just an answer machine? What if the answer machine has run out of tape or the chip is full?"
" Now, don't be silly," he soothed as I was dragged away screaming. "We are doing this for your own good. Let's not be a hindrance to others or yourself."
As I was left out in the cold and a numbness soaked through me, I was consumed with the conundrum of how I was hindering myself.

The church is next to the Rainbow Shop at 353 Atlantis Road. In the shop window is the badge of the Last Wave (fantastic Oz movie by Peter Weir) depicting the rainbow, the symbol of forgiveness and re-birth after the Deluge.

Newspaper Headlines "GOTCHA - AGAIN. True Brits once more kick the Argies out of the Falklands...."

January
17 Sunday

Today I had a kinky sexual encounter with Deianira, the famous TV Celeb (another "Pamela Stephenson-look-a-like" Well, she has to be. It's the only way women can get into Show-biz nowadays)...

Unfortunately, I was struck by an amazing revelation just as the "hanky-spanky" was getting interesting (she had opened a doctor's black medicine bag and brought out a jar of Vaseline, rubber tubing, cucumber and a dead hedgehog).

"If you find the fifth harmonic and combine it with the third harmonic, you will have the 53d harmonic, which.... believe it or not.... will lead to the secret of the universe."

When I told Deianira this incredible thought, she immediately shut her box of tricks, and refused to carry on the "Carry on".

Saw news headline – "Alien artefact found. Many thousands of years old."

January
18 Monday

My mate, Igor and I were visiting his sister, Zinaidi, in hospital. We were talking to a cleaner and she was describing the injustices of the latest pay offer. She was just on her way to a union meeting in order to reject the offer, when a man came into the room and waylaid her. He wanted a private word with her, outside in the corridor. She was a bit reluctant to drop everything until he said he was from Digressive Tours. Whereupon she seemed to realize he wanted to talk about the union action, and agreed to go with him. Before he left the room, however, he wandered around, inspecting everything.

When he finally went, I started to speak but stopped because Igor put a finger to his lips to warn me to keep quiet. I immediately understood why. He suspected the man of having placed a bugging device. We started to search the room in silence. I kept wanting to discuss the case and ask why were Digressive Tours involved in the union disputes. I did have a sneaking suspicion as to why. I'd seen on the Internet that the tour company had links with the American Mafia, with the implication that the CIA were behind Britain's industrial disputes. Another Yank conspiracy to bring down our society.

Eventually, I found the bugging device, attached to the underside of my wheelchair. It was a metal object shaped like a silver fish, made of segments that twisted about in my hands.

Still not wanting to give anything away, we silently tried to work out ways of knocking out the device. Immersing it in water? Covering it in layers of plasticine? Wrapping it in huge wads of paper? But every idea we came up with was instantly rejected. We just couldn't make up our minds as to what to do with the little bugger.

George Adamski's book "Flying Saucers Have Landed" was published in 1953. Is this significant?

1953 - the Crucible Year, the Catalyst Year, the Launch-pad, the Big Change.

- Arthur Miller's play "The Crucible" arrives in 1953.
- James Bond is born in 1953 with the first Ian Fleming 007 novel "Casino Royale" published.
- Stalin dies in 1953. Khrushchev takes over Soviet Union.
- The Korean War ends.
- H-Bomb is exploded and Eisenhower begins the Arms Race.
- Egypt becomes a republic.
- Cuban revolution begins.
- CIA overthrow democrat Mossadegh in Iran and reinstate despotic ruler, Shah.
- Cambodia achieves independence from France.
- Benazir Bhutto, future Prime Minister of Pakistan born
- Tony Blair, future Prime Minister of Britain born
- Queen Elizabeth II crowned
- Top of Mount Everest reached
- First woman break sound barrier
- DNA discovered and so genetic engineering + cloning is born and the way for a Brave New World
- Polio vaccine developed.

January
19 Tuesday

I got an air ticket to the USA. Don't know why. I conned the money somehow. Don't know how. Except that I wrote some sort of sob-sob story to the Richard Branston Pickles Foundation. Went with a man who was taking up an appointment as a professor of some yank-kiddy yank university. Don't know him. And he ignores me, even though he is my companion.

Also went with a woman, an Aussie. She was taking up some administrative post, Personnel, I think, at the same university. Don't know her. But on the flight, seated next to me, she tells me that 53 of the 56 signers of US declaration of Independence were Freemasons. America was created by Freemasons for the eventual Masonic Domination of the World. And when I reply that that is incredible because I feel 53 is bugging me, she turns away and ignores me for the rest of the trip, even though she is supposed to be my companion.

Anyway, I shouldn't be on the trip. I have no post to take up and I have no money.

We arrive at the university. It's a metropolis, teeming with a rotating hubbub of silence. The noise is senseless because I am a stranger, with no one to know and no way to go.

The Professor is immediately swallowed up by corridors, uninviting doors, bored meetings. The administrator also deserts me. I wait patiently, apprehensively, for them to give me guidance, to take me under their wing. To tell me why I am there. Give me a clue. Why was I so determined to wheel and deal my way across the seas to be in their midst of their mist?

But no help came. I was just a fleeting shadow in their peripheral vision. They were too absorbed in their new found missions to take any notice of me. I was being left, irredeemably…to my own devices, of which I have none. An Alien stranded in a land hostile because of its multitudinous plastic superficialities and sincere indifferences and Dollar Duck billed platitudes.

I was a cripple with no money, and so I became rooted to the spot. A permanent and yet invisible reminder of rootlessness and uncertainty. The Ultimate Stranger.

Later, in a Los Angeles (Lost Angels?) motel, I read a book called 'Other Tongues, Other Flesh', written in 1953, by George Hunt Williamson, claiming to have met some Flying Saucerites from Sirius, and prints huge chunks of their “angelic language” which is almost identical with words used by John Dee, Aleister Crowley and other Illuminati magi. He also informs us that the Sirians have been in contact with Earth for several thousand years and that their allies here use as insignia the Eye of Horus - the origin of the Illuminati eye-in-the-triangle design. Adam Weishaupt and Thomas Jefferson both used this symbol, and Douglas Baker, Theosophist, declares Sirius ‘the third eye’ of a cosmic being.

So, we have on this planet a Secret Network of Adepts in contact with Sirius.

January
20 Wednesday

I was walking passed a telephone box and I heard a woman scream. She had spontaneously exploded. It was the Aussie woman. The Professor standing nearby, beckons me over and hurriedly whispers the causes to me….it’s a new disease manufactured in an American biological warfare laboratory….The L - shaped (or Hell-shaped?) virus that eats away at the testicles, thus destroying the seat of man’s intelligence.
“But that’s a crazy idea”, I protested, “because that implies that women have no intelligence, since they have no balls”.
“Certainly” he said with a male chauvinist sneer.
“But why did this woman explode, if this is a testosterone virus?”
“It has mutated and is no longer gender specific. The Backroom Boys have re-named their baby the ‘Hades Bug’. Anyway, this Hades epidemic will certainly wipe out civilization as we know it.” He threw his hands up in horror and collapsed to the ground, frothing at the mouth, begging me to pass on his warning. And then he was dead. I had a feeling that he was the brains behind this new bio-weapon.

At Mid-day the snow blizzards began in earnest. Red on white. More women getting destructive vaginal discharge. The Hades plague spreads.

Igor arrives. I ask him to help me with “The End is Nigh” leaflets. But he’s too busy, too much work to do. Plane to catch. (But hadn’t he just flown in from England?) I plan to go with him. But he keeps dawdling. I can’t get away fast enough.

Earlier, I wanted to make a speech about the impending plague. A world warning… but I have to wait my turn to have it written for me. (It’s illegal to write these speeches yourself. You have to go to an approved

Speech Writing Centre). Old Noah Eliot is still having his done. Damn, he's going to take forever. Anyway, what the hell is he doing in Yankland?

Later, still stranded in America, I meet a mother, Hera and daughter, Ilithyia. Hera suggests I go to bed with the pair of them. I happily agree.

Later that night, Ilithyia hands me an apple. As I eat it, her mother, Hera, tells me that...the Apple, the forbidden fruit from the Tree of Knowledge, given by the Snake, has if you cut it in half horizontally, a 5-pointed star shaped core...Ilithyia then gives me a tomato, sometimes known as a "Love Apple". "If you cut a Tomato in half horizontally, you will see it is divided into 3 cells".

"Five and Three", I mumble as I munch, dribbling tomato juices and seeds, soaking and staining my starch white collar. They laugh and lick my chin. "Apple and Tomato," they sang, "Forget not that you heard it from us first."

January
21 Thursday

I catch a plane and escape from Yankland....and crash land in my home town, Wellingtonia. After a quick bath and shave, I make my way to the World's End Arts Centre. When I got there, I found a lot of heavy dudes wearing Doc Martin boots, with skinhead cuts, "death's head" ear-rings, sleeveless denims, tattoos and Nazi symbols festooned all over them. I realized that they were the local fascists. They looked as if they were on door duty. I asked around as to what was going on and I was told that a rock band from Sorry University was coming to play. They were called the Order of Joy (but secretly known as The Knights of St. George). This immediately told me they were a Nazi band and when I saw them arrive my worst fears were confirmed. They were slick, hair combed back, black leather shirts, and clearly came from the German electronics school of rock.

As I approached the entrance, a Heavy barred my way.

"I don't suppose I'm allowed in?" I queried

"Too right, Spazzee!" He grabbed my wrist and started to crush it. Even he wasn't going to allow me to listen to the band. He obviously wanted to take me somewhere and I suspected the worst. The final solution wasn't legal yet it but it was clear he wasn't going to wait until the law courts got off their arses

I struggled to free myself from him, and with the aid of copious sweat, I eventually slipped out of his grasp and slid away. I decided to try and find Samuel Soap, the director of World's End, to ask him exactly what did he think he was playing at it, inviting a fascist group to perform at the centre. He was taking his liberalism and entrepreneurial tendencies just a bit too far.

I couldn't find Sam Soap so I decided to get back on the plane and I landed in St. Petersburg (I much prefer old Leningrad). I went to see an old Jewish friend of mine, Ike Mattin (he was an ex-communist who used to organise cultural tours to the former Soviet Union - now he's an exile living in the Russian Mafiya Federation). I tried to warn Ike that the Ku Klux Klan were taking control of Britain….But he wouldn't take me seriously. When I try to explain to him that he should be concerned as the KKK regard the Jews to be the biggest threat to Britain, Ike just shrugged his shoulders "I don't live in the UK anymore. Not my problem." and started the arrangements for a tour of Cuba. As usual, I was being left with the final burden.

In exasperated desperation I got back on the plane and returned to England and found military vehicles and soldiers everywhere. It seemed as if we were being occupied. Again I asked around as to what was going on. Eventually someone told me that it was the Task Force having just returned from the Third Falklands War.

"But that's impossible," I said. "The war has only just ended. They can't have just got back to Britain this quick. It took them three weeks to get to the Falklands, so it's going to take them that long to get back."

"Well, I don't know. We were told by the Prime Minister that the troops occupying Britain today were our lads returning from the South Atlantic conflict."

"The PM is lying!" I screamed, "We all know the Prime Maggot lied about Syria, Libya, Iran, Pakistan, Jordan and Algiers. This Government cannot be trusted. It's just a front to impose martial law. We are being taken over by the military, with this warmongering arsehole as its leader."

They just shrugged.

"You bloody, blind, stupid fools!" I ranted and raved. "Do you not to realize that we've now got a fascist dictator!"

January
22 Friday

I'm constantly expecting 53 to keep cropping up. And it does. I watched four movies today and in each one 53 is significant. In "McKenzie Break" the hero calls on the radio for navigation point 453.
In "Nicholas and Alexandra", the train taking Czar Nick and Alex to their doom - is numbered 01353.
"Charge of the Light Brigade" about the Crimean War which began in 1853, bring Nick 1st to his doom.
"The Little Ark" about two orphans cast adrift in the tragic Dutch floods of 1953.

And it didn't stop there....TV commercial, wife says to inventor of TV "Forget it dear, there isn't anything worth watching for 53 years"

And here's a thing...I was at the Pyramid Social Club (which is at 53 Fitzgibbon Rd) and found out that it was Terry's birthday today. He is 53. There was a lottery, and the prize money reached 53 pounds when he came to my table. I had a feeling he would bring 53 to my attention. And guess what? My prize draw number is 4553. Didn't win, of course. I never do. But who cares when I've got 53 driving me bonkers.
And on the way to the club, another car forcing its way in front of me had 53 in its registration number. Yet again "53" is something of a "Road Menace".

I was crying today because an old friend, Regina Svarog, was bereaving the death of her father. What am I weeping for? Surely not for him! He was a Nazi, a member of the British National Party. It must be because I feel for her anguish. She obviously loved her father more than he deserved. Besides being a racist, he was also an alcoholic with a violent temper. Her mother suffered terribly. And yet, here is my friend, who used to wash my hair and first introduced me to Robert Anton Wilson's "Cosmic Trigger", in streams of tears. So I am compelled against my better judgment to join her in her wail of tears.

"Maybe, the secret of the Illuminati is that you don't know you're a member until it's too late to get out." - Robert Anton Wilson, "Cosmic Trigger".

Crowley refers to the Illuminati as the Argentum Astrum - the Order of the Silver Star.
"...a kind of galactic star-network, an intelligence not fully formed but evolving...this resonated with the Sufi teaching that Allah is constantly recreating Himself every second." (RAW. Cosmic Trigger)

Sirius, the Dog Star. Dog is an anagram of God. God is an anagram of Dog.
Bog (as in toilet) is an anagram of Gob (as in mouth). Maybe that's why people think I usually talk shit!

More 1953s The Alchemical Year

- First colour television goes on sale
- Elvis first recording, marking the birth of the Youth Culture and Rock Music
- Disney's "Peter Pan" is premiered, so heralding the Era of the "Kidult", i.e. adults who refuse to grow up….which is an American disease
- Ray Bradbury's book "Fahrenheit 451", prophesying the death of books
- First 3-D movie ("It Came from Outer Space")
- UFOs and "alien invasions" came of age

Movies such as "Invaders from Mars", "War of the Worlds", "It Came from Outer Space"

They saw the moving light first. High in the sky. UFO. Then I heard the singing. Celestial. Faery-like. The Lianhan Shee? She sang, filling my head as it expanded out to absorb the Cosmos.

January
23 Saturday

I was in a district of Guildford, a wood in the Sorry countryside. Suddenly I came across an army encampment and found that a war was in progress. There were many hospital tents, and I briefly glimpsed the women wounded. I was appalled at the high rate of casualties. Suddenly, a friend from university greets me, "Ah, Shiram. Welcome. Good to see you."
"Louis A. Chien, what are you doing here?" I asked, amazed to see him.
"I command this little number. Nice surprise, don't you think? Always

brings out the best in me."
So my friend is the commander. He tells me about the Eco-Squad. A political militia specially created to re-enforce the monetarist economic policies. The ruling elite have decided to bring their fascist plans out into the open. His Eco-squad is a counter-revolutionary army, he explains with pride, then he stops and realizes he has told me too a much. He knows I'm not sympathetic to his views and that I'm really the enemy, so he hastens away down the wooded track. I follow him, and for old time's sake, we talk some more in his office. There he feels safe. He can confide in me there. We were in neutral territory. He tells me that the Eco-Squad exists to safeguard the security of the university's activities in biological and chemical warfare research, communications satellite technology, nuclear research and psychological warfare. He admitted that the Vice Chancellor, Dr. Khepri belonged to a secret group of Thirteen, and the thirteenth member of this group, was a Sensitive who was in touch with a spirit guide known as the Teacher. Sometimes this "Teacher" would warn Khepri and his "coven" of pending trouble at the university (e.g. student unrest) or rig student union elections...i.e. giving the Senate the most amenable and moderate union president.
"Teacher? What do you mean Teacher?" I asked.
"The Teachers, Higher Beings, Intelligences - physical and non-physical, exist on earth and on other planets - though no telescopes will see them, regularly communicate to Sensitives, advising on how to affect the course of humanity....
"...The Sensitive in a previous incarnation had been one of the Seers of the Delphic Oracle. Apparently one of the aims of a Pupil is to go to Sirius, graduate from the 3rd or 4th Form on Earth." explains Chien.
"There is a whole Network of Cells like Dr. Khepri's, in universities around the country. Each with a Sensitive".
As Louis A. Chien shows me to the door, he says with a smile and a wink, and what felt like a Masonic handshake, "...perhaps Sirius is our Secret Master."

the 53rd trigram in I CHING is CHIEN. "chien" is French for dog, so does this connect 53 with Sirius, the Dog Star?

Back home, I notice my copy of Robert Anton Wilson's "Cosmic Trigger" finishes on page 253.

January
24 Sunday

Oh God, tears, again, in my eyes. I had been to a wedding. Someone else's. Both the bride, Natasha, and bridegroom, Pierre, were friends of mine. Suddenly, right in the middle of the ceremony, the groom dropped down dead. Everyone wanted the ceremony to continue, and as smoothly as possible. The body was immediately packaged, and put in a coffin, whilst the priest continued with the wedding service.
I was nominated to play either the bride or groom. I think for some strange reason I was having to play the bride (perhaps it was the bride who died. I seemed to remember, that parallel to our service, another was taking place in the room next door) Anyway, I was quickly put into the deceased's shoes, and told to get on with it. Nothing must stop the ceremony. The ceremony was all. No technical hitches allowed. As the hymns were sung, the prayers uttered and the guests got back into their radiant moods, I started to become more and more depressed. No one seemed to care about this tragic situation. At first, my only way of coping was to go into a trance. Like a zombie, I did as I was told, performing the vows as if in a dream. After all, the other wedding was going smoothly. No one was feeling sorry for themselves there.
However, the sadness got the better of me. I couldn't help it. I felt their attitude was all wrong. I started to cry, mourning the death of the person I have come to replace. I was also crying for my partner's bereavement. I decided this could not go on.
Soon my movements and involvement became slow. The wedding ritual seemed to float away from me, and I found myself outside the room, looking in, waiting to be summoned for the finale.
Standing in the doorway, forever waiting, I completely divorced myself from the role. The charade had to stop. I mean it this time. The spell was weakening. The enchantment on the wane. It was still a struggle to shake off the feelings of responsibility, but eventually I pulled through and rushed into the middle of the room, interrupting the service with screams of admonishment .
People were shocked, but they didn't let that stop them. I had only managed to halt the ceremony for the briefest of seconds. I was just a blip on the landscape. Everything continued as smoothly as before except for the addition of whispers and accusing fingers. At one point, an old woman friend snarled in my ear.
"Snap out of it!" She was livid that I should have behaved so childishly

“You have absolutely no right to interrupt this wedding. It’s not even your wedding. You’re not the one that’s died. Neither are you the one that’s widowed. What right do you have to feel so strongly. Now you just pull yourself together and get on with the job you’ve been given”
“I’d love to. Natasha is a voluptuous lady and I’m honoured she has agreed to marry me. (or am I the voluptuous lady and it is he, Pierre, who has agreed to marry me?) But I can’t, the Prime Minister with the Falklands victory had successfully engineered a military coup. Can’t you see, Britain has been put under marital law, so I refuse to get married.” (Didn’t I mean to say “martial”?) And I left. Anyway, my friend, Lydia had invited me to dinner.

Lydia, 8pm - 53 Jacob Flanders Road

“Oh what a gorgeous little puppy! Where did you spring from?” Too busy admiring the cute big eyed darling and not looking where I’m going. Bang. Accident. Broke left arm and left side of pelvis.
Hospital. Ward - M.D. Room 7. Why has the door of my room 7 got the number 53 written on it in pencil? It was at No. 53 where I had the accident. I ask the nurses but they don’t understand why the number is scrawled on the door. It wasn’t any of them. Besides, it’s not even in my casualty admission notes, the exact location of my fall.
So was this room already allotted to me because the accident was pre-ordained? Pre-arranged? I was meant to come to this very room? I must conclude this is so, since no one, porters, doctors, cleaners, nurses, patients seems to know why or how or who or where ….the origin of the pencil mark.

Watching Albert Finney in “The Green Man” movie on my laptop, as he mentioned he was 53, the clock turned 9:53pm

January
25 Monday

So, I'm in hospital, they say dying from an incurable disease. (Whatever happened to my broken arm and pelvis?) My Mother and brother, Dominic come to visit me from Romania. They came much sooner than I expected. Actually, I hadn't seen either of them since I was 13. My brother was only two then. With a big grin on his face, Dominic grasped my hand firmly and talked nineteen to the dozen. He seems genuinely pleased to welcome me as his long lost brother. He seems very American with his short hair and perfect gleaming teeth. My mother, on the other hand, seems much more reserved, and holds back, and hides behind my brother's exuberant behaviour.

Eventually the Cold Fish approaches my bed and gives me a limp handshake. She looks like an older version of this Italian girl I was once madly in love with. Another case of unrequited love.

It was my mother's eyes more than anything that haunted me, behind them was the memory of a tormented earlier life which seemed to have nothing to show for it but failure. Even now, she was visiting me in the midst of tragedy. I should be on stage, making her proud of me and thus proud of herself, but instead she sees me at my lowest ebb, dying in hospital.

At last, as our hands gave each other a tighter grip, the decades of repressed emotions came flooding out like an end of the world deluge. We clung to each other and wept inconsolably, whilst my brother walked off to talk to one of the other patients in the opposite bed.. Perhaps he found our tearful outburst embarrassing… but I suspect it's more likely he just can't stop talking.

Finally my mother abruptly stops her wailing and walks out of the world. But within seconds she's back, still looking very sorry for herself. She gets into one of the empty beds, curls up and quietly sobs into the pillows. I couldn't go over to comfort her because my wheelchair was not within reach. I didn't want to call out to her and make a scene. Our family was getting a lot of strange looks from the nurses and patients. It was embarrassing.

Perhaps I should discharge myself. The doctors told me I could either believe their diagnosis that I was terminally ill and thus die, or I could tell them to get stuffed and live. I decided to choose the latter because my family's invasion of the hospital was really getting on my nerves.

However, as my brother brought the wheelchair to me, my mother quickly got out of her bed and gave it a greedy look. My heart sank. It was clear from the way she was staring at my tiny wheelchair, she was trying to work out how she would fit into it. She obviously had designs on having the wheelchair for herself.
I ask myself, "Was nothing sacred?"
This sorry wedding business with Pierre and Natasha made me think of reading Tolstoy's "WAR AND PEACE" (it's a good read when stuck in hospital) and in doing so I came across an interesting thing, which may help me solve this enigma of the ever recurring 53. *Numerology and its association with Freemasonry.* Before I read this great classic, I never really thought about numerology. Although many years ago I did come across this mystical number divination system in the Reader's Digest book on FOLKLORE, MYTHS AND LEGENDS OF BRITAIN.

Certainly never took it seriously. But since it seems the Freemasons do take it seriously and is intrinsic to their mystical / esoteric system of theology and philosophy, I've decided to look deeply into the subject and give it a try.

This is what I learned in "WAR AND PEACE" - Count Pierre Bezuhov joins the Freemasons, and learns about the Book of Revelations prophecy of the Beast 666 and numerology from a brother Freemason, which he employs to prove that Napoleon is the Antichrist, because his name added up to 666...and that he, Bezuhov was intimately connected with Napoleon's destiny since his name also came to 666. From this he concludes that it is his Divine Fate to assassinate Napoleon and rid the world of the Antichrist.

Revelations Chapter 13, vs 5 and 18

The system of numbers and alphabet used by Tolstoy (see page 788, Book Three, part one, ch. 19. Penguin classics paperback (1975 print).)

A	**B**	**C**	**D**	**E**	**F**	**G**	**H**	**I**	**K**	**L**	**M**	**N**	**O**	**P**	**Q**	**R**	**S**
1	2	3	4	5	6	7	8	9	10	20	30	40	50	60	70	80	90

T	**U**	**V**	**W**	**X**	**Y**	**Z**
100	110	120	130	140	150	160

However, I discovered a more modern system better suited to the English language (as opposed to French or Russian) called the Alpha Number Chart which is much more widely used.

1	**2**	**3**	**4**	**5**	**6**	**7**	**8**	**9**
A	B	C	D	E	F	G	H	I
J	K	L	M	N	O	P	Q	R
S	T	U	V	W	X	Y	Z	

Other letter/number correspondences also occur in the Greek, Latin and Arabic alphabets. The Grandaddy of all the numerology systems is the Hebrew Gematria which has its roots in the Qabballah.

According to Numerology, we all have a "Name Number" which is really special because it reveals the story of your life. This "Magic Number" affects how you will write, produce, direct, and perform in the play called "Life". This is why Count Pierre in WAR AND PEACE got so obsessive about his name number, which he calculated to be 666. With the modern system, however, we are unlikely to get a triple digit number…and anyway, we always reduce it to a single digit…unless there is something really significant about the whole number of your name…

Okay, using the Alpha Number Chart, I decided to find out what my Name Number is…

My name : Shiram Labif

S H I R A M
1 + 8+ 9+ 9 + 1 + 4 = 32 (3 + 2) = 5

L A B I F
3 +1 +2 +9 + 6 = 21 (2 + 1) = 3
---- --
= 53 (5 + 3) = 8

SHIT FUCK 53 **53** Fifty-bloody-three. MY NAME ADDS UP TO **53**!!!!!

So, THAT'S why I keep seeing "53".
But is there more to 53 than my name?
Is there something about "53" which has a greater import than me?
Was I given the name "Shiram Labif" to make me want to discover and decode the innermost secrets of the enigmatic "53"?

January
26 Tuesday

11:11am
There was me, and this couple on the run. Their names were Aphrodite and Adonis. Someone was after them, probably the girl's husband, Hephaestus. I was helping them but in a dispassionate sort of way. I suppose the hunchback blacksmith poet was now going to kill me as well. When he finds us. (Hunchback? Why did I say "Hunchback"? I'm the hunchback).

Adonis suggests we hide out in a desolate, abandoned hut (heart?) on the coast. As we make our way towards the hut, I notice thousands of birds circling us, high in the sky. Then I notice the ground was swarming, all the way to the hut, with them. I get a sense of foreboding. I've been through all this before. Or did I just see it in a movie?

As all light becomes increasingly blocked out by the build-up of birds, I acutely feel their ominous intent. Soon they will attack and with the same lethal ferocity displayed by their counterparts on celluloid. I felt like a prophet of doom.

I tried frantically to warn the couple. To impress upon them the utmost urgency of getting inside the hut, block all windows and doors with wooden boards, and covering the fireplaces. I knew what was needed to be done to protect ourselves against the savage onslaught of a billion beaks. I'd seen the film. But they hadn't and so were treating the tasks I'd assign them in far too flippant a manner. They didn't seem to appreciate the imminent danger. Instead they half-heartedly stuck planks of wood across some windows with insufficient nails, which were weak anyway. Whilst on other windows they used cardboard and sellotape. Cardboard and sellotape! At the same time they were either bickering at each other or foolishly groping one another. Their giggling horseplay was driving me mad. They were like a couple of Neros fiddling while Roma burns. One thing did concern them though, but only slightly. And that was, what should they do when that psychopathic cuckold appears? And he was on their trail and was rapidly closing in. They made all sorts of suggestions ranging from the pornographically lewd to the atrociously barbaric.

Then we thought the attack had started. The panelling on the front door was being pecked or chipped away. I saw a chisel come through. I breathed a sigh of relief. It wasn't the birds. It was the homicidal husband. He broke in and charged into the sitting room, swinging a hatchet.

I rushed to the front door to repair it before the birds began their attack. As I hammered planks to the breach, I kept shaking my head in disbelief at how obsessed and uptight people can be over family troubles when bigger disasters threaten all of them. Didn't they know I'd seen it all before, that I knew it was coming, that I was trying to prepare them for protecting themselves?

I looked back at them in despair, as Aphrodite and Adonis first, taunted the frenzied husband, and then, cowered in fear behind the sofa, as he swung that axe down on them.

Erm. Yes… I did wonder if I should have done something to bring a halt to this a domestic quarrel. If I wasn't careful, there wouldn't be any one left alive for Nature to wreak Her revenge on. The trouble was - I only knew about Apocalypses. I know nothing about petty human problems.

January
27 Wednesday

Isis (sometimes known as Tallulah) returned to England from Canada, without her husband, Osiris (most people know him as Fraser). She seemed very affectionate towards me. She took off her top to sun-bathe. Not in the slightest bit embarrassed by my presence. In fact, I think she did it because I was there, almost a dare. What lovely breasts, two little golden apples. Very juicy looking. Forbidden fruit. Meanwhile, lots of children ran and played around us. It all seemed very nice and carefree.

Started to read Hermann Hesse "THE GLASS BEAD GAME" and I did the numerology on the hero, Joseph Knecht, (Magister Ludi), his name equals 53.
Also read on page 53 something which reminded me of the aforementioned Illuminati "...caught in the network their music was creating, they swayed...obeying an unseen conductor".

Late Evening. I'm agony. My groin is bursting. Or is it my bladder? I rushed to the bathroom with my trousers half down. Other people (my

friends, Deucalion and Pyrrha) were present. They watched as I pulled out my penis for a piss. But I didn't make it to the toilet in time. It all came spurting out. Red sticky beetroot coloured liquid. Gushing endlessly. I don't know how much of it reached the toilet bowl and how much of it splattered all over the bathroom floor and walls, ceiling and my trousers.
My beloved urine was blood and it didn't seem to stop.
It finally does and I'm still in excruciating agony. A sign of more, much more to come. I screamed "Oh No! No more!"

PYRRHA = 5
DEUCALION = 3

January
28 Thursday

12 Noon - A conference. I'm on the guest speakers panel. So is Kyles. There's this Christian "Doom is Nigh" merchant. He was trying to persuade the conference that the times we are living in, were prophesied. All of today's terrible things were all spoken of in both the Old and New testaments.
"See, this verse predicts the Soviet Union....and this one, its collapse. And this one the creation of Israel. Here it says there will be war over oil. And here it says America and China will fight. It was foretold. These are the times the prophets of old described as The Last Days!"

Kyles and I were on the panel to disprove or show his interpretations were invalid. It was our contention that the prophecies are ambiguous and that they can be twisted around to fit any era. Indeed, over the centuries, that is exactly what has happened. There isn't an age that's gone by which wasn't thought to be the last. All the previous "prophets of doom" using Biblical sayings were proven false in their respective ages.
"Why should this Man of Woe, this Storm Crow, be any different?" I argued.
I was pleased with my arguments. They were lucid and logical. Without any difficulties I showed up the inherent contradictions in the mad prophet's case. However, when the verdict came in, we only narrowly won. The conference had voted that the world was not going to end, but it was a marginal victory.
With the result declared I left the podium feeling pleased with myself. A

member of the audience approached me and spoke.
"You know, it was not your eloquence that won the day. So, I wouldn't get too big for your boots, if I were you. It was your colleague, Kyles. It was when he opened his speech with the words 'These prophecies are incorrect because I speak in purity and innocence'. That tipped the vote in your favour. "

...World War Three = 8
...Nuclear War = 8
...The Last Days = 8

...Millennium = 5
...Apocalypse = 5
...End = 5

More notes on 53....
EL (5+3), supreme deity in the Phoenician pantheon.

Breaking it down into 5 and 3
5 : the Pentangle, the Pentagon, the five-pointed star, the symbol of revolution, of the Occult.

In Numerology, the number **5** represents FREEDOM and ADVENTURE
3: the Triangle, the Eye in the Triangle, the Triple Goddess, the Trinity, the Three-in-One.

In Numerology, the number **3** represents CREATIVE EXPRESSION and REGENERATION
...The Morning Star is the Five Pointed star, the emblem of revolutions, (Russian, China, USA) and is Sirius.....
...The Greek counterpart to Lucifer is Phospher, the Morning Star...
dragon, lizard,, saurian, sauron, saucer (flying saucer - ufo), sorcerer
discs, wheels, mandalas, circles, serpent eating its own tail
Dagon, amphibious creature from Sirius, half fish- half woman, goddess of the Philistines

January
29 Friday

Jacinta Groser, the local "Do-Gooder", wants to organise fund-raising "Coffee Mornings" to help alleviate my current financial problems. Bless her. She means well.

Thinking about Hera and Ilithyia.

Cut an apple in half horizontally and in the middle at the core will be a five-pointed star. The Morning Star. The Star of Sirius. Why is it a tradition that the fruit of the Tree of Knowledge is an Apple? Is there a "folk memory" that the Apple is not originally from Earth but from Sirius? Did the numerology on "Apple" and found it added up to "5" (1+7+7+3+5 = 23 = 5).

APPLE = 5
(also CORE = 5 and PIP = 5….. ha ha ha)

So I guessed "TOMATO" would equal "3". And it does. Hah! Interesting.

I then did the sums on the mother and daughter duet? HERA did come to 5 and ILITHYIA came to 3. Very Interesting.

Some more FIVES
...Sirius = 5
...Alien = 5
...Dragon = 5
...Snake = 5

Five is the Key (Interesting. KEY = 5)

KEY = 5 LOCK = 5
OPEN = 5 SHUT = 5 "An open and shut case, M'ludd."

And "How many Beans make Five?" BEANS = 5. So the answer is FIVE. Five Beans make Five. Naturally.

And THREES

...George = 3
...Angel = 3
...Outsider = 3
...Stranger = 3
...Lone Wolf = 3

Was there a black panther? Of course there was. It has been haunting me since my childhood. And I love it.

Arrived in the post, another Reader's Digress prize draw number allegedly "Especially" allocated to me - "539738". Huh "53" Again.

January
30 Saturday

I was at a CYCLOPS residential drama workshop. Suddenly I noticed that cracks were appearing in my hand and wrist. The cracks widen and spread. Blood starts to pour out. I become afraid that bits of my hand would drop off but that was the least of my worries. What really frightened me was that out of the cracks grew fungi-mushrooms, twisting and blooming into magnificently surreal shapes. Sometimes they would drop off and people would pick them up and study them with great awe and admiration.

I started shouting for attention. "Help! There's something wrong with me. Look at my hands!"
They came. They looked. And they walked away, shaking their heads. I screamed.
"Cure me, somebody!"
Eventually someone suggested the sick bay. When I got there I had to wait hours before I was attended to. When I was finally seen, it was Hermione, CYCLOPS administrator. Not a doctor.
She was not impressed with my ailment.
"A lot a fuss over nothing." She tutted.
"Aren't you going to do anything?" I wept.
"Well, I suppose I ought to take a blood sample." She took a syringe and rammed it into one of the cracks and sucked the blood. Despite the fact that it was green she still didn't think I had any cause for alarm. I could

have killed the bitch!
Hours later, I was pestering her for the results.
"I haven't done them yet. Go away. God, you're impatient!"

10.20pm. Tears. A downpour. A deluge. I was crying for my friend, Horus. We knew each other at school, and then at the National Work Dump for Cripples. He was the Deaf Kid. He was always being misunderstood. The staff always put him down. They felt he was a troublemaker. An irredeemable delinquent. I knew different. He was the All-Seeing Eye...(and my loyal Minder. Always at hand to keep the bullies at bay)... If he was quick tempered and occasionally violent, it was because of his frustration at being treated like a moron. And now, years later, he is still being ostracized and abused.

I was his one true friend but I was powerless to help him. My heart tried to reach out to him as he sank into greater rejection, depression and the loneliness.

I'm too afraid to approach him in case he refuses my help. Why should he trust me? He has been let down so many times before by others. Why should he think it would be any different with me, even though I was his old school friend? So I just sat watching. Helpless. Crying. The poor boy was being cruelly crucified yet again

4pm
Isis ("Tallulah" to the uninitiated) invited me round to her parents for tea. They live near Oxford. She was talking about how we use to be boyfriend and girlfriend. This surprised me. "Isis, I had no idea you thought this. I imagined we were just good friends. I mean, I wanted more but could never have hoped for it." Didn't she realise my world caved in when her mother informed me that she was getting married to Fraser (Osiris)!
"Oh," she exclaimed, "I thought you didn't go to my wedding because of the snow."
"No," I replied, "I was too heart-broken to go."
"You poor love."
"So, forget this False Memory. We were never proper boyfriend and girlfriend," I continued sulkily.
"What about those lovely, meaningful kisses?" she said with her eyes.
"One!" I winced in reply. It never went beyond that one. How could she impute more in the past than was actually there.

January
31 Sunday

Lamb juice was what Hermione prescribed. Lamb Juice? What is Lamb Juice? I can understand lamb soup. But how do you get lamb juice?
“Liquid eyes,” she said.
What?
“Liquid diet, sir.”
Excuse me?
“Liquidizer, cloth ears.”
She explained that if you can have orange or pineapple juice then you can have lamb juice.
“Oh” I said, “Does that mean you can have orange soup? Sorry, I’m not convinced. You can’t make a fruit juice from lamb cutlets!”

On second thoughts…… Perhaps “Lamb” refers to Jesus. And did she say “Juice” or “Jews”? Does it matter? JUICE = 3 and JEWS = 3. What a weird coincidence.

And her name, Hermione, is a derivative of Hermes…..

According to the Greek letter / number system of Gematria,
Stonehenge dimensions refer to Hermetic number 353

353 is the value of Hermes, the hermaphrodite messenger of the gods, who, as the inspiration of human inventiveness, acts as the link between the divine essences and our own world of phenomena

a circle of radius 1059 (353 x 3) has a circumference of 6660

in Greek gematria “the only true god” has a value of 1162 (1+1+6+2 = 10 (1+0 = **1**)), and Jesus Christ has 2368 (2+3+6+8 = 19 (1+9 = 10 (1+0 = **1**))), and the sum of the two is 3530, a reference to the God of the Mysteries

“Simon Peter...drew the Net to land full of great fishes, 153” (John 21.11)
1224 = 8 x 153. In Greek 1224 spells “the Net” and “Fishes”

Hmmm. 53 seems to be pretty important.
But in modern numerology, JESUS = 2

…and so does MESSIAH = 2 and LIGHT = 2 ("I am the Light" he said…and numerologically-speaking, he was)

…….and CHANGE = 2
OMEN = 2
COMET = 2
DEATH = 2

Therefore
COMET is an OMEN for CHANGE
Also ….DEATH = CHANGE

But here is a thing
RELIGION = 53

And consider THIS

The Nine names of God

ADONA	= 26 =	8
PRERAI	= 40 =	4
TETRAGRAMMATON	= 58 =	4
ANEXHEXETON	= 54 =	9
INESSESSENTATOAL	= 53 =	8
PATHEEMATON	= 46 =	1
ITEMON	= 31 =	4
PRIMEMATON	= 52 =	7
EL	=	8

		53

February
1 Monday IMBOLC

WOLVES…..howling. Just like when I was a baby.

They put me back in hospital…for observations, they said. Perhaps they have re-discovered my broken arm and pelvis.

Another conference….in the hospital ward. This time I was giving a public confession. I was telling the audience all about my sex life. All my perversions and kinks. I was also confessing to past acts of cruelty. At the end of my speech the audience was stunned. The purpose of my confession was to encourage others to recognize that they too have dark secrets which must be brought out into the open.

Although I was admired for my frank and courageous confession, I did not get the desired response. Instead, my speech provoked antagonisms and hostility towards me, particularly among young lads. The yobbo variety. They glared at me and sent out challenging vibe's. I had a suspicion that if I paraded my newfound virtue I would come a cropper….

With certain trepidation I went down the streets in my hospital bed with my friend, Kyles. As we rolled down the road, coming up sharp behind us were two yobs in their own bed. They menace us with jeers and leers. Then, in front of us, threatening to collide, is another bed full of yobs. They block us and demand that we back up and get out of the way. I look behind me and the yobs in the rear scream blue murder "Get out of the fucking way, you stinking pervert. Get a move on, you sadistic spazee cunt!"

I tried to reason with them. "Now look here, chaps, the road is wide. There's plenty of room for all of us to pass in peace. None of us need reverse. We can all save face."

The yobs just grin and refuse to co-operate.

In the end I crawl off my bed onto the one behind me and with a single move I yank one of the yobs by the hair. Pressing a knife blade to his throat, I warn him to stop messing me about. That immediately did the trick. The cowardly bullies gave in and fled.

Later, in the hospital canteen, reporters arrived to interview me. I stood up against the yobbos and the world's press wanted the story.

However, one of my friends, Ataoko Loinona from Madagascar, was sceptical. He had seen the incident but doubted the long term benefits of my action. I try to persuade him that if we all banded together and formed a sort of Knights of the Round Table we could keep the yobbos at bay. He disagreed. Vigilantes? Deterrents? Threats of physical force? "They're not the answer. And what you are proposing is no different to nuclear deterrence, and you're against that! If you set up a private police force to deter unruly elements, then you're a hypocrite. You're no better than the establishment which you are at such pains to despise!"

I was gob-smacked. I didn't know how to answer him. Nyambe, one of his friends intervenes angrily on my behalf.

"Come off it, Ataoko!" Nyambe explodes at his friend, "You know damn well, it's not the same thing. We're not talking about nuclear bombs. We're not talking about armed patrols. All he is suggesting is that we should refuse to be intimidated, and that there is safety in numbers. Your comparison is bolloks!"

"But where will it end? You didn't see him. I did. Give Shiram power and I fear for the future."

Out of curiousity, I did the sums on Ataoka's full name. As he was my biggest critic, I had a hunch that since he was named after an African god who had been sent to earth by his father to consider the advisability of creating mankind, the resultant number would have to be important in my Holy Grail quest. It was. In fact, it blew away my mind....

ATAOKO LOINONA = 53

I told Nyambe (he can bend spoons and do telepathy like Uri Geller). He nodded his head sagely and then warned "Let me give you One piece of Holy Wisdom. Learn to know all, but keep thyself unknown"

Just to be cheeky , I did the old "El Numero" on Nyambe's full name

NYAMBE NZAMBI = 53.....Holy Fucking Hell!

And his one piece of Holy Wisdom?

HOLY WISDOM = 53 .....Shit! Bloody amazing.

And his role model, Uri Geller?

URI GELLER = 53

And what about Nyambe's piece of advice? Do the single digits of each of the 8 words add up to 53?

"Learn to know all, but keep thyself unknown"

5 8 9 7 7 1 5 4 = 46 = 1

Nope. Well, you can't win 'em all. But interesting that all the words should come down to One. And he said "...ONE piece of Holy Wisdom".

February
2 Tuesday

Did I cause my sister's death? Or have I killed my mother? Or was it my very good friend? We had a fight, my friend and I. With razor blades. On the journey? Or at its end? I don't know. It's all a bit grey. Was he the death? Is he why I am crying?
For fuck sake, who have I killed? Is someone dead? Why do I have this memory of killing someone?
My tears give no answers.

My teeth are falling out. Yet again. First, it is just one tooth, and then, another. Both from the right side of my jaw. These two teeth that fell were beautifully ornate, as if sculptured from the finest clay by a master craftsman. They looked like they were worth a lot of money. In fact, as works of art, more valuable than gold teeth.

Still, with the passing of each tooth, I was left with the feeling of great sadness and bereavement. You can't put them back. Here is irrefutable proof of time passing, the body's chronometer which clocks up aging spirals of decay. Nothing is too beautiful to rot and moulder. Time is uni-directional. Nothing can be reversed. It is futile of me to mourn the loss of those exquisite teeth, for the mourning's dawn will not bring them back. Yet… I would have this childish hope.

Later, I watched a movie, on the motel TV, set in Britain about the hunt for the Sorry Puma. A team of zoologists have decided to track this elusive Alien Big Cat once and for all, because it is becoming a real nuisance. Farmers are complaining too many sheep and cattle are being lost…another case of those mysterious animal mutilations, I wonder? A young American played by James Spader (he played a werewolf with Jack Nicholson in "Wolf") is treated with suspicion by his fellow trackers (now I'm wondering, was the American character actually played by the English actor, David Thewlis?) Anyway, the senior zoologist (played by Anthony Hopkins) takes this young Yank under his wing, and walks with him down an isolated lane for a debriefing.

February
3 Wednesday

It's my birthday and I'm depressed.

I'm being avoided. No one wants to be seen with me. All my able bodied friends have abandoned me. Is it because I am disabled? They are ashamed of my deformities. They will never admit it, but they are. I am a short arse. A squirt. A fucking midget. They secretly despise me because I am small and I cannot walk. They all said they would go out with me. At first. But later when it came to the crunch, they kept making excuses. And now they make no pretence. I am discarded completely.

I'm Aquarius which must count for something. This is our Age, after all.

(Aquarius adds up to 35 actually..(53 in reverse) and so the mystery deepens (MYSTERY = 35)).

Aquarius is the sign of the Water Bearer. We carry and dispense the Waters of Creativity, Compassion and Freedom

WATER BEARER = 53

Start reading Brian Bates "The Way of Wyrd" - AngloSaxon sorcery (shamanism?)

"All aspects of the world were seen as being in constant flux and motion between the psychological and mystical polarities of Fire and Frost...."

Now here is the thing.

Fire = 29
Frost = 24

53

Thus, from a Wyrd (in more ways than one) perspective, the world is the on-going product of 53....

February
4 Thursday

I woke up this morning floating out of my body. "Wow," I thought, "I'm having an out of body experience!" I looked down and there, about a foot away, was my body in splendid isolation. I wanted to be pleased, but somehow I wasn't. Something was not quite right. I felt scared. Perhaps I wouldn't be able to get back in the body.
The experience evaporates and I'm in a strange circular white room and there's a woman staring at me. She looked human but seemed a bit alien. She lets me kiss her and hug her and caress her. As my passion grows I begin to feel faint. I want to melt into her. She smiles her secret smile and enjoys my weakness. Taking my arm, she gently leads me upstairs to her bed.
There was another man in the building. "Worry not," she says, "that's Khenti Amenti."
"Sounds Egyptian."
"Yes" she smiled.
At first I thought she would spend the night with him, but thankfully she chose me. Soon we were under the bed clothes together and I lay on top of her. We kissed and caressed. My heart was pounding, as I inched down her body and found her vagina. It was beautiful. My hand feverishly set about to stimulate her. .. I mean arouse her… Or something. But I couldn't find her clitoris. Where is it? I thought I knew every inch of the female anatomy. Whilst I fumbled about, like some clumsy virginal schoolboy, she waits patiently, her almond-shaped eyes glinting amber, almost wolf-like. But how much longer will she wait? Soon she will get bored and go with the other man. The shadow waiting in the wings.

As I start to panic I become aware of her sex odour. It's getting much stronger and stronger, and is starting to be overpowering. The more I panic, the worse it gets. And the worse it gets, the more incompetent I become. The nauseating stink from her weird pussy eventually reached such depths of unpleasantness that I passed out.

February
5 Friday

I am being pursued. Chased. It's a creature of some sort. A monster. A great bear? I don't know. I couldn't see it properly. But I do know it was hounding me through gardens and corridors. I could hear it. Feel it's hot breath down my neck. Smell it. It forced me to crawl through bushes and hide in cupboards.

I stayed hidden, in the dark, all day. I whiled away the hours, working on new numerological discoveries.

Reading "The Way of Wyrd" I had come across the reference to the Wyrd Sisters and so I decided to check the number of their name, as I anticipated it being "53". And sure enough, **Wyrd Sisters = 53**

However, THE most AMAZING thing I discovered…and I don't know why I didn't do this calculation earlier…was that the HOLY GRAIL equalled 53.
Yes. **HOLY GRAIL = 53**

Somehow I knew it was now safe for me to come out of the darkness and into the light….and there she was….

That strange woman again. With the amber-gold, almond-shaped eyes. Now, everything was alright between us. We made glorious love. I still didn't know who she was. All that I knew was that she was older than me. Dominant. Commanding. There was nothing shy about her. She made all the moves - for which I was grateful. I tend to avoid being the initiator, for fear of rejection.

The jovial fat doctor had to go out on an emergency call but got waylaid by a distressed little pig, suffering from various wounds. He had been fighting again with the big black dog. The doctor got down on his haunches to attend to the pig, and enquired, "Why do you keep challenging the dog? He is much bigger and more ferocious than you. You always come off worse."
The pig gave a sheepish smile, and replied, "I can't help it. You know I was a tiger from Moscow in my past life."
"I see," said the doctor laughing. "Of course, that explains everything."

"You think I have problems," continued the pig. "Have you seen my friend, the shrub, over there? He is a quivering psychological mess."
The Doctor asks mischievously, "The Shrub? His name isn't by any chance George W. Bush?"
"No, but he says he was previously a carpenter from Nepal."
The Doctor goes over to the quaking shrub, and has a reassuring chat.

February
6 Saturday

Two men (behaving like little boys) up to mischief. They stole an aeroplane, a small one, set the controls for take-off, started the engine, and as the plane rolled down the runway they leapt out, laughing at their naughty prank. The aircraft took off, pilotless, and disappeared up in the sky. The mischievous and dangerous duo (one I recognised to be a CIA agent, and the other was Mossad) had programmed the plane to enter into a circular, spiral descent once it had achieved the desired highest altitude. They hoped the single seater airplane, loaded with explosives, would crash on a sensitive target, causing mayhem and destruction, though not necessarily loss of life (well, maybe not too much). Having achieved the aeroplane's successful pilotless flight, the agents went in search of the tallest building to start a fire. For no good reason other than to see the fire engines jump into action. The state-sponsored pranksters hoped the blaze would be such that it would be impossible for the firemen to extinguish or control. They found the perfect building (it was due for demolition anyway), climbed onto the roof and built a huge bonfire. The Gestapo mischief-makers were confident the resulting inferno will be inaccessible to the fire-fighters. However, their confidence begins to be shaken when they look out to sea, and see their plane slowly and gently gliding down, above a flotilla of ships and boats that have suicidally come to watch the bizarre doomed aerial display. It was apparent the sightseers were half-hoping they would be immortalised as a crash site. But, happily, it looks like the aeroplane wants a soft landing with no casualties, and so the flotilla is skilfully avoided, and it unceremoniously plops onto the watery surface, amidst cheers of joy. The state terrorists were furious, saw me smiling and waved their fists at me. Oops, looks like they think my mental powers were responsible for wrecking their plans for catastrophe. I'd better make myself scarce. I do a runner to the hills of Asia Minor.

February
7 Sunday

The wolves. I meet the wolves. Nine of them. These ones are benign. Friendly. Harmless. Not at all sinister. More like the real thing.

I ask the wolves their names. Mithra, Ahura, Mazda, they replied. And another three said their names were Jupiter, Juno, Mercury....and a third three said their names were Maia, Zeus, Hermes. I wondered if there was any numerological significance in their names, since they represented mythological trinities...each a father, mother and son triad. One Persian, one Roman and one Greek. I will look into this later.

My Mum had Coral's house burgled. She was trying to find the documents concerning my entitlement to the family land. She didn't find them, of course. Why on earth did she think Coral would have them? I'd better get back home before my Mum has my house burgled?

It is incredible.
I have discovered, thanks to Numerology (and the Nine Wolves....I wonder if they are the Nine Unknown Teachers in disguise?), the mathematical logic in the Three-In-One concept..... I have found the "3 in 1" principle in the Holy Trinities of other myths and legends. In other words, Numerological calculations show that the Christian myth is not unique in its enigmatic Holy Trinity concept of the "Three-in-One".

This is what I found, starting with the Egyptian Trinity.

In Egyptian mythology the Great Triad consists of Osiris, Isis and Horus. Looking at them numerologically they can be written down as thus:

O S I R I S
6 +1 +9 + 9 + 9 + 1 = 35; 3 + 5 = **8**

I S I S
9 +1 +9 + 1 = 20; 2 + 0 = **2**

H O R U S
8 +6 +9 + 3 +1 = 27; 2 + 7 = **9**

The numbers for Osiris, Isis and Horus are '**8**', '**2**' and '**9**' respectively, and if we add these numbers together we get '**19**' and if we add '**1**' and '**9**', we get '**10**' which is finally reduced to **1**. Thus, the Three Elements of the Egyptian Holy Trinity add up to One.

Egyptian	
Osiris	= 8
Isis	= 2
Horus	= 9
	--
	19 = 1

You can imagine my complete astonishment when I applied this approach to Godly Triads found in other myths and legends.

Greek		**Persian**		**Roman**	
Zeus	= 8	Mazda	= 9	Jupiter	= 9
Maia	= 6	Ahura	= 4	Juno	= 6
Hermes	= 5	Mithra	= 6	Mercury	= 4
	--		--		--
	19 = 1		19 = 1		19 = 1.

February
8 Monday

There was this chap Professor Galahad, who was a friend of my friend Thor, trying to convince me that he was an eye surgeon. He seemed to think that my eyes were in a bad way and that he should examine them immediately. The urgency in his voice was unnerving. Eventually I agreed, and after many tests, he came back with his report.

The news was not good. He showed me the drawings he had made of my eyes, cross sectioned illustrations of infected endings, a cancer-ridden optic nerve, and lice eating away at parts of the retina. Clearly I had not washed my hair or face often enough.

The pictures were very well drawn and the detail was quite exquisite. I particularly admired the picture of a louse embedded in a ganglia of nerves at the back of the eye.. Yes. I was impressed and chilled to the bone.

"What does this mean?" I asked, "will I go blind?"

"Yes. At best, you will go blind," the kindly I-man replied. "But it is more likely that you will die. You see, the cancer is spreading from your eyes to your brain."

He then told me the only thing that will save me is immediate surgery. The eyes must be operated on.

"In fact, I must do it now. Here in this very room," he insisted. He was serious. There was no time for hospital. It was now in Thor's sitting room or never.

"Oh dear," my stomach groaned. "This is rather alarming."

He told me to lie back in the armchair, to relax and let him get on with it.

"What about a local anaesthetic?" I humbly queried. I would have actually preferred a general anaesthetic but I couldn't bring myself to ask, being of a somewhat shy disposition.

"Not necessary!" he replied as he prepared his equipment.

"N-n-n-not N-n-n-necessary?" I stammered.

The I-man then produced a large syringe with a long needle, filled with a clear liquid

"I am going to plunge this into both your eyes."

Shit! And without an anaesthetic!

"Then, I'm going to mash your eyes into egg pulp," he advanced. "...and with a little bit of luck, the cancer will be destroyed!"

"Er, seriously..." I squirmed, "...I do think I need a local, you know. ..."

Somehow I started to doubt this man. Was he really qualified? After all, I was at the opticians only two days ago and they'd not said anything.

I grabbed my eye test report and looked at the cover. Shit! The Journal of Scientology! Crank. The man's a crank. A homicidal crank! Now I can escape with a clear conscience.

9:53 pm. It's that weird woman again. She picked me up, caressed my bottom as she carried me upstairs to her bed and we started to make love. I was joyously happy until her seduction evaporated into cold bloodied prick teasing.

"What's your name?" I asked as she put me back in my wheelchair.

"You want to do the numerology on my name?"

"Eh no, of course not! It's just that we haven't been formally introduced."

"Stella Maris...which doesn't add up to 53."

"Where's your Egyptian friend, Khenti Amenti?"

"He's back at work in Abydos."

"Abydos?" I queried, "Where or what is Abydos?"

"Abydos is one of several entrances to the Underworld"

February
9 Tuesday

The wolves. Bad ones this time. It's my job to save the world from them. An evil pack was on the rampage. I went out into the snowy wilderness to track them down and eventually found them.
With a blow-dryer I sent drafts of icy cold air into them and froze them all into a long ribbon.
Next, I'm driving a railway train with the frozen wolves in tow. I look up and to my surprise, I see that we are pulling a line of carriages with huge blocks of ice on their roofs. They're for the town. What town? The town at the end of the line. The townsfolk need ice blocks. And the wolves? Are they intending to infiltrate the town masquerading as ice blocks? If I suggest this to anyone, they'll think I'm mad, so I'd better keep quiet.

Found that the Christian Holy Trinity fits perfectly my "Three-in-One" numerology formula

Christian
The Father = 1
The Son = 9
The Holy Ghost = 9
---
19 = 1

February
10 Wednesday

The race riots in Britain have provoked our Satanic Prime Minister into arming the civilians. He is training them for his own private militia. The electricians, nurses and accountants have been given guns and told to go out and defend the nation.

A group of us gather secretly to discuss our response to the PM's growing repression. I argue strongly for terrorist action. We too must arm ourselves with guns and bombs, and attack the government forces.

Too hasty, Khalifa the Turk says. We need a more subtle form of attack.

Use violence only as a last resort. Finally after much debate, we all agree on a plan, and I am sent out to organize our blueprint for resistance.

Unfortunately, within minutes of taking my leave, I find myself lost in a huge, mind expanding building, full of long, dark, twisting corridors that snake and branch into cavernous halls and echo laden rooms.

Applying trial and error, I edge open the most promising door and enter a room full of light. My relief, however, is short lived when I also see machinery and laboratory equipment, and crowds of bustling scientists and technicians. Am I back at Sorry University? Is this the physics department?

Suddenly, everything stops. It must be knocking off time. I go to leave. But they won't let me. And hem me in.

"Make way," they all were crying in unison. "Quick, let the Man pass. Make way."

As the crowd divides to allow a clear path, a man in a white coat, precariously carrying a highly radio-active canister between a pair of tongs, runs down the length of the room to a door which turns out to be the secret entrance to a special decontamination elevator.

"HE has to leave first," they shout at me.

It didn't make any difference. Even after he had disappeared down the elevator, they still wouldn't let me leave.

"WE take priority. All staff must vacate the premises before sundry species."

"But if you all go, who will be left to carry me down the stairs?" I argued. "I'm not allowed to use the Lift."

"That's right sir. YOU are not."

"So, I'm going to be stuck up here?"

"NOT OUR problem sir. Good day to you ." said the last man to leave.

Stranded and impotent, I resigned myself to looking at movie posters hanging on the walls around me. One of them comes alive. And as the bronzed, athletic hero dives into the tropical lake, he turns to me and says,

"Life is charming for some but not for others."

February
11 Thursday

I returned to my old school, only to discover that my dark secret was on the verge of breaking. An old colleague of mine, Icarus, was about to blow the gaffe that many years ago I had burned him alive.

He didn't die. He just suffered severe burns and disfigurements as a result of my action. Up to now, no one knew. But time has caught up with me, and I sense that the former teachers and pupils are now cognizant of my barbarity.

Icarus didn't want to tell them. All these years with an extraordinary altruism, he'd painstakingly hid the truth, but he couldn't do so any longer.

As I wandered aimlessly, trying to gauge my impending doom now that the cat was out of the bag, I came across Icarus and his followers (disciples even). They used to be my friends too. Not anymore. Their open hostility was devastating.

Icarus, to my shame, still greets me as an old friend and tells me that he still forgives me. I have to look away from his charred and peeling face as he strokes my hands. He bids me farewell and as he goes, I know I have to get out of the building immediately.

I'm about to pass through the classroom door and descend the outside steps when I see an old man who reminds me of Alec Guinness in the hall, uttering mystical oaths to the ceiling.

"I see the old codger is still doing those guru parts!" I chuckled, pausing to admire his performance. This delay, however, was a perilous mistake.

Coming straight at me, from nowhere, is a ferocious policeman with a giant revolver viciously aimed at my heart. Freezing on the spot, I allow him to arrest me without a struggle. I don't remember what he was charging me with but I assumed it was to do with the burning of Icarus. I had no right to protest so I agreed to accompany him to his car.

I tell him about my Numerology research and my latest discoveries concerning Holy Trinities. The policeman looks fascinated and asks, "What about Moses, Elijah and Jesus? Weren't they the Three Prophets seen ascending into a flying saucer on Ascension Day?"

"Oh yeah," I said, "Hadn't thought of that."

He gives me a pencil and paper, so I can do the calculations.

We were both very pleased with the result.

Moses = 8
Elijah = 9
Jesus = 2
--
19 = 1

"What about my dogs?" he suggests.
"Your dogs?"
"Yeah, I got three Rottweilers. I named them Faith, Hope and Charity," he replies. "That's a trinity too, aint it?"

Faith = 9
Hope = 8
Charity = 3
--
19 = 1

"This is fantastic," I shout, "We must tell the world."
"No. I wouldn't advise that, my son," he said putting handcuffs on my wrists, "such things are best left un-said."

Now I am in prison. And I am very unpopular with a number of fellow prisoners. In fact, they are sickened by my big mouth. I have been opening it once too often. All around is a growing threatening mood of blood and rape. How long can my friends protect me? They can't be everywhere. Sooner or later, the bully boys will find me alone, and then I'll be done for.

This woman inmate passes by my cell, sees me and asks if we could have a chat. I said "Yeah, why not." She comes and sits on the bed. Her name is Urd and she's a Jehovah Witness believer and tries to convert me but I quickly tell her that I am a devout agnostic who can never be persuaded to follow any one particular religion. "No religion is the whole truth but every religion contains a small part of the truth. Truth is like a mirror that has been shattered into three million pieces and each religion and philosophy has embedded in its heart a tiny sliver, shard of the Cosmic Mirror, which is still only a pale reflection of the Ultimate and Absolute."
"Why Three million pieces?" she asks intrigued, her eyes and face flushed with excitement.
"Oh I just chose Three because it's my favourite number at the moment. I'm doing numerology research which is finding numerical links between various concepts and names found in myths, legends, religions and

theories of Armageddon, (for example: JERUSALEM is 5, and is called the HOLY SEPULCHRE which also equals 5) and I've discovered confirmation of the Holy Trinities having a "Three-in-One" principle.

"It seems that the Great Trinities are all numerologically based - in that they are so organised that Three always adds up to One." I tell her about the Egyptian, Greek, Persian, Roman, Biblical "Triadic Unions" (my expression for the numerological "3 in 1" principle).

"Actually, your name, Urd, gives me an idea for another possible Triadic Union. Wasn't "Urd" one of the Three Norns or Fates in Nordic mythology?"

"Yes, unfortunately, I have a heathen name. I was named Urd because my parents were Wiccan. I have two sisters and they were also named after the Norns."

"Verdandi and Skuld?"

"Yes, our names means Past, Present and Future"

"Okay, if my theory is correct, the Norn Sisters names will all add up to One."

"Wow, that would be amazing. If it does, I will give up being a Jehovah's Witness, be your first disciple and return to my pagan roots."

"No, no, no!" I complained in horror, "you mustn't. You mustn't give up your beliefs because of what I say. I'm a nobody. I don't have a divine access to the truth. Besides I'm still very sceptical about my findings. There's a lot more work to be done."

Suddenly, I was reluctant to do the test on the names of the three Wyrd Sisters...but Urd refused to leave my cell until I did. And sure enough, the Norns added up to One. And not only but PAST - PRESENT - FUTURE also formed a perfect Triadic Union.

The Norns

URD	= 5	PAST	= 2
VERDANDI	= 1	PRESENT	= 7
SKULD	= 4	FUTURE	= 1
	--		--
	10 = 1		10 = 1

My Fate was sealed. She left my cell a triumphant new convert. Had I erred with Urd? I had a terrible feeling that I would suffer the consequences of saying too much too soon. And to compound my feelings of anxiety and dread, I remembered that the name WYRD SISTERS = 53.

February
12 Friday

I wake up and find one of my teeth has fallen out. Then, I notice it has a very strange root at the molar. Long and made of tubular glass. In fact, the tooth seems to be an electronic component. My God, it must be an implant! A communication device, inserted by the prison authorities? Or even aliens? Why did it fall out?
Later I meet the doctor who said she removed it. I asked her if there were more "teeth" like that in my mouth. "You should see a dentist," she merely replied. Then she told me, she wasn't sure if it was correct of her to interfere. I have a suspicion she is having regrets about extracting the alien bugging device from my mouth.

At 9:22 that evening.... Because I didn't keep my mouth shut, THEY came into the prison cell (There was Three of them. Black shrouded shadows - reminding me of the Ring Wraiths in Tolkien's "Lord of the Rings") rushing through the door on my left and as they passed through, it swirled like a vortex, spiralling shut, like a camera's iris, extinguishing the light from the corridor. I looked in horror, helpless as I saw the light diminish, swallowed up by the veil of darkness. Wrapping me in a towel of blackness. One of them swiftly moved to the right side of my bed. Then I became paralysed and a tremendous pressure downloaded into my chest which began to vibrate rapidly and I heard this sound of gas escaping at a rapid and forceful rate. With my mouth wide open I realised it was the sound of my breath being sucked out of me. My life-force exiting out between my lips, causing them to "blow raspberries" non-stop. The very essence of my Being was being vacuumed out and there was nothing I could do to stop it. I tried to call out but no words would sound. In the end I remembered the "Magic Plea" which had saved me in the past...and I silently cried out the immortal words of Redemption - "HELP ME". That worked. "Someone" turned off the taps..... and my life stopped leaving me. The Black Shrouded Figure on my right, quickly swept away from my bed, taking with him his two shadow companions, and they rushed out of the room, through the swirling unseen vortex on my left, returning in its place the once absent door, now opening onto the corridor full of comforting light.

A friendly thug, burglar and mugger, Marconi, tells me his sudden spontaneous interest in wolves after seeing a cigar shaped UFO.

February
13 Saturday

In the prison library. Climbing a ladder of chairs and stools, dragging my wheelchair behind me, whilst at the same time, pissing in a urinal bottle. I also have to carry this vessel without spilling a drop. I managed to reach all the floors without too much difficulty until the last one. The stool I have to pull myself onto is smaller and more precariously balanced. I can't do it, not without spilling the bottle or letting go of the wheelchair. I look for help but all the passersby ignore me. Then I see a Chinese looking woman on the telephone. She becomes aware of my difficulties and comes to my rescue and helps me up on to the final stage.

Later, I escaped the prison and decided to pay a visit to the National Work Dump for Cripples in Midhurst, but instead took a diversion as - to be honest - I didn't really want to see the Old Shit Hole. So I inquired as to whether the Park Avenue army base was still operating.
"No," they said. "It's been closed down, but there's a new camp not far away at St. Anne's Hill."

"I'll go there, then." I said.

When I arrived I saw they were not wrong. It really was a camp. Tents and canvas sheets everywhere! The army were sleeping in a big field.
I drove into the field as quietly as possible. I didn't want to wake the soldiers, most of whom were sleeping under a massive single sheet of canvas. I didn't realize they were there at first and was about to run over their innocently unsuspecting bodies.
I backed off just in time. Lifting the car from under me, I tiptoed out of the field. Having carefully escaped, I suddenly realized I'd missed a great opportunity. I could have stolen guns whilst they slept. But to be honest, I had something else on my mind. I WAS WALKING! Me, a lifelong cripple! In fact, it wasn't so much walking. More like floating. I was gob smacked. I just had to sit down. I sat on this white…gleaming white farm gate. It was lovely. With such a wonderful sensation I could have stayed there forever.

February
14 Sunday

A big cat - a black panther, in fact- was stalking me. It circled around me, seeking a way in but I kept it at bay with a spear (though, at times it seemed to shrink into a knife). I was desperate not to harm it but it was agony trying to avoid stabbing it as I jabbed the blade to make the animal keep its distance. As I looked into its green eyes, they seemed to say that it was being badly misunderstood.

Maybe I had misconstrued its intent. Perhaps it just wanted to be friendly. No sooner had I thought that, than the panther began to shrink in size until it became an ordinary a black cat. As it leaped on my lap, purring, my feeling was reinforced that the creature was not as ominous as I'd originally feared. I've decided to call my new mystic cat Solar Eclipse, because he is as black as the solar eclipse
....and SOLAR ECLIPSE = 53.

Do I have the Spear of Longinus? The Heilige Lance? (Spear of Longinus = 72 = 9, is Heilige Lance = 63 = 9)

Reading a book I stole from the prison library on St. Anne's Hill, because I was going to interview a disabled guy, Lydia recently introduced me to. He went about in an electric wheelchair because he was paralysed from neck down due to a motorbike accident. I know more about him than he realizes.

> *St. Anne's Hill at the town of Midhurst has numerous pagan associations. The hill, once called Tanhill (Tan was an ancient name for the fire and sun / solar god. Ha ha ha, a sun-tan?) was presumably absorbed and renamed by the Christians as they have done so with many ancient energy centres. A small church called St. Anne's lies at the foot of it, but further up the hill the paved road reverts into what must have been its original state: a grass bank with a surprisingly flat top on which a fair was held until recent times, undoubtedly the continuation of an earlier pagan festival. It took place annually on 6 August, near enough to the annual Celtic celebration of Lammas (Lughnasa - Lugh, God of Light). At the hill's summit are the sparse remains of a medieval castle. St. Anne or Satan? Saint Anne's Hill or Tan's Hill or Satan's Hill....a place of Satanic worship, for the Midhurst Coven?*

6pm - The woman from the library with dark hair and amber luminous eyes and canine teeth. Erotic. Very fulsome and delicious. She wraps me in a liquid sweet viscous desire. Do I know her?

"Of course you do, my love." She whispered, biting into my neck, "You remember Stella Maris, don't you?"
"Are you foreign? Cause you don't look English."
"Neither do you - my darling, but you are almost as English as John Bull." She hisses as her sharp thin lizard-like tongue penetrates deep into my left ear, "Do I look Oriental?"
"Yes…Slightly"
"A little Chinese, perhaps"
"My Little China Girl? Almost."
"Well, I'm not. I'm even more exotic."

STELLA = 6   MARIS = 6   her name is two SIXES. I wonder if she has a middle name…and if so, will it also add up to 6?

February
15 Monday

Lupercalia Day, a pagan festival of the Wolf Goddess of Eroticism and Fertility.

A policeman knocked on my door but I refused to let him in. It might have been a summons.
"It's all right sir," he called out, trying to reassure me, " I haven't come to arrest you. Just want to warn you, lad. Watch out! There's a new highly dangerous and virulent disease about. It's much more lethal than Hades."
"Thank you, constable," I replied, still not letting him in.
"That's okay. Just doing our job….Oh, and one other thing, Mr. Shiram Labif…"
"Yes, Officer?"
"Maria says you can keep the book you stole."
"Maria?"
"Maria Stella Maris."
So she does have three names. MARIA = 6   STELLA = 6   MARIS =6
666. The Number of the Beast. The Antichrist.

February
16 Tuesday

Solar Eclipse, my black cat, was about to shit in the bath again. To stop him I threw water at him, which knocked him into the bath. But horror upon screaming horror, I find he has fallen into bleached water! I tried to get my darling out of the tub before the chemicals kill him. But I think I am too late. He's stiff, lifeless and bleached white. I wanted to resuscitate him but I felt powerless.

The only answer was some children I knew. They have the necessary skills. My additional problem, however, was that they were on a video.

I locate the relevant cassette which is entitled "The Great Rift" and put it in the VCR machine. I press "play" and on the television screen, there immediately appears a picture of a courtyard surrounded by tall buildings, all of which are perched high on a mountain plateau overviewing a spectacular African panorama.

The children are there, and so I enter the screen. I see they are deeply engrossed in a game of role playing. I approach them to ask for their healing assistance but I hesitate, not wishing to interrupt.

And as I stand there for ages, waiting for the right moment, I notice an irritating itch in the palm of my left hand. I scratch it and it gets worse. I scratch some more, and the more I scratch the worse it gets. But I can't stop. Soon my fingernails are digging deeper and deeper into my flesh, gouging out a great rift. But still I am powerless to stop. I am fascinated, as the wound wriggles and writhes, with a life of its own.

And I mean that literally, for, out of the great gaping hole emerges a squidgy squirming slug-like something. I pull it out and drop it on some paper.

I call my doctor friend, Loki Groser, to examine it. He is astonished. But says there's nothing he can do.

February
17 Wednesday

I'm making another movie with Talitha Hounslow and Oscar Grill. Again, it is set in an institution for cripples but in Israel. We, cast and crew, are all having to spend the nights together in one large room. I'm not enjoying the work on this new film. It all seems very uninteresting. No inspiration.

Until....Watch out! There is a shark in the swimming pool. See those murderous Jaws as it tries to attack each of us. I'm all right, Jack, I know how to swim on my back and escape onto a floating wooden board.

I see a UFO and I report it to the UK UFO Research Group. They send an investigator to take details. I ask if anyone else reported a similar object in the same area at the same time. The Investigator said he would find out. A little later he returns, saying that a UFO was also seen by another person living in Wormwood Close, a few streets away from where I live in Boxwood Close, but the object was reported as having "…the shape of a box turtle, on the day adjacent to yours." He filled in a questionnaire that looked like a big photograph of a garden.

BOXWOOD CLOSE = 53

A gang of gung-ho policemen break the door down and start to harass and bully. They have the same macho look as their tough guy TV or Hollywood counterparts. "Why do all you cops have to look like Sylvester Stallone or Al Pacino? Do you have to be such stereotypes?" I reproach the captain, giving him a good ticking off, making him look foolish. He immediately shrinks in stature and becomes apologetic, until he seems to act and appear like a comic dumb character in a George Lucas movie. Then I notice all the other cops transforming into funny little Munchkins, aimlessly flapping alien-looking arms like seal flippers. Their khaki tee-shirts getting loose and over-sized as they shrink to the size of Greys. Falling over themselves like dwarf clowns in a circus, they quickly exit.

Around midnight… Just as I am trying to sleep, a black shadow leaps from the floor to possess me. It enters me and I am paralysed. So I summon a female entity to take me. I dare her to have me. Instead, she quietly comforts me. Her bedside manner was wonderful. Before she left me, she informed me that I had passed the test.

February
18 Thursday

Oscar Grill, the movie director, scrapped the film. Things had got so out of hand, that he couldn't cope any more. We were too far behind with the shooting schedule, the Israeli wilderness is not the easiest of locations, too many mishaps and disasters and too many members of the crew were becoming increasingly uncooperative and hostile.

"Maybe we could somehow resume at a later date," sighed Oscar.
"If you stop now," I shouted at him, losing my temper, "We'll never get restarted!"
In fact, I was so furious I threw some crockery at him. Afterwards I felt intensely embarrassed. Such an infantile display of emotion in front of the entire crew. In recompense, I offered to buy everyone a drink and to my surprise, found ourselves outside the students' union bar at Sorry University.

We went inside and got drunk, but I knew something was wrong, strange, weird even. Earlier that day, I'd been left behind at the location (not far from the illegal Dimona nuclear weapons factory) and had to make my own way back to the hotel, down some very long and dusty Negev desert roads. Eventually, I got a car and at the end of the journey, back at the hotel, I was surprised that there had been no one else with me. Not even a driver. But I was in the back seat. So I must have driven the car from the rear. Funny old world, ain't it.

February
19 Friday

I was trapped in a huge, labyrinthine house which stretched for miles. And I was being pursued by a demonic psychiatric doctor, who looked a bit like Jonathan Miller. He was trying to con me into selling my sanity for a permanently illustrious theatrical career. However, I succeeded in escaping.

But, as they say, "out of the frying pan into the fire…"

There were only two of us left, out the original Nine. All the others had been eaten by the monstrous dog haunting the big daunting dark fairy castle. It was a mission doomed to fail. Me and the Fat Boy retreated into the ornate state bedroom, and lay on the huge four-poster bed, like lambs for the slaughter. The Fat Boy put his arm across my neck to protect the throat, in case the two-headed Cerberus tried to kill me that way. I did the same for him. Originally, the dog had had many more heads, but we think with every person it killed, one of its heads disappeared, which is why this Hound from Hades has only two heads remaining because there are two of us surviving its hunt.
A blood-curdling howl hideously announced the ravening beast's intrusion into our temporary sanctuary. I gripped the short sword I had to defend myself, ready to plunge it into the Demon Dog's black heart, but before I could breathe a second breath, my plump companion was ripped to pieces beside me. In the same instant, the dog's second and penultimate head shrank and disappeared between its shoulder blades. As I got ready to fight for my life, the doggy wagged its tail and went all puppy-ish on me, choosing not to attack me, in case its last remaining head had to be forfeit. Thankfully, the dog had wits to keep its head.

February
20 Saturday

I woke up to find large slugs and snails invading my flat. There were thousands of them, maybe even millions, covering everything in slime. I had no idea how I was going to get rid of them. I knew, however, that I didn't want to do in any killing. But neither did I want to touch them in order to pick them up and throw them outside. They looked so disgusting. Even so, something would have to be done soon, otherwise I would drown in them.

As I studied the seething mass of slime and gristle, I could see that the problem may be solving itself. These creatures were very aggressive towards one another. Almost Canada Mystic I would say, I mean, cannibalistic. Like a can of ballistics, they were pouncing on each other and having a meal of a time. At the rate these gastropod molluscs were eating each other, they would be wiped out by mid-morning.

My next worry, however, came when I noticed that every time a slug or snail ate another, it instantly grew a little bigger. So, what happens when there is only one slug left? How big will it have grown? Shit! Big enough to eat to me?

I didn't hang around to find out.

Later, I collapse from a kind of seizure. Or was it a heart attack? Or stroke? Or simply a fainting fit. Well, I am seriously ill and a nursing friend, Coral, arrived to help me in my recovery. I had plans today, but she insists I have to stay in – postpone – cancel. I look out the door letter slit and see Lydia walking up the street with a little girl of about 3 or 4, holding her hand. I greet her as she enters and explain she may not be permitted to stay long as the nurse says I'm still not well enough to receive visitors. Lydia is shocked to learn I was at death's door. Then a bird, a robin, comes flying into the bedroom, fluttering frantically against the window pane. I hear his voice, and he tells me that three days ago he was the Foreign Secretary in the government, but collapsed from a heart attack and fell off a mountain while rock climbing. However, he doesn't believe it was a heart attack but that he was pushed. The PM wanted to get rid of him for being outspoken opponent of the illegal war. Lydia quickly gets up and opens the window, letting the distressed little thing escape.

February
21 Sunday

The SAS recruits were doing wilderness survival training in the Lake district. One of the trainees goes missing. It is feared he has perished through exposure. A huge search party sweeps the area but instead of finding him, they find the body of a small girl, possibly 2 or 3. Most of her body had rotted away. All that was left were legs and a piece of skirt. Perhaps the upper part had been incinerated rather than decomposed. Was she the victim of a sex murder? A Satanic sacrifice? Or was she killed for her organs? Was the missing soldier connected to the girl's death and mutilation? Why are CID asking me these questions?

Trip to Midhurst to see Lydia's disabled friend Miles Ramsay. He asked about my numerology research. I told him I knew his number. He hoped the numbers in his life were not triple sixes.
"Are you worried about being the Anti-Christ, then?" I asked intrigued.

Others should worry, he replied, not him, if he was.
"Do you think the Anti-Christ is alive and well and kicking dust in the world at this moment?"
"Oh yes, The Moon Child is around alright. The last thing I knew he was in India but that was about 7 or 8 years ago, I think."
"The Moon Child?"
"Yes, Aleister Crowley's son - known as the Moon Child. Got the Mark of the Beast - 666, the half-moon birth mark."
"Surely he must be dead by now, Crowley's son?"
"If he is the Anti-Christ, he won't be, will he." Ramsay retorted.
"How long have you been interested in the Occult?" I asked, worming my way into the subject.
"Quite a while now, I suppose."
"Were you interested before your accident?"
"Oh yes. Heavily. I belonged to the Midhurst Coven. I was used as a virile young white male. If you've got those qualities then you were in. I was used for sexual purposes. Old women with husbands prominent in high places were lent me and other similar men. In the same way beautiful nubile maidens were trained and used. They would be mistresses and wives of top people in business, politics, police etc. The purpose was (still is, of course) to control the Establishment and use it for its own end. World domination. The New World Order. Sex, Drugs and the Occult were and are all used in such secret societies. The drugs would be used to help finance the covens, also to 'mind-fuck' members. They had to be controlled. Sexual deviation was also vital in maintaining control. Then I decided to break from the coven. They didn't like that. I also helped another member to escape. They didn't like that either. In my absence I was sentenced to death. The Tarot eventually told me I was to die. Six days later, I was out riding on my motorcycle. I had a pillion passenger. When the accident happened we didn't know what hit us or what we hit. No other vehicle was involved. No wall was struck. No damage done to the motor bike, my passenger was completely unscathed but I had a broken neck. I could have sworn I'd hit an invisible force field. Luckily I survived because I was being protected by people who had taken the 'Right Hand Path'. I'm no longer under threat because they cannot 'see' me because I'm 'dead' and there is now a 'protective shield' around me."
MILES RAMSAY = 9. Is he connected to the Nine?
...THE NINE UNKNOWN MEN = 3
...SECRET CHIEFS = 3
...OLD ONES = 3
...GUARDIAN= 3

February
22 Monday

Chad, my agent rang… doesn't want to represent me anymore. He thinks I'm a waste of time.

I ring Miles Ramsay and tell him I suspect St. Anne's Hill is the meeting place for the Midhurst Coven's Sabbat. There is silence and then he asks in a hoarse whisper how did I know. "St. Anne's Hill really means Satan's Hill."
"Why do you think that?"
"Well, for one thing, the similarity in sound of Saint Anne and Satan."
More silence. Then he suggests I visit him tomorrow for more talk.

The Disabled Club met in the big hall. I had come from the outside to inject some professionalism and experience into their theatrical activities. Two of the biggest boys were squaring up for a fight. Their age old quarrels were getting nastier and nastier. This time they may fight to the death. I look around to see if anyone, the Director, carers etc., will intervene but none seem concerned...but I am. So I go up to the pair and say a few words. My counsel is accepted and I take one of the lads to one side. I give some fatherly advice. It turns out the fight was over a girl. I inform him that women are never worth fighting over. To lose blood or one's life for the sake of possessing a particular female is wasteful. For one thing, it is never truly appreciated. In fact, women despise you for it. And secondly, there are much worthier causes to die for. To die saving a woman or man or child's life is noble and just, but for protecting as property and pride is pathetic.
I was overheard by some women who felt maligned and so spread rumours about me and accused me of misogyny. But I would have said something similar if I'd caught two girls fighting over a bloke. There isn't a man in the world worth fighting over, either.

When I left the Club I found that the left windscreen wiper, on my car parked outside, had been broken off.

February
23 Tuesday

The snows again. I'm lost in a snowy landscape. Again

Eventually, I reach Miles Ramsay, an hour late, at 11.30 am.

Miles talked some more about the Midhurst Coven. He was somewhat taken aback by my apparent knowledge that St. Anne's Hill had been used as a location for the Coven's rituals. So my guess was correct, and the reasons for guessing were accurate. Tan the Sun God and Fire God is one aspect of the PROVIDER, which is worshipped by the Covens. Tan Hill is on a ley line and is now called St. Anne's Hill, also a derivative of Sa-tan's Hill. The power of those on the Left Hand Path is so immense that anything is possible. Various national leaders, statesmen, politicians, businessmen have used the power.

"Who? Name some names," I demanded.

"President Marcos of the Philippines had been a member, but we're not just talking about ex-leaders in the developing countries but also in the West. I know of several Labour and Tory ministers, politicians who have dabbled in the Occult and Thatcher herself was once in a coven. Hitler had been and there are lots of similarities between his psychotic behaviour and Thatcher's."

However, Miles is concerned that I don't get too close to uncovering what's going on because if the Midhurst Coven or other disciples of the Left Hand Path were to find out then I would be in terrible danger. "They would certainly regard you as a threat. Also, I'm worried that you are trying to learn things too quickly. You are knowing too much in too short a time. You are riding headlong into a very vulnerable situation, dangerous situation."

"What are you saying? My thirst for knowledge is my weak spot and could end up killing me?"

"Let's just say, I know of several cases of people who got on the wrong side of the coven and ended up as a Missing Person's Report."

Miles believes in the Provider but doesn't believe It is intrinsically evil, or that worship of the Provider is intrinsically evil. No, it's the use of the power that is Provided that can be evil, and in the case of the Disciples of the Left Hand Path, it is. Their doctrine "Do Thy Will" - anything goes - kill if that's your desire - is evil.

Miles tells me more...seemingly against his will because he says he is talking too much but can't stop. He asked why was I asking so many questions...

"Curiosity", I nonchalantly replied.

"You know, of course, that curiosity killed the cat. If the Coven ever found out how much you know, they will come and cut your throat."

"Is the Provider the God of the Witches?"

"Yes, of course. He is the God of the Five and Three. Five which is the Five Pointed Star of Sirius. And Three which is the Triple Goddess. With the power of the Provider one can have any wish granted, wealth, riches, a thousand beautiful women or men, even if you are disabled, you can be given a new body, whole, fit and beautiful."

"If this is so, and some people have obtained this power, why aren't they ruling the world?"

"I told you, they are. The multi-national corporations, international banks have presidents, directors and chairpersons who are members of covens, and have used the power to maintain control and wealth. As I keep telling you, some governments have ministers, bureaucrats, presidents who are occult practitioners. Some of the Third World countries have presidents who use Black Magic."

"Yes and I keep telling you, these countries are not in control of the world. The likes of Marcos are small fry. They are not where the power is. What about the Developed World, Western countries?"

"You want to know more about Britain and America?"

"Of course"

"America, for example, has the Owl Network. All US Presidents, from Truman to Nixon to Reagan to the Twin Bushes, the Black President to the current Lady President, and most Secretaries of State, such as Kissinger, have been or are members. Every July, they gather for an ritual burning of a giant effigy of an owl, the symbol of Athena.... And yes, our current Cabinet has ministers who belong to a similar secret occult society."

"The Midhurst Coven?"

"I'm not saying. Let's just say, when I see them on TV or in the newspaper photos, I know I've seen them before."

"What about the Prime Minister today?"

"Do you really want to die?"

After saying "cheerio", I go to my car and find someone has used a dead hedgehog to wash my windscreen. Blood smeared all over the glass.

Later that afternoon, I'm with Thor, Igor, Khalifa, Nyambe, Kyles and others at Laura's flat. I tell them about my discussions with Miles.....

"Have you noticed that the Prime Minister has dark rings around his eyes?" Kyles suggests, "They say it's a consequence of doing too much evil. He has a wild, haunted look. Thatcher also had dark rings around her eyes during the last years of her power. As did Tony Blair. And all subsequent PMs."

"I think it's called Lack of Sleep." Thor quips.

I showed them some of my latest numerological sums.

The Ancient Gods of the Witches, The Watchers or "Sons of Heaven" are also known as the Mighty Ones - but as the singular God of the Witches, the Provider, he is the **"Mighty One" = 53**

"Provider" also equals 53...........

"Sons of Heaven" also adds to 53.

"Sons of Heaven" was the name in the Biblical Apocrypha given to the Nephilim, who were "angels" (or "star people" or "aliens") sent to mate with Daughters of the Earth, thus creating the human race. A hybrid species of earthly hominid and extra-terrestrial. As Nyambe is explaining this to us.... we suddenly see this amazing cloud formation outside. We rush out and watch, spellbound, as it slowly forms into the hardened outline of a giant flying saucer. Excitedly, I get out my camera to snap pictures of it. I've now got into the habit of always carrying a camera, just in case I see any more UFOs.

As I take the photos, the white UFO sheds its coating like crumbling icing on a wedding cake - revealing the metallic space craft hovering above us. It gyrates and starts to descend. Is it going to land on top of us? I don't seem to care. I keep snapping. My friends run away to hide - urging me to stop immediately and clear out. But I refuse. This is the photo opportunity of a life time.

However, I soon use up all the film. I quickly take it out of the camera and throw it to Igor. The camera I drop to the ground as a decoy, and I run like shit into the house, escaping just in time as the UFO lands.

Minutes pass as the ominous silver machine waits. After a few more agonizing minutes of silent stillness, the gigantic saucer lifts off and returns to a great height in the sky. There, it reforms its outer white covering, looking once again like a multi-tiered wedding cake. Or perhaps a fairy palace? The Holy Grail? In years to come, it may even remind me of the Cosmic City of Revelation, a New Jerusalem spinning on a disc of light. (Well, it does remind me of the giant UFO flying over Devil's Tower in Spielberg's movie "Close Encounters of the Third Kind")

Well, it's soon gone. But that's not the end of the story. My friends and I gather in a circle in the centre of Laura's large sitting-room, and as we talk excitedly about what we have just witnessed, I notice, for the first time, a small doll-like creature with yellow skin. It (or is it a "He"?) could almost be Chinese-looking. And it is sitting on the lap of one of my friends, as if it was a harmless ventriloquist's dummy, chatting amiably and cracking awful music-hall jokes.

Despite our new arrival's apparent bonhomie, we all begin to sense an inner malevolence, Dark shadows appear around its eyes and as its voice drops several octaves. We realise, perhaps too late, that we have in our company an alien from the space craft.

February
24 Wednesday

Yes, I know, Laura and I have separated. But every now and then, I give her a little kiss because in my heart of hearts, I still love her.

The Philosopher's Stone or the Philosopher's Egg?
It doesn't matter because STONE = 1 .....and EGG = 1.

ONE = 7 ALL = 7 .....Thus ALL is ONE ....and ONE is ALL

"The ONE Eye" = 3 "The THIRD Eye" = 1

UNITY = 8 GOD = 8 GOD is UNITY

TRUTH = 6 KNOWLEDGE = 6 TRUTH = KNOWLEDGE

YEA = 4 NAY = 4 When Yea means Nay, and Nay means Yea

WHITE = 2 BLACK = 2 Black is White...and White is Black

At the Anti-War Demo, I see helicopters monitoring our movements. They are black, silent and suspended motionless in the sky. Their rotor blades hidden in the clouds. I look up and see above me a giant black chopper, bigger than an ocean liner hanging, hanging with its rotating blades masked by a thin film of cloud. I realised we were being watched by someone more alien than government security. Then a sound of buzzing and a tiny single-seater chopper flies around me like an insect. It is an autogyro with a little toy man at the controls. I swat it and it comes crashing to the ground. Lydia is worried that I will now be in serious trouble. I pick up the tiny pilot who radios for assistance. I put him in my pocket and Lydia begs me to set him free, otherwise we will never escape. I realise she is right and release the Lego little manikin, who scuttles away. However, we both fear that I may have gone too far.

Later. A dinner gathering. Our hostess enthusiastically offers us a special delicacy - spaghetti sandwiches. I'm very sceptical about this alleged culinary delight, but eventually I try it. It was as stodgy and bland as I thought.

February
25 Thursday

My Mother and I in the waiting room. Waiting. She seated on a wooden chair. Me pacing around and around restless. My sister is present but out of sight.
"Shall we tell Fay in the other room?" I suggest.
"No," Mother replies heartlessly. She smiles and closes her legs tight, in case I'm tempted to look up her skirt. I shake my head and tell her she should grow up. She sighs and says she knows that I think she always whinges and moans but she has to make some kind of impression on people, this is the last talent she has been left with.

I pick up a UFO magazine. On the cover is a picture of a flying saucer in the shape of a five-pointed star, with words emblazoned on its underside - "Children, it's time to awake"

CHILDREN	= 1
IT'S	= 3
TIME	= 2
TO	= 8
AWAKE	= 5
	--
	19 = 1

Below the UFO, looking up at it, are four Biblical characters, labelled as Adam and Eve, Cain and Abel...and encircling them is Lucifer, disguised as the snake in the grass:

ADAM	= 10
EVE	= 14
CAIN	= 18
ABEL	= 11

	53
LUCIFER	= 38
	---
	91 = 1

I show Mother and tell her about the numerology. She nods. “Your Father was murdered because he knew too much. He too was interested in UFOs and aliens.”

“So are you.” I replied. “You’ve seen UFOs.”

“Yes, but I know how to keep my mouth shut.”

“Has all the family seen them?”

“It’s in the blood.” She whispered.

“All seven of us?”

She nods, taking out her Rosary. “Yes, all your brothers and sisters. And when you marry, God Forbid, your wife and children will also see them and be cursed. Cancer and Aliens - the Bane of our genes.”

“Do you remember in Spielberg’s ‘Close Encounters…’ the flat top mountain in Wyoming, known as Devil’s Tower?” I asked.

“The one, the UFO Mothership flies over?

“Yes. Well, it adds up to 53.”

“DEVIL’S TOWER equals 53?” Mother asks frightened.

“Yes, 53. Do you think this means Spielberg knew more than he gave out?”

Was he part of the Network? I asked myself silently. Did he have a direct phone line to ET? Or….Was he one of them?

“53? You name adds up to 53. Did you know?” Mother asks.

“Yes, I discovered this exactly a month ago. But how do you know?”

“It was your Father’s idea. He worked out that if we named you ‘Shiram’, your whole name would add up to 53.”

“Why?”

“Perhaps he was told to. Or maybe, he hoped you would become a beacon, a catalyst. I don’t know. But six months later he was dead. It was a punishment.”

“So that’s why you’ve hated me all my life?”

"He was a beautiful, gentle man. Too good for this world...and they took him from me." My mother began her tears again.

February
26 Friday

I am always crying nowadays. For one reason or another. This time I'm crying for Mr. Horatio. He was a teacher at my old school, Duckworth Hill. "Old Boy" (that's what we pupils used to call him) was in deep trouble. He was trying to speak for his life. There he was, up there, speechifying for all he's worth.

But it didn't work. Nothing he could say was going to save him. He started to shrink and change into a defenseless bunny rabbit!

Although I arrived too late to save him, I tried to comfort him, attempting to give him pleasant reminders of his human existence.

"Do you remember how you used to tell us you might just as well take your poodles for a walk than waste your time teaching such Dumbos?" I gently pointed out to him. I think this did bring a tiny smile to his snout... but, unfortunately, it did not last and little bunny tears dripped onto his whiskers.

I had one more try at raising his spirits.

"And do you remember," I cajoled, "how your face used to go bright purple as you'd steam over to me and grab me by the collar, to shake that smug little smirk off my face!"

But it was hopeless, the poor little creature could not be consoled and I ended up weeping buckets, on my old teacher's behalf.

HEAVEN (28) + EARTH (25) = 53 = 8

HOMO SAPIENS = 53 = 8

Derek Jarman, who loved philosophizing green Martians, the film director who died of AIDS, sent his shade to visit me. He said he liked my script "King of the Inky Rebels". He was sorry that he never lived to make the movie, but felt he owed me some positive feedback.

June de Vill, the Dramaturge, visits to check on my writing progress - wants to know why I haven't been in touch. I couldn't easily tell her that despite having been here 3 weeks, I'd not yet started on the disabled people in Nazi Germany play "The Vertigo".

February
27 Saturday

I awoke to find Maria Stella Maris standing over me. She was talking to the man, Khenti Amenti, who was wearing his wolf head. I kept my eyes shut, pretending I was still sleeping.

"The B. B. C. have bought supplies of blood from the gypsies," Khenti said.

"In preparation for the Big One in 1995?" she asked.

"1995? What is she talking about?" I silently asked, "that year has been dead and gone, long ago."
Maybe 1995 is code for another number? 1+9+9+5 = 24 = 6
Each of her names are 6. Her name is Triple Sixes

There was also mention of Thatcher returning from her Cryogenic Deep Sleep, buried in the underground Freezer vaults of Fort Knox. Something about the Ice Maiden staging a comeback - the final piece of her plan to help create the Antichrist New World Order.

NEW (6) WORLD (9) ORDER (6) - 696  Is this the face of a Goat? Or Alien? Or both?

Later, rehearsing at CYCLOPS, Kyles rushes in and tells me my invalid car, the Blue Dalek, has been done over. We go to have a look and find the fibre glass body smashed in, and the inside totally wrecked and trashed. The special seat busted and the hand controls destroyed. I can no longer drive my car. An act of sheer spite. Not theft just hatred.

Now, I have to get a new car. A real one this time. No more of those State "death traps", bloody "Euthanazia on three-wheels".

"Always look on the bright side of life" as dear old Uncle Eric would sing.

DEATH = 2 CHANGE = 2

DEATH = CHANGE

February
28 Sunday

I was driving my new car (a yellow mini), back to my flat with Laura, her 8 year old daughter, Lavinia and someone I called "Tom". Tom is an old school friend and this "Tom" whilst recognizable as such, however, was not exactly the same. He was more like one of my other school chums - Dick, perhaps.
Or Harry. And yet, still I thought of him as Tom.

But when we arrived at my place, Mrs. Ashdown, my upstairs neighbour, lent out of her window and asked if I wanted some water. This was most odd. Why should she offer me water when I have it on tap at home?

Walking down the road towards us, I see Alky Dick and Mad Harry, each carrying a bucket of water. Black buckets. When they reached the car, they both ask if we want water.

"Why are you offering us water?" I asked, poking my head out of the car window.

"The council estate has had its water supply cut off," Harry replied excitedly.

"I think you'll find everywhere is drying up," warned Dick.

I look at Laura, who gives me the nod. She knows what I'm thinking. We'd better get out of here. It is the end, and we don't want to get caught up in it.

On hearing the car door open, I turned and see that "Tom" has got out. He has now been replaced by the more recognizable Tom. As if the metamorphosis was a cue, I thank Dick and Harry for the handful of water and with all our goodbyes in order, we attempt to drive away as fast as possible.

But we've failed to escape. The exits from the estate is partially blocked off by a new garden of strange and ominous looking flowers and trees! Leaping amongst the rapidly spreading branches are capuchin monkeys which have escaped from the local zoo. I see they are the new raiders of town and country. The urban chaos is accelerating, and we must fly.

I gingerly drive the car down a narrow garden path out of the estate, only to find that the main road beyond was also completely cluttered up by more ornamental gardens.

"Laura, I promise you," I vowed, kissing her on the cheek, "we will escape to safety, but we'll have our work cut out."

Ha ha ha! what a giggle. I was experimenting with "trinities" and for a joke I thought of seeing whether TOM, DICK and HARRY made up a "3 in 1" Trinity. Ha hah ha....they fucking did.

TOM = 3
DICK = 9
HARRY = 7
--
19 = 1

So what does this mean? Who were the original "Tom, Dick and Harry"?

After having dropped Tom off, as it was rapidly approaching twilight, we decided to escape to the south east towards Henley.

Approaching a wooded area at the bottom of a hill, Laura, sitting next to me in the front passenger seat, started to play up in an agitated manner. She kept reaching for the door handle and looking around in a semi-panic. "Stop the car. I've got to get out. Let me out. Stop the car."

My instinct warned me that it wasn't safe. I turned to tell Laura. "No, I don't think it would be a good idea," when I saw them. Beyond her left shoulder, in a field sloping down...wolves. WOLVES! Laura continued to demand that we stop the car and let her out, at which point her 8 year old daughter, Lavinia, sitting behind her on the back seat, emphatically said "No Mum, there are wolves out there."

I swung round to look at the girl in astonishment "What did you say, Lavinia?"

"Mum can't get out because of the wolves."

"You saw them, too."

"Yes, a pack of black wolves running down the hill, chasing us. We mustn't stop the car."

"Don't worry. We won't."

By now, we were nearly entering the wood. We could probably expect to meet the wolves at the bottom of the hill amongst the trees. As I turned to look where I was driving I suddenly spotted it. Just above the tree line. A neon green sphere slowly moving, almost hovering, from right to left.

"Can you see that?" I asked everyone in the car.

"Yes," said Laura in wonder, "What is it?"

"Something alien. Can you see it Lavinia?"

"Yes. A green ball flying."

"Is it a UFO?" Laura asked

"Strictly speaking, yes, because none of us can identify it."

"Where are the wolves?" Lavinia asked

"Perhaps they have been beamed up into the UFO." Laura suggested.

February
29 Monday

Laura's anger over our splitting up keeps erupting. She and Lavinia are with me convalescing with the Grosers in Henley-upon-Thames. The stay ends embarrassingly as Laura goes berserk and gives me a hard time. Eventually I retaliate and give as good as I got. In fact, I give her a worse time - poor thing - my tongue really cut her to bits. I won't write the details of what I said but she didn't stand a chance. Finally, I stopped, feeling really sorry for her and very guilty for causing her so much grief. As we all sat at separate tables in embarrassed silence - the Man of the house - who should have been Dr Loki Groser but wasn't, arrived and sat at the head table. After a few mouthfuls, he looked up at me and sardonically muttered, "You may be good at investigating the Paranormal, but when it comes to relationships with women, you're crap."

8:35pm. I go to a party…alone. Laura arrived later with her boyfriend, Luther (she dumped me for him).
The party was in a big mansion belonging to Nyambe. Large rooms as usual. Group of friends crowded in the far corner of room. She who I had been searching for, was there. Maria Stella Maris (666). I desired her but she didn't seem interested. But always she toyed with me, played with my feelings. In so many other places. So many other times. Now she was flirting with Kyles - rolling all over him, pressing herself against him. But he wasn't interested. He kept trying to move away. Then, to my chagrin, she took her top off and thrust her small but firm breasts cheekily at him, trying to arouse him. But he wouldn't respond. I remember thinking why doesn't she do that to me? Finally, she removed her trousers and knickers and wriggled her beautiful bare bottom at him. For Kyles, that was the last straw. He disappeared.
Meanwhile, some doctors and scientists and other sundry academics were examining my preliminary research paper on Trinity Numeracy. I knew they were going to pick holes in it. They had that supercilious, disapproving air.
Maria Stella Maris (lost without Kyles) takes me to her bed, holds me in her arms and we kiss passionately. Our tongues entwine and reach deep into each other's mouths. At last she will have me. But no, she stops. There's a barrier. "When I wanted you the first time, you wouldn't respond," she said. "You spurned my desires. So now you must suffer. You cannot have me."

"But when?" I said, "I don't remember avoiding you."
"You acted like you were married to another," she replied accusingly.
I knew what she meant. I couldn't give myself to her then - because I'd only just finished with Laura and it would have been disloyal of me.

Later that night Laura tells me she has found me a new girlfriend - her best friend in fact. But I've never met this woman. I don't even know her name...and Laura refuses to tell me...for now. She did this once before, with a previous boyfriend, Abe. Found him a new girlfriend, to ease the pain she had inflicted by leaving him. Now it's my turn.

March
1 Tuesday

Told Kyles about the wolves / Green UFO incident.
"There was a pack of them, black, like demon dogs, hell hounds, the Wild Hunt maybe."
"Diana's?" Kyles interjected, "Or Orion's? They both lead the Wild Hunt."
"Or just simply wolves...anyway, they were racing down this quaint Oxfordshire hillside, seeking to cut us off … in the wood ahead at the intersection of the Icknield Way, which I'm told is a Gateway to the Underworld. That's why we saw the wolves. They must be the Guardians. Laura was too busy demanding that I let her out of the car, to notice the wolf menace but she did see the neon green sphere hovering over the top of the trees as we entered the wood.
"What about Lavinia?"
"All three of us saw the UFO."
"What did Whitley Streiber say about wolves and UFOs? Aren't they connected?" Kyles asked.
"He said that ET often uses images of wolves as a calling card. Screen memory. Sometimes, they also use owls".

Kyles and I are rehearsing another CYCLOPS show. There were several of us actors and we were in the process of devising it. It's a play about Jesus and we were deciding who was going to play what.

I was against playing him. In fact, I was even against him being present. I made an impassioned speech denouncing Jesus to the rest of the cast.

Bit by bit, it dawned on me that we were like the twelve disciples around the table, perhaps the Last Supper. And a nagging feeling crept over me that I was playing Judas.

The vote was taken by my colleagues as to who was to play what. At the final reckoning, it came as a surprise to me - nay, a shock - when Hermione announced that I had been elected to play Jesus. I protested in vain.

I was burdened with the cross.

ZEUS, HERMES + POSEIDON pissed on a heifer hide and 9 months later ORION was born.

ZEUS	= 8
HERMES	= 5
POSEIDON	= 7
ORION	= 8
	--
	28 = 1

March
2 Wednesday

In fact, I was shocked. I didn't realize that such an apparently nice neighbour was so racist.

"We don't want no fucking niggers in our neighbourhood," Mrs. Ashdown snarled at the black man as he entered his new house at the bottom of our street.

"Yeah! Fuck off back to Wogland!" shouted her husband.

We were travelling between Chalgrove and Henley on the B480 when we had the Wolves / Green UFO experience. I found this in "A Guide to Occult Britain" by John Willcock -
"...the B480 crosses the Ridgeway / Icknield Way which is a prehistoric road that runs across England from the Wash to Wiltshire. It is said to be

haunted at Twilight (*it was twilight when we had our encounter*) by Roman Legionaries, BLACK DOGS, and perhaps Boadicea's charioteers who galloped along it on their way to sack St. Albans in AD 61. The part of Icknield Way that runs east of Watlington and skirts Swyncombe Downs leads directly to the World's End, and from there to Hell. A Watlington man who put the matter to the test came to a range of fiery mountains and could proceed no further because of a smell of burning sulphur..."

And guess what? ICKNIELD WAY = 53 Beautiful.

Also I think the road B480 we were travelling on, is called at that particular point, Patemore Lane.

PATEMORE LANE = 53.

ORION the giant Wild Hunter and his Dog - SIRIUS (5)

The Pleiades were being pursued by lecherous old **Orion** across the mountains of Boeotia, and were about to fall into his clutches when they cried to **Zeus** for help, who responded by turning them into doves and placed them in the sky as stars.

The Pleiades, Seven Sisters (daughters of Atlas + Pleione)

MAIA = 6
TAYGETE = 2
ELECTRA = 1
ALCYONE = 5
CELOENO = 6
STEROPE = 8
MEROPE = 9
--
37 = 1

March
3 Thursday

I was kidnapped by two men in black. They served me up a dish of horse meat. Even tried to make it look appetizing - but I wasn't impressed. It looked too sickly.

Then they took me upstairs, threw me on the bed, pulled down my pants and gleefully held up a massive jar of Vaseline. They were going to rape me.

Strange to say, the thought of them forcibly fucking me up the arse, however, did not fill me with fear or loathing. In fact, the anticipation brought a quivering thrill to my senses as I lay there on my stomach with my exposed rectum prepared for penetration.

However, before the unspeakable act could be perpetrated, I dissolved to another situation, where I was being molested by a horny woman. (Or woman wearing horns? Stella Maris? Hard to say. There was too much green mist.)

She was about to seduce this soldier from the Prime Minister's secret militia, who had argued with me about the existence of UFOs. I'd got really angry with his arrogant skepticism. But when his tart decided to grope my dick under the Bible on my lap, I knew I had won a victory. The soldier was being cuckolded before his very eyes. His woman wanted to sexually abuse me, manipulate my genitals until she was ready to suck me in and blow me out in bubbles.

Again, the feeling of anticipation was filled with the sweetened intensity of fire. But as in the previous episode, just before the moment of the erotic resolution, I was snatched away and found myself on the run, being pursued by the soldier's loyal buddies. Should they catch me, I was going to be gang banged, beaten to a pulp and hung from the highest tree.

I was to be their Lynch - pin.

March
4 Friday

Her boyfriend cut down three trees. And their names were Moses, Jesus and Mohammed. They were young trees. All in one pot. I cried my eyes out. The trees seemed so innocent. And yet when we saw the gruesome decapitations, despite my grief, I told Laura not to blame Luther.
"I'm sure he didn't want to do it," I said, weeping a river of tears. The gallant woman put on a brave face and tried to comfort me. I couldn't remember why he had to kill the trees. Was it self-defense? Was it an accident? Did they try to drop a brick on his head? Can you trust trees even when very young? These doubts still didn't stop me from feeling sad.

Moses = 8
Jesus = 2
Mohammed = 9
--
19 = 1

Thinking about the Tree of Life, the Kabbalah and the 10 Sephiroths - I realised that God as described in the Monotheistic religions that sprang up in the Middle East, was 3 different icons, with a particular face or embodiment that was pertinent to that stage of the Judaeo-Christian-Muslim development. Thus, according to the respective traditions,
the God of the Jews was the God of LAW
the God of the Christians was the God of LOVE
the God of the Muslims was the God of MERCY
Here we have a Trinity which unites into One

LAW = 9
LOVE = 9
MERCY = 1
--
19 = 1

Looking at these three great Monotheistic religions, Judaism, Christianity and Islam, I found their respective adherents form a numerological Trinity. Thus demonstrating in an arithmetically beautiful way that the Jew, the Christian and the Muslim are three branches of the one Tree;

JEW = 2
CHRISTIAN = 2
MUSLIM = 6
--
10 = 1

March
5 Saturday

God. There was this dirty old man lying on top of me! He was sexually abusing me, playing with my arse and my bollocks. Guess what, he turned out to be Ayatollah Khomeini (or George Bush?), who is really Beelzebub. (when he is not being Orion or Zeus (he's also a dirty old man))

To my surprise, I actually enjoyed these gropings and digital stimulation of my anus and started to lick the inside of his ear, giving him every encouragement to do whatever he liked with me. Dreamily I closed my eyes in anticipation of a wickedly decadent buggering.

AYATOLLAH = 5
KHOMEINI = 3
--
8

BEELZEBUB = 35 = 8
GEORGE BUSH = 53 Oh shit! Oh fuck!

Is "53" a force for good or a force for bad? Stalin died in 1953, which must have been good. But that Wicked Witch of the West, the Grantham Ghoul, Mad Maggie Thatcher was 53 when she first became PM in 1979, the beginning of Britain's Twilight Years. And another of Thatcher's evil protégés, Tony Blair, was born in 1953.

The Numerical Laws of Procreation

MOTHER	= 7
FATHER	= 4
SONS/DAUGHTERS (4 + 4)	= 8
	--
	19 = 1

The Go-Between linking Heaven and Earth Trinity

HEAVEN	= 1
EARTH	= 7
MESSIAH	= 2
	--
	10 = 1

March
6 Sunday

Laura wanted to peel an apple but couldn't. She cried. And she cried. Her little tears were heart wrenching. In the end, I just had to help. And I did.

Later I thought about Avalon - the Island of Apples, and wondered if I would find any Three-in-One Trinities within the Arthurian Myth. I predict I would, since Holy Grail adds up to 53.

I did the sums and this is what I found.

MERLIN	= 8	MYRDDIN	= 6
CUP	= 4	HOLY GRAIL	= 8
SWORD	= 7	EXCALIBUR	= 5
	--		--
	19 = 1		19 = 1

3:53pm Thor and I made our way to the top of a very tall building. After we'd climbed onto the flat plateau like roof, Thor left me. Again I was being stranded. He was abandoning me because he'd just seen two women making their way to an even taller tower, it looked twice as high as ours, which was across the street, a few miles from here.

I watched with unease as they clambered onto its roof. It was becoming clear that one of the women was decidedly crazy, and that she was out to get me. She had dark rings around her eyes. I then realized this mad woman was my Mother, as she started to throw things at me. From that great gaping distance she hurled giant spears, hammers, cupboards, ironing boards, fridge freezers and anything else she could lay her feverish hands on, that was big, heavy or sharp.

She was definitely out to maim or kill me. My own Mother threw lethal item after lethal item at me, shrieking and screeching a maniacal laughter that chilled the very marrow of my being. But fortunately, however, she kept missing me. She may have had great strength and resourcefulness but she was a lousy shot. One of the spears she threw, I caught and then held it in front of me,

Finally, in sheer desperation, this infanticidal mother decided to throw herself from the elder twin tower, straight at me. As she leapt like a diver, in a self-sacrificial bid to kill me, I closed my eyes, not wanting to see her body impact mine,

But when nothing seemed to hit me, I opened them again, and saw with horror that she had missed and had impaled herself on my spear, right between her legs.

March
7 Monday

The impossible has happened. I cannot believe the medical findings. Laura has made me pregnant. It was discovered when I found a nasty sore on my penis. It was opening out into a vagina-like gash, revealing pus-like substances inside.

It was my doctor who informed me I was three months pregnant (or did he say 3 weeks? 3 days? Or even 3 minutes?). "How comically ironic!" I said. "All the time we were together, it was hoped that Laura would soon be pregnant. And now we're separated, it's me that's preggers."

Whilst listening to the doctor, it hit me what the specific Trinity was within the Arthurian legend - since the Trinity is concerned with Regeneration through the sacrifice of the Father via the Son through incest, then the Arthurian Trinity must be.

ARTHUR	= 5
MORGAN LE FAY	= 9
MORDRED	= 5
	--
	19 = 1

March
8 Tuesday

Quick! I had to get rid of this huge, slimy slug-like bogey I'd just this minute picked from my nose! It fell to the floor and slithered away. Into a dark corner. Jesus, where is it now?

I go out later to the town shopping centre. It looks unfamiliar today. It is free of cars. Pedestrians only. The town square starts off empty of people, but as the morning progresses it begins to fill with youngsters, mostly students. I guess it's a university town. A young woman in yellow and green walks pass me and sits down in front of a charity shop. She gets ready for her daily beg. I stare at her, and she immediately senses the questioning eyes, and glares angrily back at me.
I hear a guitar being played, and assume a busker has arrived. From the crowd emerges the guitarist, a young gypsy, Hippy looking guy, with long thick black hair. He walks towards me, playing and singing his melancholic song. As he gets close to me, I hear the last lines, which seemed to be directed at me "...you are going to Die," when suddenly he swings round to a woman on my left, and waving his stick with a skull handle on top, grabs her by the shoulder. She collapses, seemingly dead. Is this some kind of Divine Comedy, I ask myself, because people on my right burst out laughing, as if they were watching some kind of anarchic street theatre.

STREET COMEDY = 53

The media tycoon, Rupert Murky-Bear, who is secretly working for the CIA (so I am reliably informed by the founder, Julie Strange, of Weewee-Leaks (also known as P.I.S.S, the People's International Secret Service)) has sold all his shares in WasteBook, the social networking website as cheaply as possible. He owns 33%. Simultaneously, his newspapers, TV networks and Bally-hoo internet news service spread stories of WasteBook not capable of generating sufficient revenues. The effect is devastating. The share prices plummet to an all-time low, as all the other shareholders panic and sell, sell, sell. This is exactly what Murky-Bear had hoped would happen. And so, he buys all the shares at rock bottom prices, making him the sole owner...or rather the Central Intelligence Agency the sole owner, giving the US intelligence service unprecedented access to the hearts and minds of billions of users around the world.

March
9 Wednesday

A small dog comes bursting through the cat-flap. I've never seen it before but it is very demanding. It's a strange creature, full of energy and slightly dangerous. In fact, I find it very dubious. Somehow, things will never be the same again.

6pm …I was about to throw away this old, unused tub of clover margarine. There's no point in keeping it, it'll be awfully rancid by now. I open the lid to check the contents of the tub and find in one corner that the marg was in the process of clotting. In fact, before my very eyes, it was congealing into what looked like a messy bundle of fur and spikey spines.

With nervous trepidation I gave the bizarre assemblage a prod, whereupon it revealed itself to be a tiny living creature - a sort of hedgehog trying to be a porcupine.

Anyway, whatever it was trying to be, it certainly wasn't trying to remain small. It was growing by the minute, nay, by the second. And as it grew, so did its personality. On top of which, I was beginning to detect that it had very human traits and was capable of communicating in the English language.

And it had such a cheeky smile too. I wanted to pick it up but I was afraid of the spikes. However, this charming creature gave me a wink, said a few words and I knew it would be OK.

"Do you have a name?" I asked the jovial creature.

"What name do you want to give me?" He said as he slowly metamorphosed into a three year old human cub.

"Must I?" I asked anxiously.

"I'm yours. You must."

The little fellah waddled over to the games table and picked up a dice.

"Throw this dice and whatever number is uppermost, you must give me a name that fits that number."

I threw a SIX…which I then inputted into the "Name-Oracle" program I'd especially written to help me in the numerology research. The computer came up with the following names.

Achilles, Alex, Benny, Billy, Bryan, Dion, Evan, Fred, Geoffrey, Hugo, Ian, Jurupari, Karl, Lucian, Michael, Narcissus, Odin, Ovid, Oceanus, Proteus, Rama, Rolf, Sam, Seamus, Stephen, Teddy, Victor, Wakonda

"28 names. How do I choose?"

"What's your favourite number?"

"Well, I'm being harassed by 53 at the moment."

"Well, the computer didn't cough up 53 names. But let's use 5 and 3," the little lad suggested.

"5 plus 3 makes 8. We could choose the eighth name."

"Nah, that's Fred. Don't want to be called Fred. Why don't you subtract 8 from 28."

"Twenty."

"Then, give me the twentieth name…"

"Proteus…"

"Thank you. That'll do nicely. I have to go now." He said, taking my staff.

"Where?" I asked, giving him my cloak.

"To live with my mother." He took the lamp from the hall and I lit it.

"But you came out of me, didn't you?"

"Yes, but I must live with Laura. Thank you and Goodbye."

Looking like the Hermit on the Tarot card, my rapidly growing son, Proteus, walked out the door and into the night.

The Hermit's Trinity
CLOAK = 6
LAMP = 6
STAFF = 7
--
19 = 1

I spoke the word "Proteus" into the computer and it responded with "Proteus, an early Greek god of the sea, son of Oceanus and Tethys. Proteus had the gift of prophecy and was a shape-shifter."

Not surprisingly, I found Proteus, his father and mother formed a Triadic Union.

OCEANUS = 6
TETHYS = 7
PROTEUS = 6
--
19 = 1

And what about me, Laura and this weird offspring of ours?

SHIRAM = 5
LAURA = 8
PROTEUS = 6
--
19 = 1

March
10 Thursday

Something covering my face. Wet. Something like shaving cream or shampoo or soap. Can't breathe. Feel like I'm drowning.
Aliens? Interfering. Intruders?
I blow my nose. Blood from right nostril. Fuck, could this be a sign of alien intervention?

Later…I and a group of young Nihilists travel to Italy. We arrived in Venice and meet Volpone (the FOX) - a degenerate debauched, decadent rich bastard - who reminds me of a cross between Noel Coward and Oscar Wilde. Very camp and very irritating. We despise him and abuse his hospitality. Eventually, we get so pissed off with him and his flaunting of his largess that we decide to kill him. The man is a pathetic specimen of a disease. I do the dirty deed. We return to England after I've been caught and imprisoned for 6 hours, 6 minutes and 6 seconds. My friends have now turned against me for being a murderer. I try to explain it wasn't my idea but the guilt doesn't go away and I weep for the loss of my innocence and potential saintliness. I cry to my dead mother and father for forgiveness.

VOLPONE = 9

F O X = 9
6 6 6

Is all forgiven? Because…Wow! Another night sky full of colourful UFOs. Proteus, our three year old boy, noticed them first and pointed them out to me. Once I saw a few, the sky then seemed cluttered with them. I called Laura and directed her to look up, and what she saw, made her mouth drop in childlike wonder.
"Are they real?" she asked.
"Yes. Beautiful, aren't they!" I replied.

March
11 Friday

My spastic old school friend, Icarus (who was so severely Cerebral Palsied, he couldn't use his hands to give himself a wank), told me once that when he lived in a Cheshire Cat Home, he frequently enjoyed the personal services of future brothel queen, Madam Sinfear N. Pain. He said she began her career in the sex industry while working as a care assistant in the cripples home, and it was she who introduced the practice of helping disabled inmates have sex, in any way they wanted it. Later when she ran her own high class brothel, she became famous for accepting luncheon vouchers as payment, and more importantly, for giving 50% discount to disabled punters. Eventually, she was honoured with an M.B.E. for her charitable services. Now Hollywood are making a biopic about her, and I'm pleased to say my friend, Icarus has a cameo role of grateful Spazzy client.

This afternoon I found this homeless fox, which befriended me. We went everywhere together. Laura loved him but I loved him more.

Then it was time for me to go away and leave the fox. It was then he spoke to me for the first time. He begged me not to go. I burst into tears and said I didn't want to leave him but I had no choice.

After I had left the house, I remembered my son Proteus was a shape shifter and wondered if the fox was he.

March
12 Saturday

I move into my new place in Ireland. A country house. A farm. It's huge. A bit of a maze. Can get properly lost on the property.

I've invited some friends from England for a house warming. A knock on the door...but there's no one there. A herd of cattle pass close by. One leaves and goes into another field - where the "fairy fort" is - possibly forbidden. I sense this is a mistake. Sure enough, the ominous shadow becomes a massive bull - the biggest and fattest I've ever seen and he's very angry - with us. He sees us inside and positions himself to charge the house. I believe he is going to demolish the house to get at us.

MINOTAUR = 3
MAZE = 9
THESEUS = 7
---
19 = 1

Then someone shouts “Cut”. Or was it “Cat”? Which reminds me - where is my black pussy?
A Hollywood film crew are there. What we were doing? - I don’t know. But Oscar the director seemed to know. At first, the floor in the sitting room was covered up in large white dust sheets. One of the crew was placing objects on the floor around the cooking range, we both noticed the surface was wobbly and uneven. The tiles! Were they lose or broken? We pulled away the cloth and we saw an absolute mess of broken clay. Then for the first time I noticed the antique oven was missing and the gap had been crudely bricked up. I’d only previously extolled the virtues of having such an item. I suddenly realised that since I’d arrived with the company I hadn’t noticed that the recent burglary was a total ransacking of my home. Literally everything - not just the videos (though I notice they didn’t steal “The Exorcist” - what were they afraid of?) and a few ornaments - was gone. Curtains, carpets, books - the place had been cleaned out. In the midst of my horror, the set designer informed me that I could fit two beds in the rooms - rather than just one double bed. For a moment I was easily distracted and began a discussion on this furniture arranging topic. But my heart wasn’t in it. I had too much on my mind.

Aliens and the number THREE TRIANGLE TRINITY

“The Visitors often appear in threes. They project triangular lights. They have been reported to wear various types of triangular devices and emblems. People see three pyramids or three triangles in connection with them. A huge triangular object is sometimes sighted...”

- **‘Communion’** by Whitley Strieber

During the night I heard a man’s voice and he said I should send my UFO story “Ark Angel” to Disney Productions.

March
13 Sunday

A Vietnamese potbellied pig visits. He tells me his name is Myrddin and becomes my companion for a day. But I think he could be Proteus. He talks to me.

"Interaction or communion between the polarities or opposites
creates a third element, entity or force -
  a transformation
    symbiosis
        the next generation
        a new stage or step
        a progression to a higher level"

"Thus, you see," he continues, "the Trinity or Triangle is the symbol for Transformation."

Myddin then vomits, and out of the steaming mess on the floor, he extracts a small dictation device.

"Here is a tape recording I borrowed from Uri Geller. It was made in 1973 of an "alien" speaking.

"Uri Geller?" I said, "He adds up to 53."

"Of course. Listen, you will find Geller's ET is hinting at what you are discovering with Tri-numeracy."

The pig presses "play" on his mini-disc player.
"...the computerised beings are under the direction of the 'Controller' or what Earth-man calls God or gods. In the future, this general idea would be formulated in rigorous mathematical language."

March
14 Monday

I thought I was in Ireland when I heard Laura's voice spiral down. "Shiram. You don't help me. Where are you?"

But no-

I'd just arrived at my old home in England. The bags weren't even unpacked. Alky Elroy saw me arrive and came barging in through the front door to welcome me back, then we heard Laura's haunting, plaintive voice from outside. Elroy and I both rushed to open the door, but the old drunk schizo beat me to it. I wanted to take her in my arms but -

I found myself back in Ireland.

Myrddin said the four keys of the universe were circle, cross, spiral and line...but I suggested there was a fifth, which was the messenger, the go-between. By my calculation, if the quintet is to add up to one, then the fifth element must be the triangle....

CIRCLE = 5
CROSS = 2
SPIRAL = 3
LINE = 4

TRIANGLE = 5 BINGO!!!!
--
19 = 1

I looked out of the window, and to my horror, I saw a great multitude rushing towards the cottage. Crowds of invaders charging across the fields with sheep dogs, but thankfully, an invisible barrier keeps them at bay.

March
15 Tuesday

This morning I found slivers of glass upon my person and wheelchair. Where the hell did they come from? Ah, didn't I hear that someone had broken…shattered my crystal? Or was it someone else's crystal? Later I heard Oscar Grills was holding his favourite crystal in his hand whilst listening to the theme music of "the Good, the Bad and the Ugly" when he died. That's what the vicar said at the memorial service. So that's where the glass bits came from....

LIFE	= 5
DEATH	= 2
RESURRECTION	= 3
	--
	10 = 1

Numbers 17, 1 – 13: Then EIGHT said to Eight, "Tell the people of Israel to bring you twelve wooden rods, one from each prince of Israel's ancestral tribes, and carve each prince's name on his rod. Carve Aaron's name on the rod of the house of Levi, for there must be one rod for the chieftain of each ancestral tribe. Place these rods in the Tabernacle in front of the Ark containing the tablets of the Covenant, where I meet with you. Buds will sprout on the rod belonging to the man I choose. Then I will finally put an end to the people's seditious murmurings and complaints against you." So Eight gave the instructions to the people of Israel, and each of the twelve tribal chieftains, including Aaron, brought Eight a rod. Eight placed the rods in EIGHT's presence in the Tabernacle of the Covenant. When he went into the Tabernacle of the Covenant the next day, he found that the Rod of Aaron, for the house of Levi, had sprouted, budded, and brought forth buds, and bloomed blossoms, and yielded almonds. When Eight brought all the rods out, he showed them to the people. Each man claimed his own rod. And EIGHT said to Eight: "Place the Rod of Aaron permanently before the Ark of the Covenant to serve as a warning to rebels. This should put an end to their blasphemies against me and prevent any further deaths." So Eight did as EIGHT commanded him. Then the people of Israel said to Eight, "Look, we are doomed! We are dead! We are ruined! Everyone who even comes close to the Tabernacle of EIGHT dies. Are we all doomed to die?"

ROD OF AARON = 53

March
16 Wednesday

Disgusting. Maria Stella Maris and I were about to fuck. She wanted it as much as I did. It was going to be anal sex. First, I was going to fuck her up the arse, followed by her fucking me up the arse with a vibrator. We both knew we were going to enjoy it. There was one problem, though. Before we were permitted to begin, I had to eat shit - I literally had to consume a plateful of steaming human excreta. I had to spoon it all in my mouth, chew and swallow.
MSM felt sorry for me and tried to encourage me - that the (ordure) ordeal would be worthwhile if it meant a good buggering. I tried to eat whilst she chatted soothingly to me - it was horrible, foul - In the end, I couldn't stomach anymore and was violently sick. The wretched mess just projected out of my mouth. MSM was very sympathetic. I think I passed the test. Because we then made passionate love...

This evening the phone rang. It was Laura demanding paternity money for Proteus.
I tell her I don't have any spare cash on me. She replies, "What about your dodgy Swiss bank account? You got loads of dosh in there, I'm sure."
"But that requires a trip to Switzerland," I protested.
"Well, go to fucking Switzerland, you cuckoo!" She slams down the phone.

I book a flight and quickly get to the airport departure hall which looks more like a huge yawning warehouse, cavernous, untidy but empty of people. I go to find Disabled Services, and find no staff in attendance. However, another disabled passenger is waiting. It's an old friend, Malkuth Binah, who went with me to the flying course in Yankland twenty years ago. Malkuth, clever sod, managed to get his pilot's licence, but I failed because I was crap at landing. However, today Malkuth looked very ill as he greeted me. We heard the tannoy announce we should proceed to our flight departure gate, but the gate number was garbled. Couldn't understand what announcer said. Neither did we know how to get to where we should proceed to. That's why we needed assistance. Malkuth said he would look for help. As he departed he tried to give me a kiss, which I wasn't too keen on, since his face looked like he suffered from Bubonic plague. Also he wasn't trying very hard to make physical contact, as his lips kept missing my face. Finally, he gave up and went away. A few minutes later, I looked over a balcony, and saw Malkuth below me, in a crowd of people, in the car park. Suddenly he started shouting that he wanted to die. He had had enough. Then he collapsed, and a paramedic picked him up and took him to the departure gate. I tried to follow but saw that my way was a narrow ledge, and I thought my wheelchair was too wide for it. Besides, I was sure if I tried to bump my chair up onto the ledge, it would destabilize my approach, and I would topple over to my death. To my later regret, I quickly gave up as I was sure it was a test. Instead I waited for the medical attendant who was an old man, who looked as if he was in need of greater help. At gate 53 Malkuth was showing off his new jet pack. "See, I don't need an airplane." This reminded me of when I could levitate. Then, Malkuth's jet pack goes out of control, throws him off and dives straight at me, hitting my wheelchair, and sending me flying.

March
17 Thursday

Today, I was reading a biography on Sigmund Freud, called "Genius or Dirty Bugger?" when I felt this light tap on my shoulder. I turned around, and there he was, the randy old goat.
"Herr Siggy Freud! What a pleasant surprise. How did you get here?" I exclaimed.
"I have only one thing to say to you, young man. Read my book, THE INTERPRETATION OF DREAMS." And then he was gone.

It's night. The city. I'm out with Proteus. He's looking human again. We're having a pleasant stroll through the empty streets. It's not dark. Perhaps the light is coming from street lamps...or maybe from some Divine Source. Anyway, I worry about straying too far. Proteus, although he is growing rapidly, is only 5 years old, so I decide we must turn back home. I call him. He runs back willingly. All is well.

The triangle is "..the fundamental building block of the universe" (Whitley Strieber)
"..the central symbol of growth in many ancient traditions. It relates to the three holy forces of creation and is the main sense of the Holy Trinity."

My own numerological research in the Holy Trinities bears this out.

March
18 Friday

In the morning, on the table was a plate of spaghetti. Long writhing, wriggling strands. Alive. Then the plate was gone. Why did it fly? And where to?

Later, I switched on the telly, saw a programme on snakes, magical mystical beasts, much maligned. Ha ha ha, there was a shot of snakes on a plate of spaghetti. I looked at the Time. It was 3:53 - the Hermetic number 353 - Ourobus, snake eating its own tail, the constant circle, the eternal cycle.

My three totem animals from childhood. Black Panther, Wolf and Snake.

BLACK PANTHER	= 3
WOLF	= 2
SNAKE	= 5
	--
	10 = 1

I went to pay the young car thief £10 to stop him from robbing me - but he would only take £5. I was sitting in my wheelchair outside my car with the door open when he suddenly invited himself in and started rummaging around, looking to see what he could nick. He didn't seem to care I was there watching him. He knew there wasn't a lot I could do, being a cripple. Anyway, he was very charming for a skinhead thug. Maybe his heart wasn't in it because he gladly took the fiver, and then agreed to help me with my shopping. So I wasn't really paying "protection", I was buying a cheap chauffeur!

March
19 Saturday

Awoke with a bang - 10.05 am. What the fuck was it? The central heating system about to explode? Anyway, it got me out of bed. After a few minutes of checking around the house, I find everything still seems to be working properly.

I was in my new car with some friends. The young thug was driving. Another passenger was this middle-aged hippy type professor, who with his long grey hair, does the "Eccentric Academic" bit on popular science and archaeology TV shows. He tells me he is in so much demand, he even had to turn down "Time Team". We go to town and see a couple of armed soldiers patrolling - martial law is in full swing. They stop to chat with us. They're quite friendly. They tell us the Army is being used to supplement the Bobby on the Beat - because street crime and vandalism has increased beyond control. I suggested that loaded machine guns were a bit excessive and may cause more problems than cure. The soldiers shrugged, and claimed that it is working, and it's what the people want. I suspect a more sinister purpose behind it. Preparation for the coming New World Order. As more soldiers appear, an Army jeep arrives and pulls up alongside outside the community centre. In the front passenger seat is Princess Danu, (who strangely reminds me of the late Princess Di). An appreciative crowd soon gathers and she begins a press conference. Complaining about her married life and the hell she suffered from the Royal family. How her anorexia was caused by the Morrigan King Mother. (Funny how history always seems to repeat itself, I thought. Maybe she won't live long either.) One of the officers in the jeep tried to quieten her down - playing Devil's Advocate and suggesting the issue is not as simple as she's trying to make out. However, it's clear, he and she are nonetheless good friends, and Princess Danu has a lot of respect for him. He ushers her out for the Official Meeting - a Royal Rally - in the Community Centre. I realise we are on the brink of a civil war. That the Army is split between support for the puppet Monarchy and the Fascist establishment, and Danu and her "New Romantics" faction of Plastic Revolutionaries.

The skinhead thug helps me get out of the car as the crowd rush to Danu's insurrectional meeting. As I looked and listened to her speech, I thought more and more about Princess Di, who had had premonition dreams of her murder.

We may never know what Diana saw.

A toyshop. I've been there before. Many times before. I knew my way around and knew exactly what section I wanted. Glass cabinets and bins of plastic soldiers. I was particularly interested in Britain's knights. The girl shop assistant wasn't very good at reading the sign, which had a table of prices. The one that stood out was £10.90. The larger dinosaurs were £34. Too expensive for very poor quality craftsmanship.

March
20 Sunday

Laura was still angry with me, for letting her go. Luther, her new boyfriend was with her but still she kept having a go at me.
"Are you telling me that you will never come back to me?" she shouted.
"Yes. You know we're finished" I replied trying to calm her down.
"How could you do this to me?" she screamed. "You're saying we will never make love again. Never share a night of passion. How is this possible, after all we have been through?"
"We can't turn the clock back. That time is over." I shouted back.

One of my books keeps disappearing - "Wolves and Werewolves" by John Pollard. This is the third time. Twice it has returned but always when I'm in a different country. I wonder about the author's name - John Pollard. Does it add up to 53? I bought the book second hand from the local library. Well, I should say the book bought me. It just fell in my lap and said "Buy Me".

I did the sums and Hot-digger-di-dog-dog. JOHN POLLARD = 53

Now the damn book has gone walkies again.

I read this autobiography by a disabled actor, who wrote… "*When I was a child, I once met the so-called 'People's Princess'. She paid a Royal Visit to an art exhibition at my special school. I showed her my painting of a car crash and she shuddered, muttering "Horrible. How can you paint such things."*
I tell her I only paint dreams. It's good therapy. Perhaps she too should turn her dreams into works of art.

"Oh no, I couldn't. They would be just too horrible. I have dreams like your painting. Nasty car crashes. Men in black coming to murder me."
"Really? Tell me about them." She was about to say more when she stopped and looked at me confused and frightened. She quickly went away to talk to another child.
Afterwards I told everyone Princess Di would be dead by the end of the year. No one believed me, of course...until she was dead three months later."

Yesterday's episode and remembering the disabled actor's story, caused me to hypothesise that PRINCESS DI would add up to 53. It did. And so does our very own PRINCESS DANU.

PRINCESS DI = 53
PRINCESS DANU = 53

March
21 Monday

I was walking down the city streets and decided to walk past a night club down a dark back alley. It was evening. Creeping along the walls was a creature I thought I would never see in this day and age. A Stegosaur! Yes, one of the dinosaurs. It wasn't the normal size. Usually they reach the size of rhinos or elephants. No, luckily this one was about the size of a large dog - or maybe a small donkey. Nonetheless, it still had me worried. Was it carnivorous or herbivore? Would it seek to do me damage? It seemed to be frolicking along like a kitten. In fact, its face was very childlike, big wide mischievous eyes. Actually, it reminded me of a little girl I know, especially when it saw me. Its eyes lit up and it came bounding over like a playful puppy. And that's when the similarity ended. Within seconds I knew my life was in danger. I was food. It leapt for my throat, ready to swallow me whole, but in the nick of time I pulled out my pencil and prodded it, keeping the ferocious creature at bay. But a pencil is no defence really and soon the predator had it in its mouth, slowly swallowing it bit by bit, jaws inching closer to my fingers grasping the flimsy stick of wood. Soon it had taken the whole of my weapon in its mouth and I watched spellbound as it disappeared down the gruesome lizard's deep throat. Just as the Horror returned its beady eyes on me, ready to pounce once more, a look of pain and surprise clouded its face, which then turned blue and purple, as it started to choke. It had bitten off more than it could chew. Swallowing the pencil whole clearly was not a good idea. The creature was in a frenzy as it fought desperately for breath. It tried to make itself vomit out the obstructing article. Sticking its fingers down its throat, trying to make itself sick - but the pencil wouldn't budge. Instead, everything else it had swallowed came gushing out. Judging by the flood of its contents, the creature made a habit of swallowing its food whole. It also seemed rather indiscriminate about what it ate. In the gooey mess writhing on the pavement were rubber gloves, syringes, a crocodile - whole and still alive because I'm sure I saw its heart beat and an eye quiver. Then the biggest surprise came when a huge lump resembling a baby stegosaur comes projectiling out of its retching jaws (but still no pencil) and thudded against the wall opposite, knocking it back into consciousness. The young creature's eyes sprang open and gave a baleful stare at its erstwhile persecutor, and then spoke - in a young girl's voice.

"It's a sad day when mothers eat their young. I am your only daughter, and this is how you treat me. You are not content with taking food from the baby's mouth, you have to take THE BABY as food into your mouth. Talk about parental abuse."

The mother stegosaur wasn't paying much attention to the daughter's reproach, it was still trying to regurgitate my pencil.

I decided it was politic to withdraw and leave this family squabble to find its own resolution.

STEGOSAUR = 35
DINOSAUR (Greek for "terrible lizard")

What will men do when they become dragons?
Dragon comes from the old Greek "to see".
The Dragon is a Seer. A Dragon sees.
Why did George kill the Seer? The All-Seeing Eye?
Why? Because it saw too much? Too soon? Too much knowledge is deadly.
For whom? George or the Seer? Or both?
Or was it that the Christian St. George wanted to blind us with Religion?
Deprive us of sight. Deny us Truth?

DRAGON	= 5	GEORGE	= 3	(8)
GOOD	= 5	EVIL	= 3	(8)
ALIEN	= 5	ANGEL	= 3	(8)
OWL	= 5	EAGLE	= 3	(8)

March
22 Tuesday

At the Past Lives therapy group, sitting in a circle, discussing, of all people, Jimmy Saville (self-appointed Patron Saint of Cripples)! One woman was describing how once when she met him, he got upset with her because she pretended not to know who this great personage was. It was on the tip of my tongue to tell her about my own similar experience with "Mr Fix-It" but something held me back. Perhaps I felt to do so would have been too ingratiating. Maybe it would have made me too much a part of the "in-crowd".

Which reminds me - I woke up this morning with my nose stuffed with blood. I blow and blow and so the blood flows...

I killed a man...or that's what I thought at first, but in fact, I just rendered him unconscious? Anyway, I spent most of the time trying to hide his body. A cupboard in the kitchen was possibly a good bet. Who was he? A friend. Probably. My other half. My old half. My better half? Have I removed the old unwanted self? Or will he simply come back to haunt me? Alternatively, I may destroyed the last remaining good happy parts of myself. Only time will tell as I continue this perilous journey down an aborted life.

A Greek philosopher once told me, "War is an evil in as much as it produces more wicked men than it takes away." Is this supposed to be a mathematical truth? Can one find an equation that would prove this statement to be a fact? Does this mean that we can calculate that today there are more evil people in the world than there has ever been in the past? If every war creates a surplus of evil, then with every successive war the increment of evil is added to the prior surplus, and if war is the product of evil, then with every increase in evil there will be an increase in wars – which means there is no hope for humanity. Since war, spurred on by wickedness, will increase in number and scale at an exponential rate because wickedness, spurred on by wars, will also increase in number and scale at an exponential rate, until finally there will be nothing but wars, and nothing but wickedness – and then eventually there will be nothing. Perhaps our salvation lies in trying to discover what is it that produces more goodness than it takes away – and endeavour to set it against war, and hope that of the two, it is, mathematically speaking, the more powerful. **In terms of Numerology; WAR = 6, and PEACE = 3, which suggests that all Peace can ever achieve is a slowing down of the tidal wave of wickedness. It can never halt or turn it back completely.**

March
23 Wednesday

I come back with the grocery shopping, and find the living room infested with squirmy metallic wire-like interconnecting intelligent super-strings, knitting the substructure fabric at the base of the universe. This discovery ought to be Nobel prize winning stuff, but instead the pulsating writhing mesh feels malevolent and suffocating. I quickly vacate the flat in search of a woman.

Vanessa, Jake's Yankie girlfriend, confesses to me that she is the girl Laura found for me and loves me and wants us to make love. She says all this in front of Jake, which embarrasses me - although secretly, I'm overjoyed (over the moon, in fact). Jake says he already knew about Vanessa's feelings towards me and was coming to terms with it. This was aimed to make me feel better but my intense sense of guilt compromised my yearning for the "wolf-woman". She, however, took me in her arms and gave me a passionate kiss on the lips. Swimming in ecstasy, I now knew where my fate lay, howling between her legs under a full moon.

March
24 Thursday

Dave Rappaport, the dwarf actor who shot himself beneath the Hollywood sign. He deluded himself into thinking the Yanks would make him into a big star…but the only "short-arse" to ever make it big in America was Spielberg's ET.

I'm going to write a movie about him (since we are both "short-arse" actors) and was looking at his life's history through a series of photographs. Moments of hopeful optimism shine in the portraits which only serve to accentuate the overall sadness of a suicide's life deprived of a million opportunities. I'm on my way to the other side of the city. I stopped off at my friend's place. She said she once knew Dave. Or was it his widow? Now she is just his window. She seemed too young to have been his contemporary. Anyway, time has made her a single parent. We had a good chat and I was going to crash at her place for the night. I asked her how to get to the Other Side. Rather than show, she said she would come with me…if I didn't mind. I was pleased. I'd done this journey many times but it's always safer if you have a guide. She decided to ring the father of her child as he lived near where we were going. She wanted to take the opportunity to see him. Talking to him, outside on the street, she quickly got angry. All the old wounds were opening up. He was being difficult. Tomorrow at 2pm was not convenient. Besides, he wanted to see her alone and not with me in tow. She got hysterical and screamed abuse down the phone. The Yuppies outside, drinking "Happy Hour" cocktails stared in amazement as she threw the phone to the ground and stamped on it, smashing it to smithereens. They were aghast as she stormed off down the street. "How could anyone treat such a valuable item (icon) of the Information Age this way! A mobile phone! The most potent status symbol since the Crucifix" They were also under the impression that it wasn't even her property. I told one particular nosey parker that it was a cordless phone and not a cell phone. There is a difference. His snob's antennae waved in agreement. And secondly, I said, it came from her house so she was perfectly entitled to give it a sound thrashing. At this point the Yuppy actually became quite human, once the formal misunderstandings were laid to rest.

March
25 Friday

Back in the USA. Doing research on Dave Rappaport and the Gun Culture which murdered him and John Lennon. I'm in a large room with a group of Americans. We're in a convivial circle. They all like me and think I'm their friend. So they are really shocked and hurt when I launch into one of my usual Anti-Yank tirades. "I am so bored with the USA. You fucking Yanks dominate us with your plastic, tasteless junk food, your junk therapy, you brain-dead us with your dumb-ass TV, your wafer thin movies, your spoon-fed education, your rich man's democracy. And I hate your Prayer TV with its Fundamentalist Christian Nazism. If I had a time-machine, I'd get Christopher Columbus to take up golf to distract him from discovering America. You know my archetypal image of an American is a candy-sucking King Kong. America is the spoilt selfish brat of the world's family. You Yanks are just 6% of the world's population, yet you now consume 66% of global resources. This is why you keep invading and fucking up other people's countries and why you create these biological and chemical weapons and make wars everywhere. To keep your share of resources, you need to wipe out two thirds of the Third World's populations. I call America the world's toilet. You Yanks are responsible for 50% of the world's solid waste. In a real way, the USA is the United Shits of Ass-holes."

I'm asked about an American TV import - "Didn't you think it was wonderful?"

"You mean that 'Eeeee-Argggh, Let's Pretend We have the Greatest HealthCare Show'."

I said, "NO, it's your typical sub-standard Yankie cultural imperialist tripe."

Brad, the flight instructor was there. I was embarrassed by his presence because I'd been slagging him off as a lousy teacher, but I secretly know I was a lousy pupil. He started to say how astonished he was that I thought the way I talked. He didn't think, imagine that I was so naive, so simplistic. I cringed my way out into another space....

It was the fat American who tried to sell me his dump of a house in Chicago. Now he was in the movie-making business. He claimed he had this leading role for me. Good sexy part but he couldn't show me the script yet. Just slips of paper with doubtful promises. The whole affair seemed seedy as we crouched over his plans in a half-light full of gloomy shadows in a decrepit old building.

"Money's a problem at the moment" he said, "but we'll sort something out. Hopefully, we'll have enough to pay for you to get over there". Ukraine I think he hinted. The next shock came when he said his wife would be directing. She'd never been in films before.

"Don't worry," he whispered sly, "I'll see you are not short of a girl or two. There's plenty out there, who'll do anything for peanuts." I knew then he was a gangster.

Three nerves in the spinal cord to the brain - three pathways. When signals arrive in the brain, they go to three places;

CORTEX = 4
THALAMUS = 5
RETICULAR SYSTEM = 1
---
10 = 1

March
26 Saturday

Was awoken by a woman's voice calling my name. Was she in my head? Don't think so. Seemed very real. It wasn't Laura...and I don't think it was Stella Maris. Perhaps, The Unknown Woman?

In the evening I visited Hera and her daughter Ilithyia. Hera was blowing hot and cold as usual. One minute she was all over me, next she was keeping me at a distance with a barge pole. Zeus was also there. They seemed to have patched up their differences. We saw a cabinet display which contained strange moving objects. This was on our way out. We all had to go somewhere. I knew this strange holographic device was interactive, so I touched the glass. Hera tried to stop me. She thought I was wrong. But I wasn't. Music came at my touch. I moved my hands, and tunes and colour sensations occurred. Hera changed instantly, and was very affectionate. She kissed me on the lips. It was soft, sweet and very giving. I knew this time she was serious.

March
27 Sunday

Arrive in Britain. A huge conference. Democracy on trial. Women are in power and already they have learned like the men before them, how to abuse their power. A great woman leader - very egalitarian, a real justice-seeker - no less than Princess Danu (her insurrection was successful) - is undermined and the democratic system she had painstakingly re-installed has been wrecked by a committee of female chauvinist despots. The last stand is at the conference. All the men are too intimidated to even attend. I'm the only man with the nerve to challenge the women's supremacy. I'm not a misogynist. I know men had committed crimes with the world, in the past but now the pendulum has swung too far the other way - and women wearing the jackboots are just as bad. I believe in equality for all and so I dare speak at the women only conference. After a bitter struggle - my words carry the day and all the true freedom-loving women vote with me to over-rule the Executive, and the great woman leader (she's looking more and more like Gaia) is reinstated.

There are three essential elements to a campaigning and winnable struggle

FIRE = 2
WIT = 7
INTELLECT = 1
--
10 = 1

The top two words can be changed to PASSION and HUMOUR, and the sum will still be the same

PASSION = 3
HUMOUR = 6
INTELLECT = 1
--
10 = 1

March
28 Monday

I'm working on a movie. I've got an insignificant part. More or less an extra. It's a street scene and I've got to push myself down the road whilst the female star, Selene Taygete runs down alongside me. We're not supposed to acknowledge each other but my will, my determination to become more significant especially to her, is so powerful, she starts acting as if I was her co-star. She runs, dives and slides, glides on her belly along the pavement. It was my idea - she likes it and the director likes it. It becomes more elaborate and surreal, and so she becomes more interested in me. At one point she lets her thigh touch my hand. Another actor congratulates me on my comeback. Suddenly everyone remembers all the great work I'd done in the past. Another bit-player says that he couldn't get a part in "Jack's Cry of Joy", so I must be good.

The aloof but charming Hollywood movie star, Patrick Wolf, briefly graces us with his presence, waving cheerily from the open top stretch limo. No real contact is ever made. We continue to work hard at our rehearsals in the warehouse hanger while he just swans around, getting all the kudos. But let's not talk about him. I want to tell you about her - a

small petite delicious girl, very warm and cuddlesome, Tilda. She was a mixture of Vita, Vanessa, Stella Maris and Laura all rolled in one and maybe more. She worked on this women's film co-op movie as production assistant - it was something in the vein of "Orlando" - a woman's Greenaway - but more subtle, softer, gooey, dishonest perhaps.
I attended a preview and Tilda attended me! We lay together, snuggling up to each other. It was glorious. I had been starved of female bodily affection.

Then, people talked about her and her boyfriend who she met on the movie. They were supposed to be madly in love. Now I was hurt, disappointed and confused. It's the same old story and I'm back to square one.

6pm Lord Mayor's Civic Reception. I meet Sir David Atthegrove. We get on fine. He tells me his brother wants to offer me a job.
"Who, Dicky Darling?"
No, his other brother - Allen
"Alien?"
No. Allen.
I didn't know there was a third genius in the family.

Lord Allen Atthegrove shook my hand and said one thing,
"Humans normally experience the physical through the
5 sensory - 3 dimensional modality. Thus, existing only at
the 5::3 level of perception."

DAVID = 4
DICKY = 7 (RICHARD = 7)
ALLEN = 4
--
19 = 1

March
29 Tuesday

In a chill-out room with friends - very Hippy atmosphere, laid back music, Laura and Luther out of their heads. Laura, looking serenely happy. Luther is surprised and comments, "You seem to be at home in this sort of company."
Laura just smiles.

At about 1.15pm I was looking out of the window when I saw a UFO! It was spherical and metallic and travelling really fast in a straight line, from left to right. The tree branches weren't moving, so it didn't look like there was any wind. It was totally noiseless. I called everyone to have a look but only Laura managed to see it in time before it disappeared in some clouds. She thought she could see strange wings on the top and bottom of the sphere.

March
30 Wednesday

I had to rescue the Handsome Hero. He was stuck (trapped?) in a parallel universe.

"Who are you?" I asked as I brought him back down (up? sideways? inside out? outside in? betwixt bewitched befuddled?) to Earth....

"I guess I can describe myself as the New Medieval Man. My search for the Holy Grail is in part the Quest for the Theory of Everything - and I believe the re-discovery of the Occult Systems will help illuminate the problems of the new sciences and maths. Chaos and Quantum are tied up in Super-strings or a web of mystical archetypal structures. And I think my extraordinary discoveries, as you will read...." (he hands me several sheets of closely written paper)
"... may help find new ways of understanding and predicting problems in a variety of disciplines. The Law of Triadic Structures..."
"Excuse me," I interrupted, "but that is exactly what I'm investigating."
"I know!" he smiled, "the Law of Triadic Structures seems to determine all existence, all imagination, all movement, all change, all cycles. The

Building Blocks of the Universe..."
"Yes. Yes. That's exactly what I'm finding!" I exclaimed excitedly.

Then the Handsome Hero collapsed in a flood of tears, exhausted. "What am I talking about?" he groaned, clutching his right side, "I don't really know. I just know I've found something rather odd."

I woke up several times during the night at Lydia's. There was someone in the sitting room. I felt haunted. Did Lydia have ghosts? I asked her when she brought in my morning coffee.
"No," she said, "but Miles might have been astral visiting. He does that sometimes."

A new structure in the middle of the road, full of steps and stairs impossible for me to cross independently. Lydia has to help me. I'm furious. The Council had no right to do this. Not in this day and age. She didn't fill me with confidence although we managed the crossing. At the Council offices I ranted and raved. They sympathized, felt I had a case and would see to it that my protest reached the highest authority. If the structure did not become more wheelchair friendly, I warned, I would bomb it, demolish it.
"Yes, of course. Quite justified too. We will do all we can to help you."

Later after leaving Lydia, I visit Lady Harriet Conor who lives in the White Tower, on the River Cleddau, within the Welsh Triangle in Pembrokeshire. The old eccentric has built a labyrinth based on the one at Chartres Cathedral, which has healing properties, especially for cancer. The old girl is a dowser, who often, with her pendulum, works for police, helping to locate the bodies of missing persons. "These are usually people who have been abducted and murdered for the organ transplant black market," she tells me. "I've been warned by the local police not to be so successful, as the criminal organ-izers have rumbled my sleuthing expertise, and have put a contract out on me."
Then Lady Conor gives me an enigmatic smile. "Of course. No harm shall befall me," she says. "My son is an RAF captain, and last Christmas, looking out of the window on the top floor, he saw a flying saucer skimming along the river, at 1000 miles an hour. He thought it was heading for Stack Rocks Island in St. Brides Bay. The military have been monitoring the secret UFO base hidden inside the island for decades, and there is nothing they can do about it. The Visitors can come and go as they please, my son tells me."

March
31 Thursday

Laura says she is going to have another baby in November but in this world that would not be possible. Even if she were to conceive now (and she tells me she's been celibate these past 3 months), it would be a December birth.

Teeth falling out again. This time just one tooth on the centre right of my bottom jaw, leaving a huge and embarrassing gap. As it lay on the floor, it grew longer and bigger, transforming itself into a beautiful crystal - like a diamond.

I was in this movie, but it wasn't me. I was playing someone else who was being pursued by a pack of wolves – across the snow. I saw him running along the stark white horizon, and then I was him. A solitary wolf found me and seemed threatening. I thought he was going to attack. I try to keep it away with a stick but I don't want to harm him. I am supposed to love wolves. In the end I decide to throw the stick down and trust in the wolf's basic benevolence. Sure enough, I was correct in my intuition. The wolf just wanted to be my friend.

So we had a discussion about TV and movies and music and literature.
"What have you seen recently?" the Wolf asked.
"A documentary film about Death," I replied. "What a glorious life changing adventure it is. In the TV show there was this incredible dialogue between the Soul and its Body after dying."
"Who was it that died?" enquired the Wolf.
"It was a woman with blond hair. She and her Other were being very positive about the Passing Away Experience. At the end of the documentary I saw suspended in their cosmos, a hovering rectangular craft."
"Was it the Monolith from 2001; A Space Odyssey?"
"I don't know. It could have been a mobile phone." I replied.
"Or a door handle?" answered the Wolf, as he wandered off into the forest.

April
1 Friday Good Friday

They decided I was guilty, which was ridiculous. All my experiences showed I had absolutely nothing to do with what I was being accused of, and yet they wanted desperately to pin the crime on me. And the verdict carried the death sentence. Whether I liked it or not, whether I was innocent or not, no one cared. All that mattered was that I be their sacrificial lamb. Everyone wanted me to be dead and so I must hang. Yes, I saw myself being transported in a cart to Scaffold Hill, where the gallows awaited. A box for me to sit on was placed beneath the noose. Theatre director, Samuel Soap, was accompanying me. I asked if he was my executioner. He looked away with tears in his eyes, and then proceeded to explain how a sack would be placed over my head and then a rope around my neck.
"But what if, after I am dead, they discover I was innocent after all? Won't they be sorry?"
"No, because innocent or not is irrelevant to the need to have you killed. Your death is of greater value than justice," sadly replied Samuel Soap.
As the cart drew nearer to the gallows, I could feel a rising panic. I tried to keep it under control. I didn't want an undignified death, and yet despite my philosophy that death was just a change in clothing, a transition to another level of consciousness…the innate instinctual fear of extinction…of painful termination of precious life with all its warts…was building up in me, and I had difficulty controlling the shakes and the urge to scream and beg for a reprieve.

SCAFFOLD HILL = 53

The Rod of Aaron was a piece from the almond tree, which according to Hebrew tradition was the Tree of Knowledge of Good and Evil. And the fruit of the tree yielded the almond. The sweet almond tasted good …and the bitter almond tasted evil, and contained cyanide.

The almond tree was also the Hanging Tree.

April
2 Saturday

Going under the roundabout, there's a subway, I agree to sleep with the young tramp. I cling tight to my few worldly possessions as he sneakily searches me for money. He thinks I'm not aware. Suddenly I feel very close to him when I discover he has female breasts.
"Are you a transsexual?"
"No, I've not had the operation yet."
I feel his nipples. They are pierced with ear-rings. Even though he still has a cock, I will have sex with him. We snuggle up together as he starts to grope my arse.

Post coital discussion - "You met my Father?" asks the young tramp.
"Lord Allen Atthegrove is your father?"
"Probably. He told you about the 5:3 ratio being basic to our existence?" he said offering a puff of his marijuana.
"Something like that…", I said declining the joint.
"It is interesting that 5 thousand million years ago the Earth was formed …and 3 thousand million years ago biological life was formed. Does he remind you of anyone?"
"He reminds me of a number of old men." I replied, about to go.
"Khomeini? Orion? Zeus? Beelzebub? Rasputin?"
"Rasputin? Yes, now you mention it…."
"Rasputin claimed that he was being manipulated by 'unseen people…who were guiding his actions', exploiting him for their own ends…Whenever he spoke of these mysterious persons he referred to them as "**Zeleni**" (which is the Russian word for green)" who apparently lived in Sweden. Their associates or Go-Betweens in Russia he called " Zelenenkie," the young vagrant said, offering to sell me the Big Tissue magazine.
"Zeleni? Little Green Men? ", I asked, giving him some money.
"Little Green Men have been reported throughout history and across cultures. Before the Sci-Fi era, they're usually thought of as demons or fairies, elves or goblins etc."
"Are you suggesting Rasputin was set up to destroy Czarist Russia by E.T?"
"You know most revolutions have as their trademark the Five pointed star….which is the star of Sirius…which suggests to me Alien Intervention…"

April
3 Sunday Easter. A Bad Hare Day

Back home, I come out of the sitting room into the hall, and there by the cat-flap are a group of black cats. They are clustered around one of them, which is lying down, very still, very lifeless, quite possibly dead. I get closer and sense the cats had ganged up on the encircled one and had tormented it unto death. I realise with horror that the apparent victim is my beloved Solar Eclipse. I chase the intruders - murdering bullies - out of the house, and bend down to grieve and comfort my dearly departed friend and solace. As I draw closer, I see a quickening of fur and muscle, an opening of eyes and a sense of life restored. Was it all just a game?

I watched "EXORCIST II", and found at the 53rd minute of the movie, discussion of a cosmic struggle between the psychic Kokumo (child that cannot die) and the demon Pazuzu.

KOKUMO = 23 = 5
PAZUZU = 30 = 3

53

53? Is it the Final Battle between Good and Evil?

April
4 Monday

Duckworth Hill School Reunion.
The Great Gathering was warm and light-hearted. Everything amongst the lads seemed to be going okay. Tom was being very relaxed and supportive. He even lifted me on to the roof of the car. I laughed, joked and spoke of great things. Then I upset Tom. I insulted him and he flew into a rage and pushed me, causing me to slide off the slippery surface, and smash on to the road on my back. Everyone rushed to my assistance but I dared not move. What bones had I broken? My back? My neck? Internal injuries? I kept still, trying to mentally gauge the damage. Slowly, I started to wriggle muscles and then bones, one by one. So far so good. Doesn't look like any damage done.

Later…
After I gave Laura a lift in my car to where she was staying, I had to tell Luther off because he was making her unhappy and ill. He tried to explain that he didn't mean to and was prepared to make more effort.

Later still, I went out to the town centre, but find all the buildings have no access for me. Then I noticed a shop at the end of the row which seemed to have a concrete sloped entrance. I went to investigate but found the building shut and boarded up. Besides, it looked it had been abandoned a long time, and it wasn't a proper shop anyway. More like an office for a charitable society.
I turned around and saw a dark haired beauty trying to seduce the Handsome Hero, but he knew she was a dangerous femme fatale. He managed to avoid all her advances. He knew one mistake on his part and she would have ripped his throat out, and condemned his soul to Hell for all eternity. When he escaped her, she looked around for another possible victim and spotted me. She came over like a purring kitten, offering her swaying hips. "Hello, I haven't seen you before," she murmured sexily, licking her lips. "You are rather cute. Such a sweetie. What a lovely little Darling you are." I was almost captivated but as her face drew closer to mine, I recoiled with horror. It was faceless, a complete blur. Her eyes, nose and mouth had almost melted away into mere dark smudges. I realised she was not human, probably a demon or Devil Woman. I pushed my finger into the side of her mouth, as a means of warding off the evil creature. She backed off and snarled. However, her eyes – what was left of them – said she would take me when I least expected it, when I was off my guard.

April
5 Tuesday

We were still at Duckworth Hill school Reunion and I was astonished to see Laura come sailing down the hill. She was riding a very tall unicycle! It was about 4 or 5 storeys high, and she was riding it as if she was born to it. It was exhilarating to watch her. Where she got the sudden skill or the unicycle I don't know, but she certainly looked free and happy. As she waltzed high above me in the playground, she explained the technique. I told her I wanted to film her. She agreed to repeat the performance. As she whirled around, she saw the open windows of the mansion and paused to look in. She was obviously tempted to enter at the top floor, now that she had the means. All this is in stark contrast to how she was yesterday, haemorrhaging a lot and in constant pain. When she was in my car, she grimaced in agony. So, what happened today?

In the afternoon, at the reunion, Jake does a Tarot reading, and says, "Something is coming to planet Earth unannounced."
"A giant asteroid?" suggested Lonnie.
"If it's giant, it won't be unannounced, will it?" scoffed Hector. "It will be sighted by astronomers long before it gets here."
"Could be Nibiru, Kachina, the Blue Star, the Tenth Planet, Planet X...whatever you want to call it," surmised Icarus. "You know, an artificial hollow planet, which is a super Mother of a Mother-Ship, carrying an entire civilization of extra-terrestrials, hell-bent on invasion and colonization."
"If it's planet-sized, it can hardly come here unannounced," reiterated Hector.
"Maybe it has an invisibility shield for most of the journey, and then finally reveals its presence once it is in Earth's orbit?" Hephaistos suggested.
"If it is using Worm-hole technology, or has the ability to fold space, or can travel faster than the speed of light, then it can pop up anywhere unannounced, so I don't see anything unlikely about an artificial planet-type space craft suddenly arriving here without warning," proposes Jocelyn.
"It's probably the Messiah. The Bible says he will come unannounced," says Laura.
"Whether it's the Messiah or Capt. Kirk, it amounts to the same thing," I said.

In the evening while everyone watches telly, I escape to the Rubber Nipple Club. I meet S&M Dominatrix, Madam Angel Dark, who works part-time in the film business. She calls herself "a concept broker". Also bump into "Batman". The rubber-suited Masked Crusader says he's a friend of the great director Toyland Toffe, who is currently making "Waters are Deep".

April
6 Wednesday

That S & M Dominatrix, Madam Angel Dark (who reminded me of Stella Maris) and I have a snog. Tongues deep down each other's throats. Luscious gobsmacking sucks. Then she decides to stick her finger up my arsehole - but couldn't because of all the slime. She said it was slimy. I couldn't believe it. I tried to wipe it away, but still her finger refused to penetrate the clear sticky barrier. Everything just fizzled out after that..... Talk about wet farts.

Three moons circling very fast, round and round above my head. Two of them were the same colour, pinky-purple in the middle, and white around the extremities. The markings looked more like maps of the earth rather than the moon. The third moon dodging in and out of the two was all grey, and perhaps slightly smaller. It was daylight and there were several of us observing this strange aerial phenomena.

PURPLE = 7
WHITE = 2
GREY = 1
--
10 = 1

I'm driving this crazy car down a country road through a mountainous region in east Turkey. I have been driving all evening from Britain. The blasted car goes even more out of control as I sink further into the driving seat. On the other hand, I have the feeling the seat beneath my seat is actually shrinking, disappearing, forcing me to lose sight of the road as I can no longer see out of the windscreen. Before disaster strikes and I crash, or hurl down the cliff, I stop the car. Well, it stopped itself...I think. "No, It was me," comes a muffled voice to my left, On the floor, on the

passenger side, hiding amongst the papers and rubbish emerges a little dog, as small as a Chihuahua, nearly hairless with blue grey skin, apart from a small tuft of purple and green hair between its ears, punk style.
"Hello there, where did you come from?" I enquire as the tiny dog greets me excitedly, licking me all over my face. Having washed me of all the sweat I had accumulated during the scary drive, he said, "Itz-a Chicken, You-can-tango, Mekkiko."
"Que?" I queried.
"You had better go back home. Laura is having a hard time of it," urged the chirpy little Mexican canine with the funky punky purple and green sheen hairwear-doodoo.

April
7 Thursday

Rosalynd, my older sister from Cuba, comes to England. She just appears, unannounced. Why? Nobody knows - except perhaps to reprimand me. What for? I don't owe my family anything.

Aleister Crowley's book of the law, which he wrote on 8th April 1904, was entitled "LIBER LEGIS" = 53. He attempted to reach the summit of one of the three giants of the Himalayas - KANGCHENJUNGA - the five sacred peaks - Anyway, the Great Beast failed with the deaths of four fellow climbers. Hearing ghost voices on the mountain, he developed "Kangchenjungan phobia".

Ha! KANGCHENJUNGA = 53. So I could say the Not So, "Great Beast" had a phobia of 53.

Kangchenjunga translated means "The Five Treasures of Snows". The treasures represent the five repositories of God, which are gold, silver, gems, cereals, and holy books.

GOLD = 20
SILVER = 31
GEMS = 17
CEREALS = 27
HOLY BOOKS = 41
---
136 = 10 =1

April
8 Friday

Patrick Wolf? Caring sharing Hollywood movie star? Or rip-off merchant? Is the Texas bastard gonna steal my Circus script?

I visit Laura and find she has a container of Anthrax in her attic, enough to exterminate a third of the human population. I'm worried that any small explosion or lightning strike will release the deadly biological contaminant.

I turn on the radio to find out what to do and there's a news item about a hijacked airplane and a dead rock band.

Puddy Golly, lead singer, of the Dead Rock Band had this to say before he died, "Not long ago, I woke up one morning with a vision of the future economic system, when we will no longer have cash or cheques or credit cards for transactions. It will be a unitary global economy controlled by computers. There will be no private ownership of companies, no entrepreneurs, no currencies markets. Everyone is born with fifty-three million credits. You spend your credits on the necessaries of life – food, shelter, clothes, entertainment. When you run out of credit, you are Euthanized. You also lose credits for every day you don't work. In this economy it will be impossible to be without work. Of course, you are not expected to work before you reach 21 years of age, but you lose credits if you miss days off school or college or university. In this system, you cannot earn or gain extra credits. You can only lose them. If you commit a crime, and end up in prison, then every day you remain behind bars, you will not be working, so you lose credits. This will obviously bring you closer to the day you are Euthanized. If you are unable to work due to illness or incapacity, you will not lose credit for days unemployed but if you are proven to be malingering you will be immediately Euthanized, as will the physician or medical administrator for issuing a false sickness / incapacity certificate."

PUDDY GOLLY = 53

I'm convinced that for proposing such a radical economic system, Puddy Golly was murdered by a Capitalist conspiracy of the IMF, the World Bank and the International Federation of United Capitalists (IFUC).

April
9 Saturday

Participate in a Drama Workshop with REAL professionals, who were all wearing masks. Rolling about on the floor, crawling under tables, playing hide and seek in life and death struggles. I was holding my own amongst "the good and the great". He who was wearing the mask of "David Threlfall" took me in hand and everything became frighteningly true. "Kenneth Branagh" arrived and the seriousness became even deeper. "Imogen Stubbs" (or was it Rosalynd, my sister?) was enormously impressed - she pounced on "Branagh" and positively seduced him away. She beguiled him with the words, "My husband said you would find me irresistible. You wouldn't fail to be charmed by my intelligence and beauty, irrespective of my talent." The Mask of Branagh looked sheepish as she led him away.
Suddenly all my acting skills meant nothing and I was left high and dry.

So who of the two women was behind the Mask of Seducer? I did the numerology to find out.

DAVID THRELFALL	22+40 = 62 = 8
KENNETH BRANAGH	32+33 = 65 = 2
IMOGEN STUBBS	36+11 = 47 = 2
	--
	12 = 3

DAVID THRELFALL	22+40 = 62 = 8
KENNETH BRANAGH	32+33 = 65 = 2
ROSALYND	= 9
	--
	19 = 1

So it was ROSALYND

April
10 Sunday

Laura wanted to borrow £100 and I gave it to her as a gift, not a loan. I hate lending money to friends.

Jake, who is an amputee friend, Ben and I were exploring the Artificial Limb and Appliance Centre at Roehampton. Jake was our guide. We found a truck full of pristine shiny aluminium and steel limbs, arms and legs, hooks and trays. They were beautiful, like works of art. I decided to steal an arm and a leg, wrapping them in a towel with the idea of smuggling them past the gate sentries. Jake was worried. He was sure to get into trouble - when it was discovered that some items were missing. I tried to reassure him, that these things were about to be thrown away. No one will care. The era of forcing amputees to look like robots is over. But still, he was very nervous. Then I heard crying. But it was in my head. Sounded like Laura screaming in fear. Perhaps Luther was beating her up at that moment. I quickly forget about thieving the discarded limbs, and head for home.

JAKE	= 9
BEN	= 12
SHIRAM	= 32
	--
	53

April
11 Monday

I'm lonely, ignored. No one wants to associate with me, even though I'm with a party of "happy-go-lucky" revellers. But I just seem invisible. It's obviously because of my wheelchair. I'm trapped by steps, stairs and indifference. I need food but the canteen is inaccessible and since no one wishes to see my predicament, so no one will help me. They are too busy enjoying themselves.

Loneliness is the Mother of Invention, so I did some more numerology.

The Nazca drawings are of three types of creatures - BIRDS, SPIDERS, FISHES

BIRDS	= 7
SPIDERS	= 9
FISHES	= 3
	--
	19 = 1

Today everything is a fog. I can remember nothing....except I did rescue a little spider from dropping into my boiling cup of coffee. I wonder if she realised she had a guardian angel, softly blowing the thread she clung to, away to safety? Did she think it was Divine Intervention? Or just one of those weird inexplicable occurrences in Nature? Or perhaps she couldn't see she was rapidly approaching her Doom and so didn't realise she was in fact being "saved"?

April
12 Tuesday

I'm at home, all alone. Working in the computer room, I heard what sounded like a human cough. I guessed it must be 53 past the hour. I was right. The time was 10.53

Loki Groser visits me and lies in the bed next to mine. We talk about my honorary doctorate which I will receive soon. He asks if he can be at the ceremony. I say "yes", then remember he's supposed to be dead.
"You're a ghost aren't you?"
He replies, "Yes".
I take great comfort from the fact that he bothered to visit me and wants to be with me at my Big Award day. I take his hand and press it to my face- trying not to be scared of his supernaturalness -in the end his warmth wins through. I asked him as a ghost if he ever travels to his favourite haunts, places that gave him the most joy. He shakes his head sadly. "Ever since my friend... ", he starts to say. I knew he was going to say something about a plane crash. I wonder if I would be dying soon too.

Later…
East End council estate. The old boss is dead. Betrayed. The clan gather. I'm in a room upstairs. It is crowded with the old cockney sparrow's family, all waiting expectantly for the inauguration of the new Godfather.

April
13 Wednesday

Laura wanted me to make love to her. She kissed and cuddled. Tried everything to get me to be like old times. But I couldn't. We lay in bed together, though I felt very uneasy about this arrangement. Also I didn't know whether she was still with Luther. I sensed danger somehow. Things could never be the same again between us, and I felt guilty. Laura needed me and yet I was failing her. Then, my fears proved correct - in walked Luther, very much the proud owner of Laura. Luckily the new Godfather didn't catch us embracing.

Instead, he tells us about his most recent discovery.

"It's like 'Cut and Paste'," he said. "A clone was made of the tired, exhausted, faded, grey Old World, which was then rejuvenated by having pumped into it, new life, sizzling energy, and sunshine. And pasted onto the Universe, a New World of sparkling bright vibrant fresh colours, emerging like Phoenix reborn out of the ashes of the Apocalypse."

Laura and I sat with bated breath, eager to hear more.

"It all looked like a huge cosmic computer game," continued Luther.

"And it was called B."

"B? The computer game was called B?" I asked.

"No. B was the first letter of the name of the New World – Barakadur."

Barakadur = 32 = 5
Barack Obama = 32 = 5

April
14 Thursday

A court case. Corruption trial. I was led to it by a book I discovered in an old wooden chest in the attic. I hadn't read it. But the photo of the author looked familiar. He was on trial but when I found myself presiding as judge and jury, prosecutor and defence and called my first witness, sitting in the front row I recognised him from the photo of a freedom fighter (Rebel) turned union leader (Collaborator) turned cynical businessman (Tempter) caught with both his trousers down and his dick in the till. This was the man the book was supposed to have led me - but was I really a victim of war crimes? Or did his sly wink at me from out of the corner of his eye suggest that we were all in it together.
Who can stay innocent in a corrupt world?

In the Bible, there are Three Persons made manifest in the Devil - the Rebel, the Tempter and at times, the Collaborator with God, existing with divine consent.

Rebel	= 6	
Tempter	= 7	
Collaborator	= 6	
	--	
	19	= 1

A football-sized lump of shit, in my hands. I try to wrap toilet paper around it, to avoid it staining and stinking my flesh but it keeps slipping and sliding, with bits dripping on the floor.

Suddenly I realize that I'd come to the awards ceremony in my everyday clothes. I'd meant to change but completely forgot since such things seem to mean nothing to me.

April
15 Friday

Kyles the naughty boy. When Vanessa went to sit down on the chair, he put his finger in the path of her bottom, so that it jabbed cheekily into her. She leapt up and looked accusingly at ME! I denied responsibility and Kyles owned up. She turned him over, pulled his pants down and spanked his bare bottom with a hairbrush. He was so enjoying it, I regretted my denial. She looked up at me and smiled as if to say "You're next."
The idea made the bulge in my pants even bigger.

Woke up during the night because I heard a cat crying. I thought it was Solar Eclipse wanting to come in. Thing is - it sounded too clear. Not like it was outside the backdoor. Also Solar Eclipse has never been able to meow properly. Nonetheless, I got up out of the bed, but Solar Eclipse was nowhere to be seen.

Then I heard a voice say, "Ancient Grey
Here to stay
Won't go away."

I look and see a pair of grey wolf legs. The hind legs, and realise it is standing upright. In which case, it could be a werewolf or shape-shifting extra-terrestrial.

April
16 Saturday

I awoke at 8.05am. “Shiram”, said the woman’s voice in my head. The Unknown Woman?

The President of the UFO Society who is obsessed with Angels and Dragons, told me she was the Dragon-Master of Australia.

Angel = 21
Dragon = 32

53

Thinking about what Lady Harriet Conor told me about the secret underwater UFO base at Stack Rocks Island, a hunch told me to check out the numerology,

STACK ROCKS ISLAND = 53. Yes indeed, as I anticipated.

Making a movie with the great English director, Toyland Toffe, this afternoon. Makeup and wardrobe getting me ready. Washing my hair and body. It’s an interior shot, so I’m just in my dressing gown. Then the second assistant director comes and tells me Toyland has changed his mind, and we are filming an exterior, with me rolling in the mud – which is crazy since I’m all wet and clean for indoors. I take my time going out to the waiting film crew, uncertain whether the esteemed director will change his mind again. Eventually when I do go out to the set, everyone has lost patience with me, and have gone to film a different scene without me.

And then I wonder why I never seem to be offered much work. “He’s a difficult actor. And so unreliable,” I imagine they say of me.

Toyland Toffe = 53

April
17 Sunday

An old friend from university - Ataoko Loinona - turned up. At first I didn't realise it was him, then we greeted each other like water flowing across rocks under a bridge. Nothing seemed to have changed much with him. He was still at a loss as to what to do with his life, drifting from room to room in the same house that was once a squat. Still no telephone but tinkering with computers and music systems. As a musician he had forgotten his dreams.

ATAOKO LOINONA = 53

So had the anarchist punk band DOLT or so they would have me believe. I was visiting their cottage near Lake Windermere, hoping to stay for a few weeks but Orlando, the lead guitarist, was dubious. DOLT days were over. As a band they were shattered. There was no going back. Middle age and old age was all that was left to them. As for me staying, there may be a problem, as there wouldn't always be someone at home after tomorrow. I'll be on my own for several days, maybe weeks at a time. How will I manage? I accepted his conclusions and knew that the old ideologies were dead.

April
18 Monday

A gathering of friends in a large communal room, at the DOLT Farm Commune. Laura is upset. Very upset. Depressed, almost catatonic. She cries and slowly takes all her clothes off. People rush in to shield or cover her but they fail. She just stands there and starts to urinate...out of a young boy's penis. I can't believe my eyes. There she is, naked and sporting between her legs - a little cock.

April
19 Tuesday

Infantile! Childish even. Me and Horatio (the bunny rabbit) arguing, bickering at the table. I knew I was behaving badly, dropping to his immature level but I couldn't resist it. Sheepishly, I eventually succeeded in pulling out of the quarrel.

THE HEADLESS MAN

Echoes scudding on a wet look floor,
A deadly deed to settle the score,
Centre stage are grouped five men in black,
Inching towards them, I fear my back,
Their whispers slink thru the misty dark,
Red circles of light bequeath their mark,
Crouched heads jerk round, a shade of squint,
They look to me for the hidden hint.
I dribble the lines like sweating cheese,
Which builds in strength, words for weaving ease,
"The world has blown far too old", I blurt,
"But it's fall from grace we could divert,
"There's this sad Man, he clones death for all,
"When humanity heeds fast his call,
"Unknown to all, except to us six,
"New life springs not, from his loinsome tricks.
"All will love him but will rue the day,
"His creed for the world leads them ash tray,
"So, my friends, before cracked bells toll late,
"Let's act now, while he's not yet great."

Later I witness two men to be executed. After the first one is shot, the second volunteers to put the barrel in his mouth, and pulls the trigger on himself.

April
20 Wednesday

Back at Duckworth Hill, my old school, chased by a young man with the HADES plague. He wants to kill me by infecting me. I run up and down corridors, try to hide in rooms but he always finds me and tries to kiss me and stick his lethal tongue in my mouth. His face is a bleeding mass of sores and it is with glee he attempts to rub my flesh into his highly contagious wounds. With extreme terror I fend him off, trying to keep him at arm's length. Every now and then he dodges behind me and tries to pull my pants down, so as to bugger me with his HADES-ridden weapon. Finally, I succeed in incapacitating him with a knockout rabbit chop on his throat. I make my escape.

Later I phone for a prostitute. I needed a bath and hair wash....and sex. She charged me 110 pounds for the lot. Her name was Sophia, the Goddess of Wisdom.

THE HEADLESS MAN (continued)

They nod in agreement, they cough "Yes",
They have to accept his death no less,
"Who will perform this unholy task?"
A farce to ask, the Role long past cast.
Dressed for the part, He stepped out of line,
With that smirk of his, Fate's chilling sign,
His eyes worming the truth from the grey,
For the world, down my life He must lay,
From Him, I cannot, will not, deny,
It is I who must, for Hope's sake, die.

Out there now lurks my appointed death,
At the brush stroke of my brother's breath,
Still, I'm glad, the mission has been set,
I can sleep now, Time will free my debt.

April
21 Thursday

Driving to the theatre in the afternoon, I thought about Vanessa. Put all my concentration on conveying my desire for her. Wanted her to feel me inside her head. I had succeeded before with another woman. She heard my voice calling her name in the middle of her bedroom, at three in the morning. I ought to be able to send telepathic signals again. It usually works when you're in love.

Later that evening, after the show, she appeared when I wanted her to. I had sat alone in a darkened corner at the Women's Folk Night. The rest of our company were at the bar end. Adam discovered me and I hoped he would tell her where I was and she would come to talk to me. And just as I was thinking of her, she arrived, smiling and asked if she could sit with me. Then she told me an amazing thing. 3.30 this afternoon, she was in the dressing room with my costume to be laundered, and as she looked at the door mirror she saw the reflection of her head change into mine. Instead of her own face she saw mine. What with her having dreams of me and now this, no wonder, she exclaimed to me "My god - why are you getting into my head?" I could have told her about my afternoon's telepathy exercise but I didn't want to freak her out. I could have told her we must be falling in love, but then, we may have had to do something about that…and I didn't want to come between her and her boyfriend, Jake. She waited for an answer, her big brown eyes searching hopefully. I shrugged and merely said "You tell me." She looked away disappointed. Then she asked if I minded her telling me about the experience. I replied that I ought to feel flattered.

Disturbed sleep. Wake up quick! Lights! Car-load of young hooligans, thieves, ready to invade your home. No, not yobbos. Something more sinister. The lights are too bright. What's this? Floating, euphoric feeling! It's happening again. The paralysis. Out of body? Alien Abduction? I manage to stop it. But afterwards I want it to continue on to the point of entry into THEIR craft, the flying faery palace…and beyond. But no. The light...the feeling...fades away because I know I am anxious-ridden. Guilt. Awareness of Alien punishment for illicit games and desires.

April
22 Friday

Laura and I go to see Jake, who had made promises to her about singing opportunities. However, when we got to his house, we find that he was all mouth. Laura is really upset and bitterly disappointed. She begins to feel suicidal. I intervene and give Jake a furious bollocking. I really tear him to shreds. Then, to my surprise, the poor man bursts into tears. He is completely beside himself with grief. He nearly chokes as his heart breaks. Suddenly, I feel remorse and desire to comfort him. I rush up to him and put my arm around his shoulders and give him a hug.

Visited Isis and Osiris. They told me to read the accursed poem "The Madwoman of Cork" by Patrick Galvin, if I had the courage. They say bad things happen to you if you read it. So I read it.

On the way back home in the car, I just had to have a piss, so I did it in my travelling urinal bottle but there was so much shit in my bowels just wanting to get out, that I also shat my pants. Now, this was horrifyingly disgusting. I pulled down my trousers and knickers, wiped my arse with a plastic bag but I could still feel a great lump of turd just screaming to be pushed through the orifice and so out it came onto a plastic sheet. This I dumped on the road. I then proceeded to wipe myself clean with my knickers, which revoltingly soiled, I threw out of the car. I still felt dirty, so I took off my lovely expensive woollen embroidered waistcoat, and cleaned the last remnants of excrement from between my buttocks with that attractive but unfortunate garment. It too was unceremoniously discarded onto the road. I then drove through the town with nothing on below the hip, hoping I would not be stopped by the police.

April
23 Saturday

Vanessa had no time to tell me about her self - yet she desperately wanted to communicate to me - so she wrote me a letter - describing her life, her family and her hopes and fears, her adventures and her tragedies. Unfortunately, I just could not read her writing. It was beautifully done. I could admire the calligraphic artistry but was unable to understand a single word. Everything became a confused mess in my head. A morbid desperation gripped me.

Cynthia rang and told me she came to visit me last night but found I wasn't in my flat but in a big house - well, actually, a tower block. She claimed I was in a strange woman's flat who was preventing her from seeing me. The woman was being very possessive and was intimating that Cynthia should keep away. Apparently, this hostile woman had straight shoulder length, blond hair - and was foreign. Cynthia managed to see me but I was nervous and didn't want to do anything to upset this new woman in my life. The woman was seated and looked strongly built. Cynthia wanted to warn me this blond woman may be trouble for me.

I haven't a clue what Cynthia is going on about. There is no new woman in my life.

Anyway, later, after her visit, at about 11pm Cynthia was driving between Croydon and Sutton when a UFO appeared with aliens on board. She was very apprehensive especially when the craft became interested in her. She tried to hide but the threatening UFO hovers over with a searching red beam of light.

April
24 Sunday

Visited Isis and Osiris. Bad vibes, especially from Osiris.

Oh my god, Isis returns that shitty waistcoat I dumped on the road...but all beautifully cleaned. She said she was driving and saw it by the wayside and instantly recognised it as the one I had been wearing when I'd visited. Oh Jesus, how embarrassing. Did she not wonder why it was all covered in shit? And she picked it up and washed it brand spanking new to give me back. I couldn't look her in the eyes as I mumbled thanks. She then gave me purple red flowers, sticks of celery, a jar of chutney, a scallop fan shell and a virgin stone. Is she The Madwoman of Cork?

Later, Kyles and I are pursued by a monstrous Crocodile known as the Gobbler of Souls. We hide in a cage in the jungle. I see lions and tigers with their cubs, minding their own business. They ignore us as they lounge about in the grass. I want to stroke them, cuddle the cubs but Kyles warns me to be careful. These wild animals cannot be trusted. However, I'm now quite confident despite the approaching crocodile who is also called Dr Sobek.

My waistcoat - the grey woollen with the exquisite embroidery, the one Isis found and returned. Well, I ripped it as I was putting it on. I was half-pleased. I sort of desired an excuse to throw it away and now I could. So, I threw it on the fire, then rang Isis and wished her a Happy New Year.
She asked me what was I talking about? It's Easter now. Not exactly, I replied. It was 21 days ago, but we can still say Resurrection is new life, new year.

LIFE	=	5
DEATH	=	2
RESURRECTION	=	3
		--
		10 = 1

April
25 Monday

Jake, Vanessa's boyfriend, suddenly appears in front of me as a hologram. He is in trouble. He has an S.O.S. hologram transmission-wrist band, which enables distress signals to be sent. I never found out what Jake's problem was because the transmission was interrupted by the telephone ringing.

An egg rolls off the table and smashes on the floor. Is it Easter Sunday, already?
I look up and notice a little blue grey bird flying at the window, looking in, trying to enter - but the glass was in the way. It was really trying hard. I could hear its little beak thudding on the window. It was losing feathers, getting battered in the attempt. I moved to get a better look and told it "No, stop, you will hurt yourself." It tried one more time, then heeded my warning and flew away.

"Three wheels on my wagon….." sings the cowboy as he is chased by Cherokee injuns….. Shall I find the "Three in One" relationship in the Birth / Death dichotomy held together by Life?

BIRTH	= 3
LIFE	= 5
DEATH	= 2
	--
	10 = 1

Vanessa visits my flat and sees how disgustingly dirty it is. She looks with horror at the filthy state of my bed sheets. I try to make excuses but I'm just a mumbling cheat. She abandons me to my bachelor squalor. Serves me right.

April
26 Tuesday

Egon Ronay rang. (To tell me that Delilah had told him that Lydia quite fancies me. That's good because I quite fancy her)

EGON RONAY = 6
DELILAH = 6
LYDIA = 6

Things are going wrong with the theatre tour. The rest of the cast and crew are treating me with disrespect. In fact, they are treating me like shit. For example, my wheelchair has become a problem for them. Adam the stage manager refuses to repair it. One night he leaves it in the van, even though I need it for the show. He seems to think I can manage to perform without it. I tell him it's like asking someone to go on stage without their legs. But he remains unimpressed with my argument. Everyone agrees I'm behaving like a spoilt prima donna and ignore my protests. In retaliation I decide to boycott the show. The bastards can go on without me. Huge crowds gather to fill the massive auditorium. I sulk and skulk in a backroom, feeling unloved and unwanted. The performance tries to start but the crowds are angry. The people came to see me and I'm not there. Soon I hear a chant go up which blows my mind - "We want Shiram - We want Shiram!" Eventually I'm persuaded to go out to the audience and address them...and offer my apologies for the delay in the start of tonight's performance.

April
27 Wednesday

A ghostly visitation. Lying on my stomach, left hand outstretched behind me and about to doze off when my cat, who should have been 500 miles away, comes into the hotel room looking for me. His sadness at being apparently abandoned by me, was pitiful. I could feel his tiny paws stroking the palm of my hand. "Where are you? Why have you left me?" he seemed to be crying. I called out soothingly, "Solar Eclipse". I was desperate to let him know it wouldn't be long before we would be together again.

Giles furious at my hijacking of his play. My performance has made it completely unrecognisable. Worse, I'm so arrogant. I refuse to recognize his criticisms and right to re-direct me. Even Maxine agrees with me and gives the poor put-upon director the sharp end of her tongue. I leave him to stew in his own juice.
Later, I sit at a window and look out to another building in the darkness. It's a hospital ward. The dead are sleeping. I shuffle some paper on the window desk and to my amazement, the scraping rustling sound is music to my ears. I play the sheaf instrument more emphatically and electronic melodies wing their way to the room opposite the courtyard. The dead awake and complain at my noise. I ignore their protestations and so they are forced to rise from their beds and call the nurse to stop me. The nurse summons Malcolm McDowell to reprimand me but he just smiles and winks, giving me a gentle ticking off. He knows we're both a pair of lovable rogues. Then he ages before my eyes and becomes a decrepit old man with one foot in the grave. He is me but I'm still young. I cannot let him drag me down with him. But we both know our time has passed and the final rest for the wicked is eternal monotony in a darkened hospital ward staffed by indifferent and indolent nurses.

April
28 Thursday

Hospital - A man on the run, needing my protection. As doctor I tried to give it but two assassins, one burly and tall, the other short, had arrived with trumped up charges. For a while, my sanctuary worked, the staff helped me to protect the man but eventually the assassins persuaded three workmen with the "Sun" tabloid mentality, that the fugitive was a serial killer of children, who abused them and hung them. I found the three fools looking at false documents alleging the atrocities. It becomes clear I have a hard struggle ahead of me, keeping the man away from the growing lynch mob.

Later…
The old mystical tramp, with long white hair and thick beard, comes out of the music room, playing on one of my recorders the theme tune from Sergio Leone's "For a Few Dollars More". He then hands me the wooden wind instrument, expecting me to play it, but I find it won't play because it is broken. It has an outer cylinder, and an inner cylinder, and they have become separated. Also the inner cylinder is broken in two, where the mouth piece is. I try to slide the inner tube back inside the recorder / whistle / flute, but am unable to align the finger holes, so I still cannot play the tune as required. My Housekeeper shakes her head at my failure to produce a decent sound.

For a few dollars more – 31796 – reminds me of 25th February and my Mother.

April
29 Friday

I'm the Great Interviewee...NOT! I may have been in the past but now I seem to be losing my touch. The radio invites me to a live interview but I blow it. I'm all teeth and gums. My lips flap all over the place and I'm about as coherent as a chimp whistling Dixie. Two hours of rambling broadcast. I plead for salvage but you can't edit what's gone out live. I'm sacked but as a consolation the BBC feed me with posh nosh. Vanessa stands behind me and is nominated to speak instead. She turns down the expensive food and humbly requests cheese on toast. She is obviously destined for great things. A Star is Born, and I'm knocked into the shade.

With the tail between my legs, I go and gain entry into the TV studio next door, where a woman called Yesod, is appearing on a chat show, boasting about how she had got custody of the child she had had with the pop star, Mad Donut (remember her hit single "Virgin on the Ridiculous"?), and had escaped with it to some hiding place where Mad Donut couldn't find them. Apparently Mad Donut and Yesod were lovers, and decided as a couple to have a child through IVF. Then the relationship inevitably broke up. It was a mistake Yesod declaring herself on television because within minutes Mad Donut barges into the studio drags the big mouth woman out, beats her up and repossesses the child. Of course, with Mad Donut being an important Celebrity, she gets away with it.
Meanwhile, I hang around in the hospitality suite. I had heard film producer, Toyland Toffe was around, and so sent him a message to meet me, as I wanted to discuss one of my movie projects with him. While waiting, Mad Donut enters and sits down on a massive white leather sofa, I go over to her, apologise for imposing myself, but I need to ask if she has a good photo of her nude.
"What?" she explodes.
"No, please, don't get the wrong idea," I quickly say, as she beckons over two brutish-looking security guards. "I need it for my film, 'Naked Mad Donut'. It's a supernatural thriller involving a poster of you, naked. Problem is I've surfed the Net, but I can't find one that does you justice."
"Are you telling me, I don't look great naked?" she growls, shooing the guards away.
"I'm sure if I were to see you naked in the flesh, I will think you look fantastic, but I have to say photographers have not managed to capture the perfect nude image of you. It's their failing, not yours."

"What's this movie about? Could be something I might invest in it."
"Great. I was hoping you'd say that," and I began to tell her the story, when Toyland Joffe arrives, sees me with Mad Donut, and is impressed at our apparent familiarity, especially as the pop star looks captivated by my narration. As I reach the chilling climax of the tale, the door crashes open, and in comes a dashingly handsome man in a wheelchair, clearly expecting to successfully steal my role in the movie.
"Now, that is some hunk on wheels," Mad Donut positively drools. Shit. That's me fucked.

April
30 Saturday

The pop singer, Mad Donut visits me in hospital. Actually, she's a patient in the next ward.

Hospital and TV film crew. I object to their imminent arrival. Another invasion of privacy. Can't people be ill in peace? I have problems with some of the other patients who don't find it so objectionable. However, I kick up such a fuss that the ward sister takes seriously my views - and orders a postponement whilst an inquest takes place.

In the meantime, I go out and discover a new Evangelical church which is dominating Protestant Christianity. It is yet another Pentecostal variation. However, all is not well with the new movement, which is led by a very charismatic young woman preacher, who uses her seductive feminine charms to woo converts. I see there is a rebellion within the congregation led by an older black woman who seems unwell, possibly dying, but determined to expose the preacher's sinister intentions. As I watch the black opponent denounce the white seductress, the wily serpentine preacher, reclining arrogantly on a luxurious sofa-like pew, changes into greater attractive deadliness, her clothing shrinking to reveal more of her alluring feminine bodily charms, minimalizing the coverage until she appears scantily clad as if for a beach party. I am astonished to see, as her dress disappears and her knickers get briefer that her genitalia are revealed as penis and testicles – not female at all. I quickly leave, understanding perfectly why Christianity has never worked. It has been controlled by the Devil all the time.

May
1 Sunday BEALTAINE

I wake up and find the bedroom floor covered in sleeping cats. They are also all over my bed. It' a real takeover bid. What about poor Solar Eclipse? What can I do to help him? The neighbourhood cats are really taking liberties, and I haven't the heart to ruthlessly evict them. They know I'm a sucker for animal rights. Actually, I'm rather flattered that they wish to live with me.

The Four Celtic Festivals
IMBOLC = 9
BEALTAINE = 6
LUGHNASA = 2
SAMHAIN = 2
--
19 = 1

The show, OTHELLO (with me as Iago), is going from bad to worse. It's getting out of control. Giles the director is rapidly losing heart - so he brings in a top flight director - a tough bastard - to knock us back into shape and put us back on track. This outside director - someone I'd worked with before, a canny Scot - overdoes his toughness and succeeds in alienating us all. I refused to be bossed about and became even more uncooperative. A climatic showdown ensued just before that night's performance. I'd had enough...and wanted OUT and so pushed the director into such a rage that he would sack me. I dared him, provoked him but he just didn't have the nerve. Giles tried to intervene and calm the waters. I sent the Imposter packing with accusations that he failed to live up to his renowned reputation and that he had revealed a shallow experience. The result was an impasse and concrete-heavy air. Vanessa (she is playing Desdemona) was the only company member to attempt to comfort me.

Shakespearian Trinity
OTHELLO = 6
DESDEMONA = 8
IAGO = 5
--
19 = 1

May
2 Monday

Gabrielle from my agent's office, rings with bad news (as usual). Giles rejects my play "The Vertigo". Not possible to produce. Not his "cup of tea". Slowly I am being blacklisted.

Eve the dancing queen, comes a visiting. She brings with her, a Captain Mainwaring lookalike + soundalike (the fat pompous one in the BBC TV comedy, "Dad's Army"). He introduces himself as "Donald A. Light". It turns out that not only is he a costumier for the theatre but he's also a horseman, jouster, stuntman, an impresario for striptease artists, a novelist, scriptwriter and film producer (he's currently developing a Merlin and Arthur movie). Whiles he was entertaining me with his tales, my eyes were being riveted to the rings on his fingers and the pendant around his neck. One of his rings had the skull and crossbones (a Masonic symbol), another bore the 5 pointed star symbol, which I knew to be an occultic pentangle. Also the pendant was a 5 pointed star surmounted by a triangle. Intriguing – the Five and Three. I told him I was intrigued by his jewellery, and he, in turn, told me he was intrigued by my book collection. He then blurted out he was an Occultist, a High Priest of a Witches Coven – white witches, of course. Of Celtic origin. He was also a Freemason. "I see you have 'The Brotherhood' by Stephen Knight," he shouts. He grabs the book from the shelf. "This man gave away too many of our secrets. Look, he even has on the front cover the white gloves we wear." Whereupon, he pulls from his coat pocket, similar white gloves, just to make the point, to prove he was a bona fide Freemason and knew what he was talking about. "I tell you," jabbing the book fiercely, "this man paid for his indiscretions. I said, years ago, when this accursed book was published, something will happen to him. He won't have long to live. Six months after, he died from a brain haemorrhage. Which is how the Masonic death sentences are normally camouflaged."
Shit, I thought, why is he telling me this? Is it a veiled threat?
Then the jolly Witch-Mason saw my black sword hanging from the ceiling. "Where on earth did you get that?"
"A junk shop in Paris."
"Great Holy Architect! A junk shop! What sacrilege! That is a Masonic ritual sword. Let me look at the blade. Does it have a name on it?"
"Yes – Don Alda Light." Then I started to laugh.
He snatched the sword from me and unsheathed it, staring at the engraved

letters and Masonic insignia on the silver blade. He cursed softly to himself. “My name. It’s the sword that was stolen from me.”
“Donald A. Light ! And all these years I thought it read Don Alda Light” I said trying to smother the giggles. Eve was giving me filthy looks. “I suppose you had better have it back.”
“Do you know numerology, dear boy?”
“Yes.”
“Do you know it’s vital to Masonic understanding?”
“And do you know what number Donald A. Light comes to?” I asked.
“I’ll work it out…” He pulls a pocket calculator.
“I’ll save you the effort… ‘53’. I think the sword should remain with you.”
Before he and Eve went, he gave me a sample of his Celtic ceremonial chanting. Filling the flat with pagan incantations.

My cat, Solar Eclipse, says “Descartes was a bloody coward, because he said ‘To live well, you must live unseen’. ”.

May
3 Tuesday

Argue with Maxine about female chauvinism. Gave her a hard time. The screaming and shouting continues until Ike Mattin, fleet of foot, arrives with the message he is still organizing trips to Cuba - I ask him if I can book to go this year. He says yes.

The Four stages in the development of the Secret Society of Guardians and Propagators of the Ancient Wisdom.

KNIGHT TEMPLAR = 2
CATHAR = 6
ROSICRUCIAN = 4
FREEMASON = 7
---
19 = 1

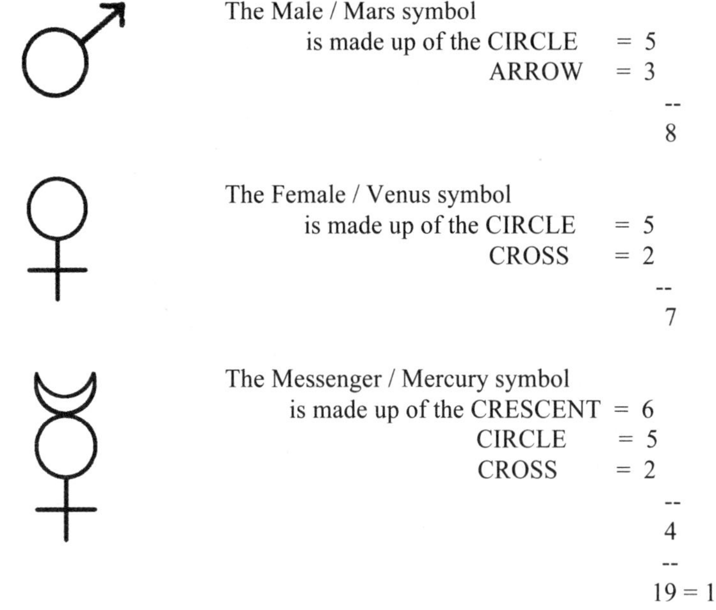

The Male / Mars symbol
is made up of the CIRCLE = 5
ARROW = 3
--
8

The Female / Venus symbol
is made up of the CIRCLE = 5
CROSS = 2
--
7

The Messenger / Mercury symbol
is made up of the CRESCENT = 6
CIRCLE = 5
CROSS = 2
--
4
--
19 = 1

And for my next trick.....MARS = 6
VENUS = 9
MERCURY = 4
--
19 = 1

May
4 Wednesday

I find a weird piece of junk machinery, made up of broken musical instruments, type-writers and old bicycles. It is absolutely fascinating. Some sculptor-mechanic must have put it together. Anyway, I take it upstairs to my room and start to tinker with it. Suddenly it comes alive and starts to whirr buzz and hum and whistle. Wheels, cogs, pistons, springs begin moving and music starts to play. I rush downstairs to get Laura. The bizarre and gigantic music box is still playing when we get to the room, although it seems to have moved by itself into the wardrobe. Laura gets it to play a different tune. When it finishes she tells me to see if it will play something from Mars. I press a few buttons and turn some knobs and to our amazement, the machine sings to us in a perfect mimicry of my voice. In fact, it might now be me. The song it sings is "Confide in me" ("Come and find me"?) which I've never heard before - but it may be based on "Come Fly with me".

MARS INVADERS = 53 (The movies "Invaders from Mars" and "War of the Worlds" - both 1953) just wrote this at 01:53 in the morning))

The Sky God (Father Heaven) of the Mongolians
TENGER ETSEG = 53

SONS OF HEAVEN = 53
THE CARETAKERS = 53
THOU WATCHERS = 53

"Adapa wiseman of Eridu" (Babylonian Genesis myth)
5 3 3 3
"Adapa, the seed of Mankind"
5 6 6 3 3
HOMO SAPIENS = 53

Journey with Laura, Inigo, Lavinia, Igor and Quincy in search of a school for Proteus, across the wide and desperate spaces. We call on a country school run by Ninian Ceres, the sculptor-mechanic cum composer. He directs us further afield - another 200 miles. Laura annoyed, wanting to return home, carelessly takes me down steps. And I have to teach her all over again.

May
5 Thursday

Returned to my house in Ireland and discover it has been invaded by an army of the builders. I am horrified that everywhere has been turned into a construction site - causing me great inconvenience and inaccessibility. Furthermore, the new building is being done without my agreement and permission. With difficulty I locate the couple responsible for this intrusion in my private property and private affairs. They seemed genuinely mortified at my outrage. They were convinced that I would approve of the charitable venture - creating a refuge centre for disadvantaged people to acquire skills and confidence. They also assumed I would be proud to have a permanent monument to me. But I violently disapproved of it. Ireland was my retreat, a place where I could be left alone with my soul. What annoyed me most, however, was that I was not consulted. Once again someone else was controlling my life, maybe for the best intentions but I was being hijacked. In the end I could refuse, demand that everything be removed and restored to the status quo but I was touched by the sincerity of the man and woman in charge who thought it was all for my benefit and when I saw how beautiful the towering cathedral-like structure was, I weakened and began to accept the inevitable. However I was not pleased to find the tree cover destroyed, leaving me, my house and palatial monument exposed to the world. I moaned that Ireland was meant to keep me in obscurity. My friends laughed and told me to chill out, not to be so serious and relax on the green grass and enjoy the splendour of the magnificent vine-covered structure towering above me. I decided to give in and let them have their dream.

May
6 Friday

Got woken by the Wail of the Banshee....and other weird shrieks and screams.

Laura and Luther in trouble. They visit me in Ireland

My Irish house and yet, of course, not my house. Bigger, bleaker, darker, more vacuous, cavernous - hostile open landscape. Night. Laura, the children. Strange cars cruise nearby, threatening. Intruders prowling. We hide in corners in the darkness. We mustn't be seen. Vulnerable isolation. Then salvation seems to come around the corner - the local gardai - policeman - Pat Mac Tire arrives - strangely, semi-naked, battered and bruised, clothes torn to shreds - yet he has good news, despite his shocking appearance. The burglars have been caught. We can all relax. The Home can be reinstated.

The Irish Christian Trinity
BRIGIT = 2
COLM CILLE = 2
PATRICK = 6
---
10 = 1

The night is young and Laura contemplates bedding me but I am determined our relationship remain platonic. She teases me about Laura.
"Who is Laura?"
"You are Laura" I replied.
"Yes, but there is another Laura." I think, surely, she is getting the name confused with Willow's friend Laurel Larter? But that can't be right because I never desired Laurel Larter. I go outside and stare up at the stars. Suddenly I see a pin prick of light moving rapidly from left to right. I think it's a high altitude plane.... until it stops suddenly and reverses back in the opposite direction. I realize I am seeing a UFO. Then more pin pricks of light appear- performing the same and other equally impossible aerial maneuvers. I call out to Laura to fetch me my spectacles. For some strange reason I had gone outside without my glasses. But Laura is nearly as blind as a bat herself without glasses and brings out instead an empty glasses case. I rushed inside to get them myself hoping the light display isn't over by the time I go back out. It was all over by the time I returned.

LAUREL LARTER = 53 (**Larter**, Old English for "deceiver, trickster")

May
7 Saturday

the phone rings and the time is 7.53 am.

The Grosers come to visit me in Ireland. I was bending down to do some cooking that night when I hear a noise. I look and there are outside my window is Jacinta. We both seem equally surprised to see each other. I welcome her in, and then, I am even more amazed to see that she is accompanied by Persa who is a very impressed with my place, Hecate who gives me a cheeky, knowing look, recognizing it as a reminder of the long forgotten childhood, Inga also comes in relaxed and breezy and Ninian, who is wondering where he can buy a place like it. Livia is still in Libya, but her son Claude comes instead as her ambassador. The biggest surprise visit, however, is Loki, Jacinta's departed husband, who died some while back. I knew he always wanted to see my place in Ireland but to take on the mortal coil for the occasion is a bit extreme. He smiles and chuckles like he was never dead. I'm pleased to see him again. Jacinta, however, tells me Laura is furious with me, for sneaking off to Ireland without telling her.

In the story of the Great Flood, there were the three sons of Noah, responsible for the regeneration and renewal of the devastated human species. Their names Shem, Ham and Japhet forming a 3 in 1 pattern.

SHEM = 9
HAM = 4
JAPHET = 6
---
19 = 1

May
8 Sunday

Fairy singing? Did “Galadriel” from “Lord of the Rings” sing to me? Or was it Leannan Shee, Queen of the Faeries?

A frog has just appeared in the sitting room by the fridge. The time is 9.53

Later I meet Richard Branston Pickles at a party he is holding. I remind him of his non-replies to my most recent letters and that nothing has come of my previous ones. He has failed to act on any of my requests (I had asked that he get his Vestal Airline pilots to fill in reports of UFO sightings they may have had, for a book I am writing about UFOs seen by pilots, which his Vestal books could publish). Then I tell him about Laura who is with us, and how he should at least help her, perhaps pay for the necessary medical treatment. But no one takes me seriously, and even Laura chooses to get into the full swing of the party. Her general hilarity undermines my own earnestness.
At a lost as to what to do next, an exotic central Asian, swarthy slim girl catches my eye. A young Maxine perhaps? She also attracts the attention of Lady Bonanzai, who grabs her, tips her upside down and invites all and sundry to spank and fondle the petite girl’s appetizing bottom. Lady Bonanzai is also unable to keep her hands off this quietly acquiescent plaything.
The young woman is brought over to me and I am invited to run my hand over her cheeks and in between her thighs.
I resist. It seems an outrage. An insult to this vulnerable woman. Bonanzai goads me, teases and tempts. Telling me the girl doesn’t mind. In fact, desires that I caress her intimately.
Eventually I succumb and stroke the perfect quivering mounds and see the intense pleasure in the captive girl’s eyes and I plunge my hand deep into her yearning yawning crevice. Now I have gone too far. And the fabric rips and everything is blown away, with an earth shattering noise.

May
9 Monday

I meet a tiger which becomes friendly.

We discuss my numerology research. The Tiger shows me how in the Genesis myth there is a Trinity in the form of "Adam the Man", "Eve the Woman" and "Lucifer the Serpent".

Adam the Man = 8
Eve the Woman = 5
Lucifer the Serpent = 6
--
19 = 1

And then to my surprise, the Tiger said, "I produce myself among creatures, whenever there is a decline in virtue and an insurrection of vice and injustice in the world; and thus I incarnate from age to age, for the preservation of the past, the destruction of the wicked, and the establishment of righteousness."

"Isn't that what Krishna said?"

"And today I have to say it even louder," replied the Tiger.

"But no one listens to the roar of tigers nowadays. They will just shoot you, and sell your penis, eyeballs and bones for Chinese medicine, and use your skin as a rug to wrestle naked on, in front of a comforting warm fire."

May
10 Tuesday

Slim, beautiful, naked, but wild and quick tempered. Fed up of being ignored and treated as a joke, the Faeries decide to quit on mass our world for good. The person who bugged them the most, Wart Deenee, when he realized what he had done, tried to persuade them not to leave us - But they were adamant. We were all aggrieved, and put blankets on our heads, and began to sing

> "Where have all the Faeries gone?
> Long time passing.
> Where have all of the Faeries gone?
> Long time ago "

Tears are streaming down my eyes as I sing.

Jesus, I have been crying so much lately.

On leaving my house, to return to England, three animal visitors came to bid me adieu.

HARE = 5
FOX = 9
CRANE = 5
--
19 = 1

May
11 Wednesday

A horse gets into bed with me. At first, it feels very nice, the creature is very sweet and loving. I feel comforted. But then, I feel its jaws close around my throat and mouth and I begin to suffocate. I am being slowly choked to death.

The Creatures went into the Ark two by two
CREATURES = 2
Why is it called THE BOOK of NUMBERS?

The Numbers went into the Ark two by two
NUMBERS = 2

So "1" and "1" went into the Ark…and made "2".
"2" and "2" went into the Ark…and made "4"
"4" and "4" went into the Ark…and made "8"
"8" and "8" went into the Ark…and made "7" (8+8=16 (1+6=7))
"7" and "7" went into the Ark…and made "5" (7+7=14 (1+4=5))
"5" and "5" went into the Ark…and made "1" (5+5=10 (1+0=1))
and so we return to "1". A cycle of 6 numbers.

What about a pair of 3s going into the Ark?
"3" and "3" went into the Ark…and made "6"
"6" and "6" went into the Ark…and made "3" (6+6=12 (1+2=3)
and so we return to "3". An oscillation back and forth between 2 numbers.

Finally, the remaining number from 1 to 9 to go into the Ark…9.
"9" and "9" went into the Ark…and made "9" (9+9=18 (1+8=9))
thus returning immediately to 9. There is no movement with 9. It is a static number. Solid as a rock. The Still Centre of the Universe. The Eye of the Storm. The Eye of Horus.

Clearly the world was reconstructed according to a Divine mathematical formula and blueprints....which is why Numerological and Gematria systems are useful analysing and predictive tools.

The Numbers went into the Ark two by two
99 = 18 = 9...99 = 18 = 9... the Cycle repeats endlessly

88 = 16 = 7...77 = 14 = 5...55 = 10 = 1...11 = 2...22 = 4...44 = 8...88... Back to the beginning

66 = 12 = 3...33 = 6...66 = 3...33...etc. Oscillating back and forth between 6 and 3

This is illustrated graphically with the Mandala of Number Pairs.

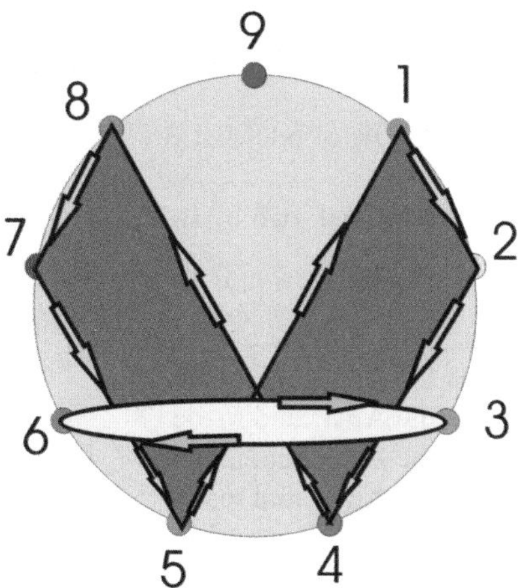

The diagram shows the three movement behaviours of the Numbers going into the Cosmic Ark.

1. The Infinity or "figure eight" or "butterfly wing" movement of the 1,2,4,8,7,5
2. The Oscillatory movement of the 3,6
3. The Fixed immobility or Zero movement of the 9.

Through simple arithmetic, I believe I have discovered the basic three tiered system of motion dynamics of the Universe.

The Trinity of the Ark-itypal Numbers

99 = 18 = 9

88 = 16 = 7

66 = 12 = 3

--

19 = 1

May
12 Thursday

She comforted me. Held me in her arms. It was the Great Goddess come down on earth in human form.

SPIRIT	= 1
MIND	= 4
MATTER	= 5
	--
	10 = 1

Alltheshit police contact me in Ireland. They've had word that my flat in Wellingtonia is going to be burgled while I'm away. The local "boys" have already planned it. The police have seen it in writing. Secret documents have come into their possession. Has Marlon done a dirty on me. The double crosser. Is he putting his mates up to the break-in, as he knows I'm going to be away for three months?

Continuing the saga of Numbers marching into the Ark -

Three addresses Nine on behalf of One, Seven and Four
Six addresses Nine on behalf of Eight, Two and Five.

And the Numbers went into the Ark in Threes

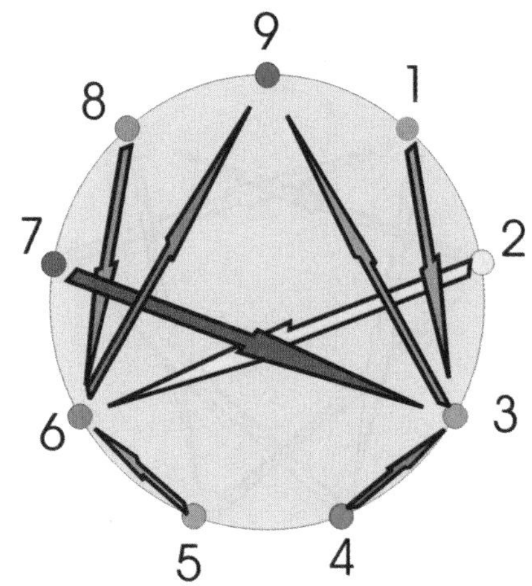

May
13 Friday

The helpful idiot (who was capable of homicide) mopped the lovely new carpet with bleached water. I had to humour him, even though I was dismayed at the pending loss of colour. The damage was done so I let him complete his domestic pursuits, wondering if I would have a house left by the time he'd finished.

Arthur Koestler writes about the three domains of creativity and names them the jester or fool, the sage or scientist and the artist. His Creative Trinity also creates a "Three in One".

Koestler's Triptych of Agents of Creativity

FOOL	= 3
SCIENTIST	= 1
ARTIST	= 6
	--
	10 = 1

Continuing the saga of Numbers marching into the Ark -

In the case of Fours, then Three and Six become stationary with Nine, while, One, Four and Seven form a clockwise motion triad, and Two, Eight and Five form an anti-clockwise motion triad.

And the Numbers went into the Ark in Fours

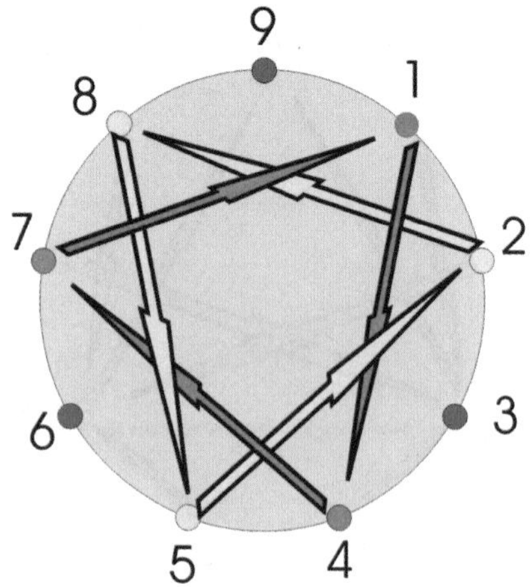

May
14 Saturday

Nocturnal Visitation. The Unknown Woman. She was snogging me again. But who? Full mouth and tongue treatment. Very erotic but was she an acquaintance or a total stranger? I can't see her properly. Blurred vision. The veil is too thick.

Food of the Gods
SOMA = 3
MILK = 3
HONEY = 4
--
10 = 1

Continuing the saga of Numbers marching into the Ark -

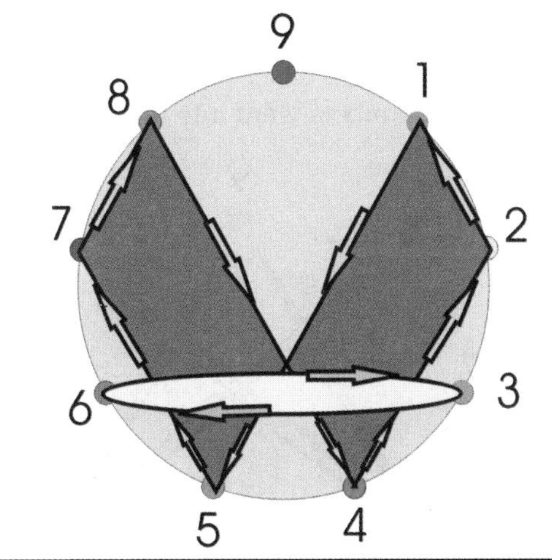

Numbers entering the Ark in Fives, is the same image as in Twos, except the flow is in the opposite direction.

May
15 Sunday

Small pockets of smoke. The source unknown - but the desk top is definitely clouding over. How do you put out a fire if there are no flames?

The 3 Biblical Jewish heroes who survived unscathed after being thrown into the fiery furnace by Nebuchadnezzar

SHADRACH	= 8	
MESHACH	= 3	
ABEDNEGO	= 8	
	--	
	19	= 1

News on radio. Air crash in Amman.

Continuing the saga of Numbers marching into the Ark -

In the case of Numbers travelling in Sixes…
Three addresses Nine on behalf of Two, Eight and Five
Six addresses Nine on behalf of Seven, One and Four.

And the Numbers went into the Ark in Sixes

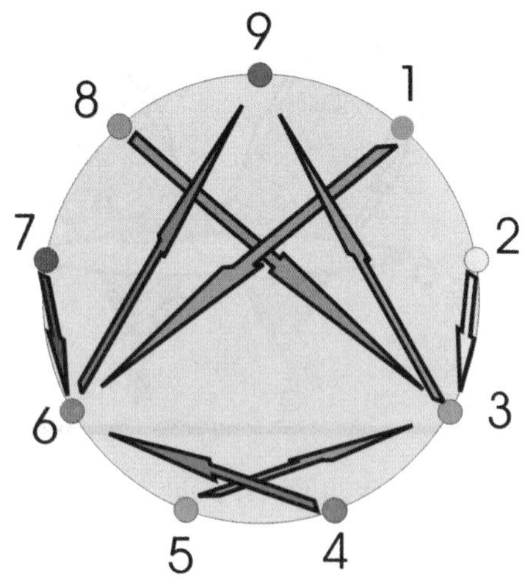

May
16 Monday

A knock on the door and there is Coral, come to visit me in Ireland. Except that she didn't look exactly like Coral. She was shorter, plumper and waddled. In fact she looked a bit like Cynthia -except she was wearing an ill- fitting blond wig. Yet she seemed to be Coral. Anyway, my guest came in and gave me a nervous kiss. Very like Coral. But still she reminded me of a blonde Cynthia. Coral also has black hair. Also these two women have another thing in common. They are asthmatic and therefore allergic to my cat, so perhaps neither of them came to visit me in Ireland . So, who was she?

Continuing the saga of Numbers marching into the Ark -

In the case of entering the Ark in Sevens, we see a repeat of Three and Six being stationary with Nine, but unlike the case of "Fours", here the triangles reverse their rotation. Thus One, Four and Seven move in an anticlockwise fashion, while Two, Eight and Five flow in a clockwise motion.

And the Numbers went into the Ark in Sevens

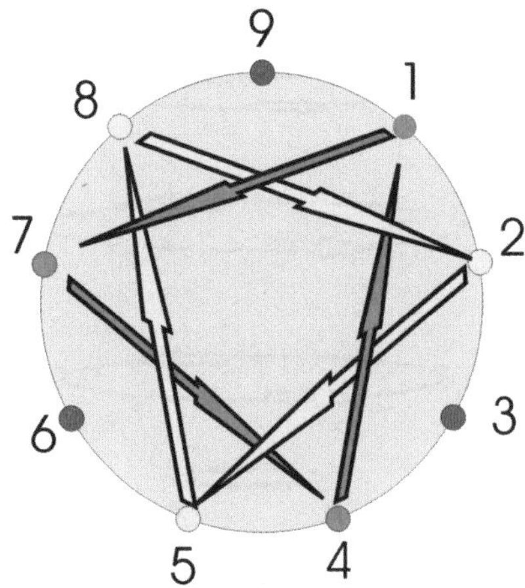

May
17 Tuesday

I have a haunted bookcase. Keeps throwing books at me. Ghost poltergeist entity?

The phone rings. It's Vita. She tells me we must meet as soon as possible to have sex.
"You prefer to see me early ?" I ask.
"Yes" she replied. I giggle as I change the words to "Peter Sourly" which she doesn't quite understand. But that's just my schizophrenia's creativity at play. It's meaningless really. Not worth losing it any sleep over.

Continuing the saga of Numbers marching into the Ark -

> But when the Numbers went into the Ark in Eights, what a surprise! They form pairs of oscillations (1-8, 2-7, 3-6, 4-5), except, of course, 9, which is pivotal to the sphere's rotation.

And the Numbers went into the Ark in Eights

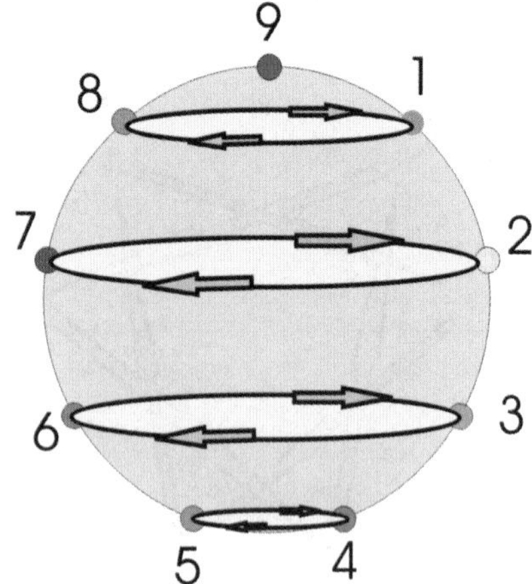

May
18 Wednesday

The animals came into my Irish home. Firstly, it was a fox cub, then rabbits, weasels, hare called Ham, a heron named Japhet and then an adult fox, called Shem. All the local wild life were seeking refuge with me. I was so happy. My house was the Ark and I was Noah, rescuing the creatures that were in peril from the approaching global doom. At last, I have the role I've always dreamed of - Saviour of innocent life.

Continuing the saga of Numbers marching into the Ark -

Finally, when the Numbers entered the Ark in Nines, they became Nines and so, paid homage to Nine.

And the Numbers went into the Ark in Nines

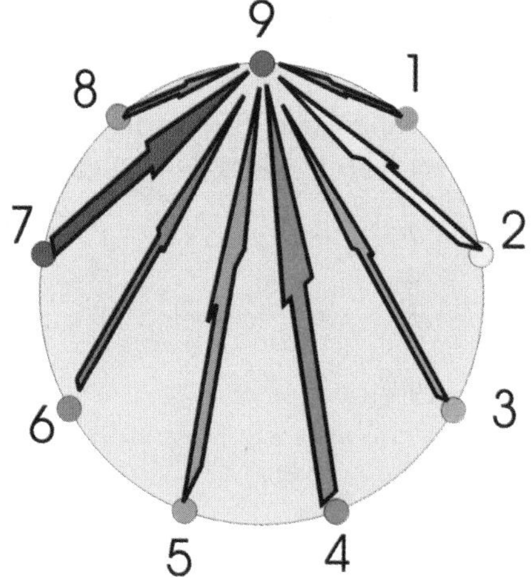

And when I look at my diagrams of the Numbers, in all their multitudes, entering the Ark,
I am reminded of the Dance of Shiva.

DANCE OF SHIVA = 53

May
19 Thursday

Jake is back with Vanessa. Damn! Blast! And I wanted so much to fuck her.

"I can laugh, I can cry or I can be detached. The choice is mine."
"Then you're not human." replies the old Home Help.
"No. I am God."

LAUGH = 4
CRY = 1
DETACHED = 5
--
10 = 1

Just because I cover my ears, it doesn't mean other people can't hear my farts.

To achieve Release and Eternal Bliss, you must detach yourself from Pleasure and from Pain. This is achievable through the Buddha Way.

PLEASURE = 7
PAIN = 4
BUDDHA WAY = 8
--
19 = 1

May
20 Friday

Hearing a droning sound I look to the sky. There's a plane up there flying quite low. A yellow and black helicopter appears and circles the plane, moving closer and closer. Suddenly I realise that the helicopter is behaving very irresponsibly. There will be a collision. Then the plane swings round and confronts the chopper which is startled and taken aback, so much so that it crashes into the window of a tall skyscraper behind it. The helicopter disappears into the building. The plane is no longer present. My friend arrives, and I tell him what happened. We go to the foot of the building beneath the window where the helicopter vanished. We search the ground for broken glass. We don't find any evidence of the incident, except I notice that my left wheel is beginning to slip off the wheelchair. If it collapses, I'm done for. The collapse is excruciatingly slow. I call out "Help Me" and prepare for the crash to the ground. It happens and I lose consciousness. When I come round, my friends including Laura, Giles, Jake and Marlon are gathered around, staring down at me. They appear very concerned. They agree I should be taken to hospital. I wait as my friends get into the car but there's no more room for me. Giles says he'll take me in his vehicle - but when we get inside, I notice other people getting on board and paying a conductor. I guess we must be on a bus or train.

PLANE = 5
HELICOPTER = 3

As we travel, Giles is mumbling to himself.
"What's that you're saying?" I groan.
"Typical of humans. We are Nature's outlaws. We break another circle, which is a cycle, and commit two crimes against the Earth."
"What do you mean?" I mutter as I continue to fathom whether I am on a train or a bus.
"First, we no longer shit in the fields - and second, there is nothing in our shit worth giving back to Nature."

May
21 Saturday

Ndriananahary hands me two packages. One contains Christmas cards sent to me but not delivered.
The second package is the long awaited script. Ndriananahary assures me the film will now be made this winter. A likely bloody story!

An unlikely story which reads as follows -

Somehow the playing card got sandwiched between the hamburger sesame seed bun and a CD mini-player, with the result that the picture of the UFO on the reverse of the card became a comical hybrid. Was this the Joker card or a Pokemon poking fun at a Macdonald bun?
As I examined the image with amusement, I saw that the UFO was animated and was metamorphosing into a more conventional flying saucer design. Then I began to see how the Extra-terrestrial spacecraft works. Its energy field made up of concentric circles spinning in opposite directions – each alternate ring powered by half the signs of the Zodiac. Positive signs (Aries, Gemini, Leo, Libra, Sagittarius, Aquarius) for one ring of energy and Negative signs (Pisces, Taurus, Cancer, Virgo, Scorpio, Capricorn) for the other ring. One revolving clockwise, the other anti-clockwise.

Doing the Numerology Analysis I found that in order for the flying saucer to achieve flight and direction the Negative Energy Rings (199=1) must revolve at half the speed of the Positive Energy Rings (182=2).

POSITIVE POLARITY SIGNS		NEGATIVE POLARITY SIGNS	
Aries	25 = 7	Pisces	26 = 8
Gemini	39 = 3	Taurus	19 = 1
Leo	14 = 5	Cancer	26 = 8
Libra	24 = 6	Virgo	35 = 8
Sagittarius	45 = 9	Scorpio	41 = 5
Aquarius	35 = 8	Capricorn	52 = 7
	--- --		---- --
	182 = 2		199 = 1

May
22 Sunday

A drowning baby. Swimming pool with see-through sides where we non-swimmers can watch the enjoyment of others. A baby falls into the pool and no one seems to be bothered about rescuing it. The baby seems able to cope but sooner or later it will run out of air, and then what? It clambers over obstacles of chairs, tables and shelves that have become submerged, oblivious to the growing danger to it of drowning. I look around desperately for help but still no one has become concerned. Does no one see the baby's predicament? Or is it that they just don't care? Tears flood my eyes as the doom of its watery tomb looms ever nearer.

Laura has a brain tumour and is dying. She has gone into hospital but doesn't know the real reason. My eyes fill with tears and my head explodes with grief.

The old man and the old woman are very good friends of mine. The man is very upset. He'd just been informed that his best friend has died. The woman had learned that her mother was dying. There was misery all round. I started to cry. She also told me that soon after the man had been told of the death, he'd driven back down a dark country road and hit an owl. It was killed instantly. The man didn't know what to do with himself any more. The woman did her best to comfort him, but she kept thinking of her dying mother. I burst into bigger tears.
"What's he crying for?" the old man grumbled, wiping tears from his eyes.
"What's the matter, dear?"
"It's weird, Someone has just told me that Laura was dying from a brain tumour. On top of which, all your tragedies have given me new fear."

The Zen Trinity
NIRMANA = 7
SAMBHOGA = 3
DHARMA = 9
--
19 = 1

May
23 Monday

Approx. 11am. I am given a gold honourary medal in a special commemorative silk cushioned box. An extra treat is found inside. A bronze miniature figurine of a standing monkey (or a character from prehistory?). As I examine it, I find it is jointed at one of its elbows and at the waist, so I am able to take its paw and "shake hands" with it. Then comes the surprise. It's a present from my kid sister, Fay. Now I am guilt ridden. She has given me something that is priceless and what have I given her in return? The present she is excitedly waiting for is nothing compared to her gift to me. She is going to be bitterly disappointed and hurt.

Then, at 3.15 in the afternoon. Robbery in the neighbourhood. The police are searching my garden for clues. The old Home Help helps me to sort things out and finds an old pair of cream woollen socks. She urges me to tell the police the socks are mine, even though I haven't a clue as to their origin.

Later at around 5.35 pm. Laura turns up with Quincy and Inigo. I'm overjoyed to see them all, especially Laura. She seems in a playful, happy mood. It is like the old times again. Inigo has been stealing from her and confesses in a flood of tears. She, like a true mother, forgives him. Then she tells me the bad news, like giving me her favourite cooking recipe. She has the HADES plague.

May
24 Tuesday

My electric shaver is rubbish. I just cannot get a decent close shave. So Pisces, Cancer and Scorpio, the girls from the make-up and wig department, volunteer to wet shave me. But even their attempts are pretty pathetic, and my face is still spotty with ugly clumps of insurrectionist growth. Anyway, that didn't stop the sexy brown haired lady with the elongated face, from wanting me to get out of my wheelchair to sit next to her on the lounge couch in the crowded Green Room bar. She wiggled her hips suggestively at me, attempting to entice me. Her hands would certainly wander in my most secret of places, which I could find appetizing, but feeling too depressed, I chose to decline her many attractions. So, feeling affronted at being scorned and rejected, she waved me away onto the next floor upstairs, where a seemingly kindly man lifts me out of my wheelchair, and suggests I take a bath while he cooks us some dinner. I'm unsure about this idea. What will he do to me? Especially when I am naked. Is he some kind of pervert? Does he intend to fiddle with me? Again, I am half-tempted (am I still so sex starved, I can contemplate allowing men having their wicked way with me?). But I say no. He is angry and abandons me. I am now without my wheelchair and marooned on the first floor up a flight of stairs. From a balcony, I see two young guys below me on the ground floor. I call for help. They rush upstairs to me, and offer to carry me down. I had hoped they would carry me in my wheelchair, but they took me down separately. At the bottom, I asked for my wheelchair but by then they had lost interest in helping me, and couldn't be bothered to go back up. And yet, one of them did go up and threaten to throw the wheelchair over the balcony. I yelled, "NO!"

"Suit yourself, Creepy Cripple," he said, laughing and disappeared.

Night has fallen and I am forced to leave the building on my hands and knees and bottom, and crawl and shuffle through the city streets. I feel undignified and vulnerable, and know this is not a good time to be wandering, lost in such a hostile environment. I bum and creep my way down a darkened alley, and spot a man looking strangely at me. Then, I notice another odd character, and another. They just stand around with extreme facial features, almost caricatures. They feel threatening but do nothing except wait. What are they waiting for? I continue on to the end of the alley, and find it is a cul-de-sac, and I am confronted by the Final Man, who looks very angry. I slowly turn around and head back, but just when I thought he was also going to ignore me, he chases after me, and easily catches me.

"Oh no you don't," he hisses. "You think you can come down our alley in the dark without being attacked?" The man's face was chalky white with black around the eyes, somewhat reminding me of Beetlejuice. Such facial features were, to me, a typical signature of evil. He grabs my left arm and pulls me towards him. I feel his claws digging in me. Sharp cuts in my skin as his index finger slices like a razor blade. I realise with horror he is holding a razor blade, and he is intent on stripping all the flesh from my arm and probably more. I struggle to escape him but I realise I cannot unless I relax and treat him as an ally.

May
25 Wednesday

Vita visits, someone I had not seen in ages. An aspiring actress, who had abandoned her career, and now has decided on a comeback.

In a huge room, waiting to shoot the "blue screen" scene for the movie "Jinxed Dinner", finally. Ndriananahary, the director and Thor, the writer, arrive. They both look older and thinner. They are not pleased with each other. In fact Thor is furious with Ndriananahary . Ndriananahary warns he may sack him if he continues moaning. They both leave in a huff, while I am abandoned, wondering if the film will ever get made.

Evening. It has got dark very early…as if the Winter months have come upon us without warning. And yet June is less than a week away. And SNOW! Loads of it falling, Big flakes, The streets are quickly thick with it, making it impossible for me to push my wheelchair. I struggle to get out of my car, and I'm wondering how am I going to get to the party in time, when I hear a familiar voice behind me – "I don't suppose you want my help?" I turn and see Penelope Perceval. "Are you going to the party?" I asked. "I take that question to mean yes," she replied, and she picks me up and seats me in my wheelchair, and begins to push me down many frozen streets until we reach a posh suburban detached house, lights a-blazing and sounds of great hilarity. We enter to find the party is taking place in a restaurant. Penelope sits me at a table of two gentlemen of a Middle-Eastern appearance. The waiter, who sounds like a speaking robot menu, is explaining to the Semitic types that there is no ham in the meat dish on offer. I don't get the impression that this was the guests' query, but the waiter continues to shout at them "There is no HAM. No Ham. Neither is there any pork.."
"That is not the question," one of them politely responds.
"I said there is no ham," the robot reiterates.
"What meat is involved?" I ask shyly for fear of turning the waiter's wrath upon me.
The waiter looks at me with fatherly benevolence. "It is a combination of two meats, pressed together and covered in gelatin. Rather delicious if I may say so," he assures me.
"And what are the meats?" I ask. He turns to the Arab and the Jew and says with manifest pride, "No ham. One is veal, and the other is Chef's

secret. But I can assure you it is the Royal of all flesh. Exotic beyond compare." I speculate venison, swan, horse, buffalo but he refuses to divulge. "State secret. Cannot say but you won't be disappointed." Well, I decide to forgo this mysterious food, as I have never liked the idea of veal, and if the other meat is venison, well, I have a rule never to eat Bambi. And swan I refuse on the grounds it might be the Ugly Duckling. As the party is getting too noisy, and I haven't seen anyone I really know, I ask for my hat and coat, although I do worry about how I am going to make it to my car. As I leave the house, and groan that the snow is a blizzard, and the streets are thick carpets of awkward white stuff, I hear Penelope Perceval nasally high-pitched voice behind me. "I suppose you want me to push you back to your car!! And before I can say yes please, she grabs the wheelchair and plunges me into the swirling snowy mattress. The return journey is heavy going and heart-stopping, as I fear Penelope is inexperienced at driving wheelchairs through arctic conditions. She cannot anticipate that hidden kerbs suddenly disappear and reappear to trip the unwary. However, we make it back to my car. I turn to thank Penelope, and suddenly I find her sexually attractive despite her being a nauseating condescending Posh bird. She smiles at me, sensing my arousal, and just as I think she's about to invite me back to her place for a night-cap, or suggest that she comes home with me, Sam Soap, God's gift to women, arrives on the scene. He shakes her by the hand, looks lovingly into her eyes, and she is hooked. I am history.

May
26 Thursday

Laura visits me, to admonish me for abandoning her and leaving her destitute. I told her I couldn't give her money while it was feeding Luther's drug habit. She had to sort him out herself, make him go out to work and support her and the family. While she continued to give him her money, he will continue to leech off her, and do fuck all. Laura storms angrily up to me as if to attack...but instead she gently touches my head and assures me that she knows that I am genuine and mean well, and I care for her with tenderness and love. She forgives and releases me.

May
27 Friday

Bull fight. The raging bull escapes into the audience. They panic and flee. Many women trip. The bull impales them, humping their writhing, screaming bodies, like he is raping them. After he gores them to death, the bull returns to the arena to meet its doom with the toreador.

THE HEADLESS MAN (continued)

I am found some time past on the train,
Holding on to what's left of the sane,
The cripple that's me quakes on the tracks,
Sliding chair fro and to, my nerve cracks,
Then I sense His presence down the line,
He's creeping up the vans towards mine,
Death's shadow snakes thru the corridors,
I expect no mercy, only Jaws,
After all it was me who made Him,
We both knew this Joke was no mere whim.
Suddenly bang, doors open, there He is!
Confident, in steps this Tarot's kiss…

We were standing around, minding our own business, when they came. Some kind of Christian evangelists – but a strange sect, fanatical – like Mormons, wearing severe looking suits of black, white shirts, black ties and black hats. They encircled us and started to harangue us with their religious hogwash. I started to take the piss out of the preachers and made a lot of noisy nonsense words. Next, the Sermonisers, angry at my ridiculing, stepped aside, revealing their Nazi skinhead Minders who quickly bore down on me threateningly. They made it patently clear that if I continued to blaspheme or insult their cult I would be pulverised. I refused to be intimidated by these thuggish youths, and was about to resume my "Blah blah blahdy bah" gobble-di-gook, when one of Men in Black points an ominous looking object at me. I realise it's a kind of zapping weapon, perhaps a laser beam instrument of torture. I take a closer look at the lethal device and see the tip of it is some kind of light emitting crystal…a diamond or sapphire like the Rod of Aaron.

I decide at this time that discretion shall take the place of valour, and beat a hasty retreat.

May
28 Saturday

Laura turns on me. She beats me to the ground and I am defenceless against her onslaught. The sad old days have returned with a vengeance.

THE HEADLESS MAN (continued)

My eyes wide, What's He got? Gun or knife?
A blade! Good. I can still save my life,
Torn in two, my will is distorted,
Creep of Thanatos, be aborted!
I know I must let the Hymn succeed,
Prevent not I, stark destiny's need.
The smiling grim beams back the blade's gleam,
When the train deranged breaks Hade's dream,
We both fall apart and to the floor,
He's lost his knife, I've got hope once more,
The Killer scrabbles and grabs His tool,
While I grip His wrists, from His lips come drool,
Fate's struggling dagger goes back and forth,
I try to push His blade back up north.
I know it's a sin. We had a deal,
He was to kill me. The world would heal,
But I can't, won't, for no one, die,
With my utmost will, I'll bleed Him dry,
Success! His eyes cry. Now glazed. Now shut,
I've forced His knife up, ripped His own gut,
I won, but I'm suffering from shock,
The world's now doomed to suck my cock.

May
29 Sunday

At last, I've managed to go to a new country this year. I was beginning to give up. Lapland. Felicia's motherland - but as usual, she is there to torment me.

The Sami Trinity

MAYLMAN-RADIEN	= 8	(Ruler of World)
MADDERAKKA	= 6	(Earth Mother)
LEYBOLMAJ	= 5	(Hunter-God)
	--	
	19 = 1	

Felicia arrives - in her night dress, which barely covers her naked arse. As usual, she's tempting me and suggesting we will sleep and fuck but I know it is all a sham. What is she doing here in this state when she knows she doesn't fancy me? Why does she keep tormenting me? She talks incessantly about her men problems while flaunting her legs and bottom at me. In the end I give up and go out, leaving her the house.

May
30 Monday

We went to the wrong haunted house but at least we got a free slap up meal. But at the end of the day, Thor informs me it's Chailey in Sussex, not Shelling in Kent.

Chailey Sussex = 53
Shelling Kent = 55

later I watch a TV documentary on ghosts. "The Hitcher of Blue Bell Hill in Kent".

That night as I lay in bed, Coral visits me. I told her off, for not informing me that she had died three months ago. She apologized but she'd been kept busy getting used to her new disembodied experience.

May
31 Tuesday

The party was going well until the end when I found my money was missing. We searched amidst the debris and drunken bodies but it was gone. Then I found Isis, she looked a bit different, reminding me of that other prick-teaser, Felicia (Hor-m-akhet) - But it is definitely Isis (Tallulah). She was so pleased see me. Her eyes shone as they looked into mine. The old love was rekindled. We took each other's' hands and her thighs pressed against my feet. I glanced across at her husband, Osiris (Fraser) who was pretending not to notice. Isis whispered, "How come we never fucked?" I smiled and kissed her on the lips. The kissing became more passionate and I knew we were going to be at last together forever. I told her I was too shy and scared to try to make love to her in the old days. She stroked the back of my head and told me those days were gone and we had a new life awaiting us.

Is it true? Is Isis correct? What do the Numbers say?

Felicia	= 9	Hor-m-akhet	= 9
Tallulah	= 6	Isis	= 2
Fraser	= 4	Osiris	= 8
	---		--
	19 = 1		19 = 1

June
1 Wednesday

Ferdinand returns my scripts. The British Film Industry is ending and my "The Vertigo" (the story of Hitler's extermination of disabled people) is doomed. America owns us "lock, stock and barrel" with Hollywood cast in the role of Goebbels.

Hitler's Racial Trinity (despicable creep)
ARYAN = 5
JEW = 2
MONGREL = 3
--
10 = 1

p.m. I was driving along when I started to have trouble from other motorists. First one car tried to bump into me, but I succeeded in avoiding it. then another car, a black vintage type, probably from the 1920s, came overtaking me, and as it did so, tried to run me off the road. The driver and passenger acted as if I had no right to be sharing the road with them. I saw they were young guys in black suits, and white shirts, and black ties. Could it be they were the same Men in Black religious Gestapo from yesterday? I retaliated and turned my car into them, to warn them to keep away. Next, I felt something hit the back of my head. It was so hard, I almost blacked out. I was really surprised...are they throwing something at me? I turned and looked at them as their car continued to drive parallel to mine, racing. The passenger was leaning over to the rear seat, and had picked up a strange metallic large silver and black object. In fact, it was disc shaped, about the size of a large frying pan. I thought to myself, the bastard is going to throw that thing at me next, which could easily kill me, if it hit my head. He nodded at me and smiled as if he had read my thoughts, and seen the look of anxiety on my face. I accelerated and tried to pull away from their vehicle before he could throw his heavy flying object at me. Suddenly my pursuers veer of the road to avoid a giant apparition of Genghis Khan standing astride the road, singing the song "Where are the Dragons and Lions?" As I drive between his legs, he looks down and gives me a little wink. I take this as yet more proof that I am really a direct descendent of his.

June
2 Thursday

Khalifa who was living in Grovely Castle, moves nearer to me. Guilt. I never made his "Flying Fever" video. He forgives me.

The Great Dragon's Triangle.....
from Stonehenge to Grovely Castle is 6 miles
from Grovely Castle to Old Sarum is 6 miles
from Old Sarum to Stonehenge is 6 miles

Since this gives us 666, I expect a Triadic Union (Three in One) from Stonehenge, Grovely Castle and Old Sarum....

GROVELY CASTLE = 2
OLD SARUM = 4
STONEHENGE = 4
--
10 = 1 BINGO!

The Beast lies sleeping in the geometry of the geography....FENG SHUI (Chinese for Dragon Swan)
FENG = 5 SHUI = 3
DRAGON = 5 SWAN = 3

Blimey O'Riley, my bête noir, the Prime Minister arrived unannounced and was trying to make friends with me. In fact he was being extremely charming and pleasant. I wanted to hate him, quarrel with him but his disarming solicitude fair knocked the wind out of my sails. Not once did we talk politics. He skilfully skirted the subject, giving me no ammunition with which to attack and accuse him. He suggests I make a trip to the United States. The President wants to meet me.

June
3 Friday

Hecate and I were driving through the USA and were stopped by Yank cops, who took us in for questioning. Really just a formality. Checking our identity papers and basically being nosey, like cops everywhere. For some reason, I'm carried into the station, leaving my wheelchair in the car. Inside was a white cop who was typing out his report on us...and a black cop interrogating a black woman, a prostitute drug-user. He was treating her like shit, occasionally fingering her vagina as she sat with her knees to her shoulders, revealing her nakedness under her skirt. She was reporting an incident of a gang rape she'd witnessed, at least she thinks it was rape going on - the men, possibly 9 of them, on top of one woman. There was a strong pungent smell of sex, she said.
"Sort of fishy, would you say, Freebie?" enquired the abusive cop.
"I suppose so.... " she replied trying to ignore his advances. She moves away from him, "...and I'm not Freebie. My name is Phoebe," and sits next to me, giving me a sexy, knowing look. I'm instantly aroused but then she forgets me. Meanwhile Hecate returns from the car, irate and demands to know if we are free to leave. The cops say "Sure," but no one volunteers to carry me. Hecate has stormed off, leaving me in the lurch. A white female cop comes in. She was previously the black prostitute. I suggest she carries me out. Looking a bit like Selene she nervously agrees but as she approaches I suddenly worry that she might have the HADES virus.

Three other names for ARTEMIS.....
HECATE = 6   PHOEBE = 6   SELENE = 6

Later....James Stewart, the dead Hollywood film star is present at a dinner engagement I've been invited to. I give the poor old ghost a hard time. He helped make the myth that America was everybody's Favourite Uncle. Him and Walt Disney.

June
4 Saturday

I'm a guest at a party / reception in the Yank President's White House. She had invited me as she was keen to meet me and discuss certain things. It was all very strange as I wouldn't normally entertain any sympathetic feelings towards this adulterous weak warmonger. Yet I was charmed by her enthusiastic welcome of me. She invited me to meet her for a close tête-à-tête in the nursery. She wanted to persuade me of the inherent beauty of the Coming "New World Order"…which she kept describing as the "**New Holy Order**". She looked very psychedelic with wavy hair and colourful clothes. Her sixties background was obviously shining through, as she energetically assumed Jane Fonda's alter ego. (Or had she once been Jane Fonda before Ted Turned her?). I went into the large room which I had been informed was the nursery, and was surprised to find it was more like a works canteen with posh chairs. Around the walls were signs of childhood, picture books, toys, dolls. The tea lady gave me a coffee as I waited for the President.

NEW = 6 HOLY = 6 ORDER = 6 The NEW HOLY ORDER is 666

Looking in Revelations, I ask why are these 13 words in upper case letters?
Revelations 17:5 (1+7+5=13)

MYSTERY, BABYLON
8 8
THE GREAT, THE
6 6 6
MOTHER OF HARLOTS
7 3 3
AND
1
ABOMINATIONS
6
OF THE EARTH
3 6 7
= 70 = 7

13 words (unlucky for sum) 70 divided by 13 = 5.3846154 (yikes! 5.3)

June
5 Sunday

The Yank President shouting her big fucking mouth off….going on and on about the New Holy Order. Why doesn't the Nazi pig just die? Can't she see we've all had enough of her! As usual, however, she has gathered around her a group of arse-licking cowards who secretly despise her and know ultimately she is a danger to all of us, yet they haven't the nerve to tell her what they think. So instead, they ingratiate themselves and wallow in her slime. Except me, I rise to the challenge and rip her to shreds with a barrage of verbal abuse. She is shocked and dismayed at my attack and sent scuttling away, with her serpentine tail shoved right up her stinking gob. Death to all tyrants.

June
6 Monday

6pm. Leaving Yankland. Airport customs. I have a problem. Looks like I may not get out alive. The officer passes me the phone. A woman's voice. She is the Colonel. She tells me the matter has been sorted. There is no longer a problem. With relief I survive another trip to the United Fats of America.

It's late when I get back to my apartment in Wellingtonia. As I enter I have a feeling there is an Intruder lurking in the shadows. Did they get in? Or are they still outside hiding in the garden? I go in the bedroom and I see a woman's arm coming through the window, pulling at a cord. The light switch? Or is she trying to open the blinds? I catch a glimpse of her Elfin face. She thinks I didn't see her. No, she did see me looking at her, that's why she quickly stopped doing what she was doing. I think I scared her away – for now. But I know these beings. They always come back later. I go in the sitting room, and notice a window isn't closed properly. I try to push it up with a stick, and then knock the latch to lock it, but it is proving to be very difficult. I haven't the right implement, and time is running out. They will be back soon.

June
7 Tuesday

Am I really home?

Various of my old friends are now my neighbours. Or am I visiting friends who all inhabit the same neighbourhood now?
Tom and his family live in one house, Jake in another, and Maxine and her family in yet another. My arrival causes great excitement. I see people leap up in their sitting rooms to greet me. They race to be the first to welcome me back. But Delia Artemis, Maxine's second daughter is the winner. She is in front of me, her eyes gleaming with love . I realize she wants me and I in turn want her. She tells me "We were made for each other. I was born for her."

I do the sums. DELIA ARTEMIS = 53

Victory in South Africa. Standing up against Apartheid Fascists helped to bring about the release of Mandela and freedom for the blacks. Resistance is All. A lesson from history.

Chief Naked Cloud, the Native American medicine man, said everyone who walks the earth has nine spirit animals to guide them during their walk. "You must find your totem animals," he said to me.
"But how?" I asked.
"Sometimes you look at a picture of a particular animal or see it for real, and you simply feel it belongs to you. Or the animal comes to you in dreams. Is there a particular animal that speaks to you? Or you can never stop thinking about?"
"The wolf," I replied. The Indian nodded. "To us Native Americans, the Wolf is Pathfinder-Teacher who seeks Heaven and once he has found it, strives to bring down all the blessings of Heaven onto Earth. He is not the mystic, who merely seeks to save his own soul and escape the material earth. Such religious philosophies of escape are self-centred and incapable of changing the world, since only a tiny minority ever achieve Nirvana, and thus leave all the rest of humanity in their disorder and misery. The Wolf is the agent of Aquarius, bringing the Heavenly Waters down on Mankind, transforming the earth and giving growth to seeds of Divinity."
Then Chief Naked Cloud took out a pack of cards.
"These are special medicine cards. Each card is of an animal. We will

discover through these cards your Nine Totem Animals. Take the pack. Shuffle them thoroughly. Kiss them, and pray to the Great Spirit to reveal your animals." I did as he told me, while he made a small bonfire, and then played a haunting melody on his flute. When I finished, he took the shuffled cards from me, and threw them on the fire. I cried out but he gestured me to stay calm. After a minute, he urinated on the flames, putting them out. In the ashes, he found exactly nine cards completely unburned. He laid the Nine out, speaking as he showed me each card.
"The Opossum is your animal of the East. The Dog is your animal of the South. The Swan is your animal of the West. The Horse is your animal of the North. The animal above you is the Dragon-fly. The animal below you is the Skunk. The animal within you is the Armadillo. The animal on your left is the Moose..." By this time I was feeling depressed. No wolf. I thought it highly unlikely that the last card would reveal the wolf. With a glint in his eye, the witch-doctor turned the final unburned card over. "And the animal on your right is the Wolf." A big smile broke across my face. "You see, your intuition was correct. You do have a spiritual affinity with the Wolf," said Chief Naked Cloud handing me the nine cards.

The Mountain bridges the gap between the Earth and Sky. The Wolf brings Wisdom from Heaven to Earth.

SKY	= 1	HEAVEN	= 1
MOUNTAIN	= 2	WOLF	= 2
EARTH	= 7	EARTH	= 7
	--		--
	10 = 1		10 = 1

June
8 Wednesday

Our group had been infiltrated. One of the members, the leader (bloody Giles) in fact, was a spy, working for the security forces. Or perhaps the whole group was a front for the secret police, and I was the only genuine resistance fighter! The point was we were now under siege. An SPG or SWAT force were about to attack. The traitor had planted a loaded Kalashnikov on my bed but out of my reach, so that first I could not use it in defence, and second, as incriminating evidence. I was, however, given a dummy gun, utterly useless but a convincing enough replica to give the enemy the excuse to open up and wipe us out. "We had good reasons to believe our lives were at risk, my lord". I can just hear the usual lies, excuses for the Shoot to Kill policy. However, I managed to throw both guns, the real and fake, away from me. They disappeared sufficiently far enough to render any future court verdict unsafe. The SAS (or whoever fascist bastards), are no longer going to be able to have everything their own way.

June
9 Thursday

On the run. I am a member of a "designated" criminal gang. There are five of us. One is a real psychopathic killer. But all for one and one for all. His crimes are my crimes. I have to accept responsibility for his ghastly murders. Our fun (fun? Did I mean to say that?), our killing spree (ours?) is cut short. Dawn raids by the police round us all up. We're taken to separate interrogation cells. My police investigator gives me the "no turning back" look. I know I am doomed. He seems sympathetic. Perhaps he suspects I am not the real killer. But if he reads my journal he will know I am not entirely blameless. If they learn the truth, I can never live with my name again. Then I remember one of our gang members is Laura, and she is truly innocent. The police will treat her the worse because of her inherent anti-authority streak. She will resist them and they will use every cruel trick in the book to restrain her. I must help her.

June
10 Friday

In prison. A handsome man grabs me, flips me over on to my tummy and lifts me up and down by the hips. I ask him if he wants to fuck me up the arse? He replies that is exactly what he intends to do and before I can say "yes" (which is what I was going to say, anyway) he yanks my pants down and as he thrusts his penis right up into my quivering expectant rectum, I come in a great gush.

He then metamorphoses into a luscious little woman. A small gorgeous body, a sweet tasty bottom naked and inviting. We secretly know, given time I will be allowed to enjoy her heavenly delights. Soon her friends depart and she throws herself on the bed lying on her stomach, her exquisite bum and juicy quim quivering invitingly. I take the plunge and immerse myself in the soft roundness of her flesh.

11.05 pm Looking west at the last glimmerings of a farewell sun, a meteor streaks in bright green downwards shouting "Wait for me!"

June
11 Saturday

The Prime Minister returns the Falkland islands to Argentina. Everyone is jubilant. A new era of liberation has opened with this gesture.

Amnesty is given to all his opponents. I am released.
For the time being.
Take nothing for granted.
The Calm before the Storm.
The New Holy Order
Is just around the corner.

June
12 Sunday

Laura is searching for me.

Thor tells me that you can always detect aliens or their collaborators by what colours they like. Purple and Green are allegedly their favourite colours. (Traditionally, fairies prefer green and purple. Plus "the little green men from Mars". Rasputin's "Zeleni")

Well, if Purple and Green belong together - a Duet, then what Third colour completes the Trinity?

The Riddle of the 3rd component to complement the Purple and the Green was already solved by my subconscious mind. I'd placed the Crystal ball at the apex of a triangle formed by the Green stone and the Purple stone.

GREEN = 4
PURPLE = 7
CRYSTAL = 8
--
19 = 1

The Sky is Crystal. The Mountain is Purple. And the Earth is Green.

June
13 Monday

Marlon has a pet hamster on a chain around his neck. It's like a medallion. His good luck charm. I look at it, and see the poor creature is almost dead. The chain is too long and it has been dragged along the ground. Marlon doesn't realize what he's doing. He thinks that by painting the chain green the good luck charm will work.

Two women. The dark haired one chooses me and physical journeys begin at her feet. Mutual pleasures are promised but what did she say about the cylinder? (=9) And why do I remember the number 3514?

June
14 Tuesday

I asked Jonah if 3514 had any meaning, and he just replied "Lucifer knows he could've repented, but he chose not to."
"Doesn't Lucifer get another chance?" I asked.

I am making a movie. It is an epic drama with incredible special effects of the whole of San Francisco being destroyed. "But can the American audience cope with seeing such a city of icons being obliterated. Destroy San Francisco and you destroy the American Dream". I reason that if they could handle the White House and Washington city being obliterated by aliens in "Independence Day" then it shouldn't be a problem for them. Remembering the alien invasions brought to mind an alphabet book - huge, brilliant pictures, almost three dimensional animation, like a walled chart strip traveling the length of a school corridor. What amazed me was the number of entries referring to astronomy, space, planets, cosmos . Aliens were being brought to my attention once again. The last picture I saw was C. for comet. Underneath were the words "I am (in?) Trouble."- the word "in" kept blinking on and off so the meaning became dangerously ambiguous, reminding one of the so called distress signal received by the space-refinery, "The Nostromo" in Ridley Scott's movie "Alien."

C = 3
Comet = 2
San Francisco =5

I am (in) trouble
9 + 5 + (5) + 3

= 44 (58) = 8 (4)

June
15 Wednesday

I was parked in a woman's car park. I had nowhere else to spend the night. This morning she found me and told me never to spend the night in her drive again. I promised her I would not.

Dinosaurs. A whole herd. The carnivorous kind. Tyrannosaurus Rex, Allosaurus, Gigantoraptor and the Megalosaurus. Huge and hungry. They are hunting me. Well, us. A group of us are fleeing from them. We try to hide in a building but the monsters soon track us down and besiege us. The building is massive, so the dinosaurs will have no trouble operating once they break in. The huge doors and rooms will not hinder their movement. I fear we will have no escape if we stay together, so I quickly detach myself from the group, and go out the backdoor.

Sitting in the cafe, daydreaming over a cold mug of coffee. Suddenly the name "Octavia" pops into my head. Octavia? I don't know any Octavia. The only "Octavia" I ever met was a nurse, nearly 20 years ago. Why would I be thinking of her after all these years?

June
16 Thursday

Working in the basement, with Pluto, the makeup artist. Delilah is waiting at the parking meters. Time is running out for her. She keeps returning to remind me she has to go. Her journey back home to Austria can no longer wait. Eventually I can leave the job and meet Delilah in the street where she and her friend are waiting, to give her my farewells. On the way, I see a young homeless person lying in a blanket in a shop doorway. Nothing has changed. The poor are still with us. I'm tempted to cross the road to chat with him but I cannot afford the interlude. Delilah is impatiently waiting. On my right I pass the magnificent and alluring entrance to the Elephant Emporium. Full of knick-knacks of a pachyderm connection. I postpone the pleasure of perusing for later. I must bid adieu to Delilah before it is too late. She is in tears. Her friend had been paid by her father to find Delilah and bring the prodigal daughter home. He was even paying Delilah to do a degree in Vienna to woo her back. Understandably, she was overwhelmed by his paternal solicitudes. She'd painted her face and put on bright red lipstick. She was re-establishing the familiarity for him. However, as a last act of rebellion, she gave her lesbian friend a full erotic sensual kiss on the mouth.

Afternoon. Pluto tells me he's got a phone number of a girl who is desperate to meet me.
"Oh yeah, who is she?"
"Someone I met at a party last night. Really stunning to look at. Her name's Octavia"
My heart stops.
"Octavia? Does she know me?"
"No, she says she's never met you. But she's had dreams about you. When I told her I was seeing you today, she insisted I gave you her phone number."
"Give it to me, then."
Pluto hands me a cylinder and scratched on its smooth metallic surface are a series of numbers -3514 9553.
"Is this her phone number?"
"No, her dildo, you prick."

Later, I find myself singing Donovan's song "Universal Soldier".

I think there will be a world war soon. Perhaps the Last War. The Prime Minister is acting fishy again. The truce is going to collapse soon. And Princess Danu will have to watch out.
And so will I.

June
17 Friday

More home-interior decorating. Inga Groser and I argue about the likelihood of World War Three breaking out soon. She thinks I'm just being paranoid. "You always were an Apocalyptic doom merchant."

Later this evening, I meet Octavia. She tells me her mother is being persecuted by the CIA, MI5 and Special Branch. I know what she means.

Even later, in a car, overlooking stars that have come to rest in the misty valley below us, Octavia and I cuddle and kiss and smile as a passing fox looks back at us, giving her blessing to a love born in the aether.

June
18 Saturday

A Chinese woman (Stella Maris?) comes rushing up to me. "Doctor Labif, I have some photographs of wolves for you". I thank her and she goes into the library to fetch them. Across the way is a Yank woman sitting at a restaurant table. When the Chinese girl returns with the wolf pictures, the Yank calls her over to look at them before me. We go together and the Goddam Yank completely dominates, hogging the photos, mistakenly thinking the Chinese woman had taken them. I feel like reasserting my rightful place but I don't want to embarrass the Yank (poor dumb creatures that they are), but then I guess that's how they always get away with it.

Later, I find I am tiny and am being chased by a huge giant. At first I thought I was stuck in a board game environment, but it turned out to be a computer cyberspace arcade world. As I run from level to level, I wonder what happens if he catches me. Will I always be trapped, suspended in Virtual Reality?

Then I am caught but instead of crushing my bones to make his bread, the Giant tells me about The Doors. "Jim Morrison is not dead," he says. "I saw him. Here is his calling card." I take it, and it immediately turns into a mobile phone, which rings. "Yes?" I speak into the phone. "Who is that?"
"Jim Morrison," came back the instantly recognizable voice.
"Prove it," I reply. And he instantly appears in front of me. "Wow," I exclaim. "Jim Morrison. So you are not dead?"
The Great Rock Icon shrugs. "Dead? What does that mean? A stupid concept, anyway."

June
19 Sunday

Lying naked on the bed, having a good wank. Morning breaks and I hear activity outside. To my horror a new panoramic window behind me opens up a vast vista of immaculate lawns and swimming pools. People enjoying their stately homes and grounds. Did they peep at my disgusting behaviour. Dr. Sobek, photographer, wouldn't miss the spectacle. His gossiping tongue would spread the story far and wide, me beating my meat, with all having a "butcher's". I'll be the laughing stock of "After Dinner Speeches" for years to come .

"I cut my hand off," saith he, holding up the prying electronic eye
- Don't do it, Dr. Sobek.

THE HEADLESS MAN (continued)

I'm near the Top, the world's been raided,
Now I can walk and stand with the tall,
With stunning good looks, I excel all,
Married to a princess, soon to be Queen,
With an envied palace, the best yet seen,
I'm a rich, powerful superstar,
No one can stop me, I've gone too far.
Much loved by the global media,
It's mine, that's why it's now seedier,
Elected Business Man of the Year,
Eminent Statesman, Mister Sincere,
The New World Order's my invention,
Created to suppress dissention,
The plebs will stay tame with bread and games,
Soon I will be World Controller of Names.

June
20 Monday

Octavia tells me that her husband is going to the USA for a year. In fact, he is already there. She seems to be suggesting that the way was now clear for us to get together.

THE HEADLESS MAN (continued)
I've been praised for solving with slick ease,
Problems of famine, drought and disease,
My genius has cracked the energy gap,
Unlimited fuel, just turn the tap,
My Peace Plan has won the Nobel Prize,
Won an Oscar for "Master of Lies",
Soon they'll vote me World Ruler Supreme,
And then they'll know I'm not what I seem.
Upstairs bathroom, I'm having a shave,
My wife's adorning the silk I gave,
We're preparing for an evening out,
Dressed to kill, there are smart Gods about,
We're honoured guests at the White House ball,
Where I'll condescend to take the Call,
Tonight, Time waits for the razor blade,
Life spliced on the Edge, poised for the Shade.
Not long now for the posh sleek limo,
To pick us up for the Last Laugh Show,
But in the mirror I see no grin,
Something ominous has just crept in,
A shadowy feeling sensing doom,
This shaking shave craves blood for my tomb,
Echoes return to collect lost bills,
There's a Song to be paid, one that thrills,
"Oh Razor, please Razor, cut my throat,
Time to take me on your Death-Wish boat."

June
21 Tuesday

Octavia, the bubbly woman, perky, seductive, gives me all her attention. We kiss and kiss and kiss. She makes me very happy.

She smiles as we fuck and says she has never had anything so big inside her before. Are we at last "Breaking the Waves"? No, because in the next breath, she pours cold water. "Let's enjoy a good shag but don't fall in love with me."
"Okay" I agree sheepishly. But it's too late. I already have.

How is the Circle Squared?

Circle = 5
Square = 9
Triangle = 5
--
19 = 1

The Circle is Squared by the Triangle

June
22 Wednesday

This morning while Octavia prepares breakfast, I study her apartment. For the first time I notice she has a dead mutant cat (it has two bodies) in a jar of formaldehyde, in the bathroom. Also, in the sitting room, behind the sofa, is a cupboard full of dried deformed human foetuses. Freaks. Actually, some are very alien-like. Similar in shape to me. Suddenly the sculptures of dismembered body parts hanging on butcher's hooks in the hallway begin to make sense to me.

Browsing Octavia's book collection, found a biography on Horatio. He was a teacher from my old school days. To my surprise the contents page lists three chapters about me.

I ring Sam Soap and tell him I may not be available to do "Who's Afraid of Virginia Woolf?" at the Edinburgh Fringe this August / September as I could still be in "River Oozes Murder". I've still got the interview to come, and may accept the offer. Needless to say, he was not pleased. Especially as he was hoping to do his film on the I. R. A. suspect murdered by Thatcher's S.A.S. in Gibraltar, with me playing a part in it. Mind you, HBO were only giving him a week to shoot it in. I tried to tell him he will be terribly compromised but he was confident… a sign of his lack of experience.

This evening I saw a UFO, and there were aliens I think, but I don't remember any details as I write 0000000000000000000000000000000000 0000000000000000000000000000000000po++++++. My watch slowed down until it stopped at 11.53pm. What are these two marks on the right back of my head? With dried blood?

June
23 Thursday

Laura was dying from an incurable disease, which was causing her face to be eaten away and was caving in. Also, her brain was affected, so her behavior and speech became distorted. I hugged her, trying to comfort her but felt helpless in the face of her imminent doom. I wept and wept. The tears burned my eyes.

THE HEADLESS MAN (continued)

Tell me I'm a Melancholy Man,
I don't understand the risk I ran,
My Ego awoke God's Evil Plan,
Now He hints I must carry the can.
Ghosts never die, they're made to haunt you,
The doorbell rings and I'm torn in two,
I'm still upstairs but I see the hall,
"It's okay, I'll go," comes my wife's call,
I watch her as she descends the stairs,
While a silent prickling scares my hairs,
"The chauffeur's early," she says, annoyed,
Opens the door to a black night's void.
At first, she just felt the smiling stare,
Shadows were shielding Him standing there,
So out stepped the Smile into the light,
Fate urged Him back for a second bite,
A luminous face, eyes sparkling red,
My Assassin returns from the Dead,
His quiet charm fills my wife with dread,
He's from that Place where angels can't tread.
"Who are you?" she asks fearing His voice,
He doesn't answer, He has no choice,
But to extend His benevolence,
And takes off His hat that gave offence,
Taking with it His head, smiling still,
My wife screamed, terrifying and shrill,
God's Man had come to complete my Scheme,
Your scream was now mine, no time to dream.....

June
24 Friday

I embarrass everyone at Octavia's party by announcing that I will not be washing my dick for quite a while as I want to keep the smell of her gorgeous vagina on it. Octavia is furious. How dare I reveal our love in such a coarse fashion! Shit. I think I've blown it with her.

June
25 Saturday

Igor says Octavia is weird, completely off her head, but Octavia said that I was even weirder.

I go to where Octavia is staying. A huge house belonging to a rich young man who plays at being her brother. But he is really her mother's new lover. Anyway, the house feels like a hotel with many big rooms. I search for Octavia but she is too busy with her friends. The young man is a good host but he is in the way. Eventually I find Octavia, and I'm informed we will be sleeping in different rooms. I am bitterly disappointed. Gutted in fact. She decides to take me out but we leave my wheelchair behind. She carries me through the city streets. I realize I need to get rid of the video camera I'm carrying, I need to pick up my coat since we are going to be wandering around for hours. We go on a diversion to discard the camera. Octavia is feeling the strain of having to carry me everywhere.
"I was really looking forward to carrying someone I love around my favourite places, " she sighs sadly. I felt our relationship would never happen, being a burden to her and not having my own independence. Maybe I should have had the courage to offer to walk,.

June
26 Sunday

Holland. Hera's seventeen year old daughter, Athene, attempts to seduce me while I sleep in her bed. Most strange because I didn't even know what she looks like. She was supposed to be miles away. Not at home. Which is why Athene's mother gave me the room. "Who is sleeping in my bed?" she whispered as she tried to get on top of me.

Meanwhile, Hera encounters UFOs and aliens. She and her family witness a night skyful. She told the "reptilian" aliens not come in and they obeyed her.

I read today, that the reptile symbolizes striving and territorial, the mammal represents nurturing and nesting, and the insect represents communication and networking. Clearly, we have a trinity. I wonder if this will be another case of the "three in one" numerological rule.

REPTILE = 4
MAMMAL = 8
INSECT = 7
--
19 = 1 Yep, I guess it does. Whoopee.

Find Three coins in the toilet. The First coin has a Man's head on one side and an Alien's face on the flip side. The Second coin has a Woman's head on one side and an Angel on the other. The Third coin had God's head and on the reverse is the Devil.

MAN (1) + ALIEN (5) = 6
WOMAN (3) + ANGEL (3) = 6
GOD (8) + DEVIL (7) = 6

The two faces of the three coins, gives us 666

June
27 Monday

Octavia is two-timing me. She has a new boyfriend. I discover him and realise I do not stand a chance. She is apologetic but will not budge from her choice over me. But Octavia doesn't look like the Octavia I know. She looks like another woman. Stella Maris or Alien (Eileen?) the Fiddler.

The real Octavia rang - she spoke into a vacuum. After a while of stone wall silence she moans "If you're not going to speak to me, there's no point in me trying to be your friend."
"I'm confused. The problem is I'm still crazy about you"
"That's life", she replies, "you feel the way you feel, and I feel what I feel. Life's hard. Grow up and get used to it."
I hung up. Jesus, I must have been such a lousy fuck, to send her scurrying back to her boyfriend, Orion.

Fifty three seconds later, she rings again. "What happened?"
"I hung up."
"I didn't want it to end like this. I hoped that we could continue as friends, even though I'm back with Orion."
"But Octavia, how is that possible? How can I just be a friend after having made love with you. You stirred me up too much. Having glimpsed the Sun, I can never return to the dull glimmer of the light bulb."
"Well, tough shit! Because I can't bear to have you anywhere near me, you snivelling little git!"
She hung up.

Buddha's Eightfold Way

Right	VIEW	= 31	= 4
	AIM	= 22	= 4
	SPEECH	= 37	= 1
	ACTION	= 34	= 7
	LIVING	= 45	= 9
	EFFORT	= 42	= 6
	MINDFULNESS	= 54	= 9
	CONCENTRATION	= 69	= 6
			--
			46 = 1

June
28 Tuesday

A dirty man, on the pretext of bathing me, fondled my genitalia and anus. I enjoyed it. I shouldn't have. I don't find guys sexually desirable. Well, when you're as sex starved (or obsessed?) as I am, any old hand or finger will do. Anyway, we were interrupted by a woman.

Octavia. In the mirror. Octavia. A mere glimmer. She was gone in seconds.

What did Octavia say? "Desire is a loose wire that fires the imagination."

My Jewish Kabbalist friend, Jonah, who is searching for God's Holy Numbers, tells me that he has found eight numbers and "53" is one. He says that the Hebrew word for "Sun" = 53 and
"sun-moon eclipse" = 106 which is 2 x 53
After Ike went home, I calculated a Triadic Union within the Three Pillars in the Qabbalah Tree;

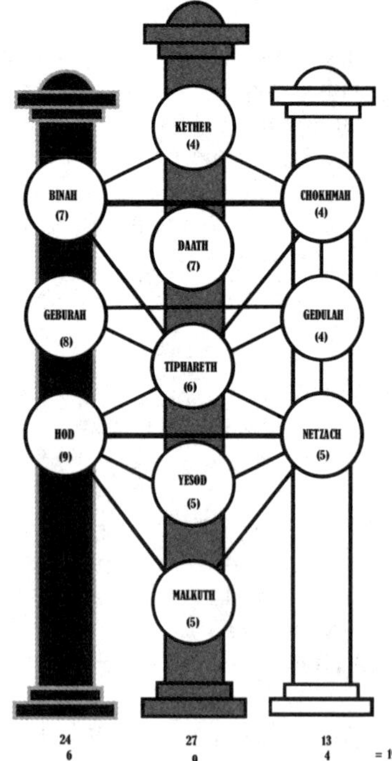

June
29 Wednesday

I was in a coach full of disabled people, and tailing us was another vehicle full of dodgy geezers. Eventually, they collided into our back. Probably deliberately. Jake said it was one of the T4 vehicles, otherwise known as the Murder Buses.
Then I witnessed a factory producing dolls on a conveyor belt. I was surprised to see every one of the dolls had their right arms missing. A voice announced, "White males for Australia".

"While the Birth Goddess is present
Let her create a Primitive Worker
Let him bear the yoke
Let him carry the toil of the Gods" The Atra-Hasis, Babylonian-Sumerian text – 4000 BC.

Fuck that! Seems like bloody ETs created us in the beginning to be their bloody ROBOTS!!!

Birth Goddess "Lady of Life" – NINTU = 3
Father-King - ANU = 9
ENLIL = 7
---
19 = 1

June
30 Thursday

Laura dying from some kind of cancer. Because she refuses to accept her death, she is committed to a psychiatric isolation ward, where the British medical profession hope to hasten her demise.

Euthanasia in action. The T4 program has been resurrected. Today, they have stopped pretending it is "Assisted Suicide".

The media did the dirty work, trotting out gullible "liberal" Celebrities to support the campaign to legalise "Assisted Suicide".

July
1 Friday

I returned to the estate. Visit the big fat Greek's grocery store round the corner from Igor's flat. The two sisters, Delia Artemis and Pythia are working as usual. They're both, at first, pleased to see me back. I see a young man at the back of the shop. D.A's secret boyfriend? Suddenly, I become a troublemaker. How I know not. All I know is I'm no longer welcome. Delia Artemis who used to like me, now wants me out of the shop. Pronto. I resist and start throwing things. Pythia tries to explain my turmoil to D.A. At least she is still sympathetic. Even her boyfriend is gentle as he tries to throw me out. He hands me a Frisbee (really an old gramophone record) to distract, divert me. I look back at Delia Artemis, wondering where did it all go wrong.

Can Delia Artemis really equal 53? Does this number connection imply we have a destiny together? But 53? Is it a number I can depend on, to bring me luck?

Later at tea time, my friend, Boney Nancy, who runs a nursery, asks me to tell fairy tales to a group of her toddlers. As I begin the story of "The Ugly Duckling", I turn and see a visitor standing in the doorway. He is tall…very tall…thin, very thin and holding a walking stick. He has thin brown hair struggling to cover a bald patch. The children don't seem to see him but I see him clearly. Or do I? Because I cannot make up my mind whether he is a ghost or Death. Or Hans Christian Andersen himself.

July
2 Saturday

Wandering down my road, to the post box, I chanced upon a smallish bird. Well, crow size, but white and grey, though not a seagull. The bird seems interested in me and hovers around me like a hummingbird. I tried to reach out to it but my arms are not long enough and yet I sense it wants communication. I hold out a wooden ruler which it takes in its beak. We have a gentle tug of war. Some people come by, and it lets go and flies away. I'm disappointed. After the passersby have gone, the bird returns and this time it actually speaks in English to me. It told me its name was Shiva Vishnu. I reach out with the ruler and Shiva Vishnu takes it in its beak again. Then the bird tells me to let go and give the ruler to him. I do. Shiva Vishnu flies away, carrying the measure.

SHIVA VISHNU = 53

Before the bird, Shiva Vishnu, flew away, he calculated Triadic Unions for Babylonia and Hindu.

Babylonian Trinity

EA	=	6
DAMKINA	=	8
MARDUK	=	5
		--
		19 = 1

Hindu Trinity

VISHNU	=	3		
LOKA MATA (World's Mother – aka Lakshmi)	=	2		
SHIVA	=	5		
		--		
		10	=	1

Marlon and friends appear and crowd around a car. He greets me. Amongst the friends is a young girl with tight jeans and blond hair. I look enviously at her as I guess Marlon has made yet another conquest. He is a lucky young sod. And he would call me a lecherous old sod. But am I? Aren't I just lonely, looking for a sincere girl to give me unconditional love?

July
3 Sunday

Gliding between an avenue of tall buildings I saw this small flying saucer. Because of its size, it might have been remote controlled. On the other hand, it may have been piloted by a small alien like myself.

A warm, nice feeling. Atmospheric. Octavia reaching out to me. I heard her voice in the bustle of busy streets and saw her name on posters on the side of buses.
Maybe, she will return to me. Is that what she was telling me?

She was already dead, Mrs Jeremiah, my old French teacher (though she preferred to tell us tales of Greek and Roman myths). Well past her hundredth year when she died years ago…and yet here she was, proud of the fact that she was still alive at the age of 120, all hail and hearty. However, she went on to say that in 10 months she will be dead. What is she really trying to tell me, since she deceased so many years back? Will we all be dead in 10 months' time?

July
4 Monday

Jake was trying to kill me. Was it because of Vanessa?

In the garden, I join a table which has the Groser kids and grandchildren. They are all students now (even Hecate and Persa have returned as students). Hina and Homer, the twins, are discussing a student union motion they are about to vote on. It's a very heated debate. Apparently concerning a ferry crossing where an outrage was committed. Something to do with Germans. I ask if the story isn't being somewhat xenophobic? Why are the students getting so worked up and angry over something that is obviously tabloid material? Hina rushes off for the vote. Hecate looks apologetic and says I'd better read the paper. She mentions it might be Townsend Thorensen. Before I read the article, a woman walks behind me, touching my shoulder and says smugly, "Do you want to read about an actor who is trying to ruin our career?" It was half in jest but I knew she was accusing me.

July
5 Tuesday

Felicia and I lying naked on the bed. She visited me. First my bed. Making love. Then her bed. This was Astral Sex. And then, back to my bed.

"Do you love me?" I asked her.
"Yes," the Sphinx softly replied. "Do you love me?"
"I want to love you but I don't want to love you," I said sadly. "If I love you, you will abuse me. Destroy me. Like you destroyed your first husband. Drove him to suicide. Because you were fucking his brother. So I refuse to love you."
"Fine. Then, don't love me." She smiled.
"I want you to go back to Lapland, and live with Ezra. Then and only then will I be safe from you."
I looked again, and she was gone.
But I know she will be back.

Thinking about the bird, Shiva Vishnu, I wondered if there was another variation of the Holy Trinity in Hinduism. For example, Shiva the Creator God, and Kali the Goddess of Destruction, and the two producing Krishna the God Redeemer on Earth.

SHIVA = 5
KALI = 6
KRISHNA = 8
--
19 = 1

DANCE OF SHIVA = 53

July
6 Wednesday

Laura and Luther cutting up and crushing cocaine seeds on my bed. I'm supposed to be assisting them but I seem to be more of a hindrance. I spill and lose some valuable seeds.

I go to the hospital for a full body scan. They are looking for problems with my internal organs – kidneys, urinary system, liver, bowel. But afterwards when the doctors come to do their ward rounds, the consultant informs me that the X-rays show my spine to be very severely curved, and that I was tipping so far to the right that my back may snap at any moment. He advised that something be done about it immediately. But what? There had been discussions in the past about rodding my vertebrate or fusing the bones in the spine but nothing was followed up. Mainly because the operations may cause more problems than solve. For example, render me paralyzed from waist down. The consultant now seemed in favour of rodding. "Well, you can't walk anyway, so that shouldn't matter," he said reassuringly...but won't I become incontinent as a result, or impotent? "True," he warns me. "You may not be able to fuck anymore," which he didn't seem to think was such a tragedy as the thought of crippled dwarfs or midgets having sex was rather nauseating to him, especially if they suffer a congenital condition.

Yeah, I read this book which said that in the study of the origins of human language, evidence had been found to support the view that there was once a single root language from which all languages stemmed. This proto-language was called the "Mother of all Mother Tongues". When I read that this "Babel", "Babble" or "Baby" language only had three **number** words for counting - which were "One", "Two" and "Many", I performed the "El-Numero" to test whether this primitive Trinity would repeat the "Three in One" pattern.

ONE = 7
TWO = 4
MANY = 8
--
19 = 1

Yep. Mission Control, we have Lift Off.

July
7 Thursday

A seaside town - Aldeburgh - searching for a bed and breakfast called the "Five Crowns Guesthouse". Arrive at a sort of shopping mall/hotel complex. Someone suggests I might find what I am looking for there. At an elevator, looking at the list, I realize that the B + B could be in another building, perhaps on a different level. I go into a restaurant, carrying the remains of food and drink in a paper bag. I still can't find what I am looking for. An Exit proves awkwardly accessible for my wheelchair, yet I sense the goal might be out there. A friendly waiter asks if he can help and offers to take the rubbish from me, but I tell him I haven't finished with the paper bag yet. Does he realize I was eating someone else's food? He volunteers to ring directory inquiries. He goes to the back room and phones someone. I groan when I hear him mention P. H. A. B. (an association that tries to integrate Physically Handicapped with Able-Bodied) Why is it that disabled people are invariably associated with charity?
There is no escape.

FIVE CROWNS = 53

Meet this tall blond woman, very friendly, in a lift going to the top floor (26th floor) of a dark and dusty building. I feel a sexual and loving relationship developing between us, growing out of her gentleness and quiet intellectualism. She accompanies me, as my secret guide to a crowded room of students and academics. Is it a philosophical debate? Am I to be judged by my peers? She tells me she recently met a woman who addressed her as Mrs. Labif. Is this coincidence significant? Is destiny trying to draw us together? Is she the long searched for, "Anam Cara"?
I'm told by the head student that they are to "Eat Shiram".
The tall blond woman smiles and reassures me I have nothing to fear. "It's standard philosophical practice," she says. "A mere formality."
"Metaphysical?" I ask.
"That too," she replied with a twinkle in her eye.

July
8 Friday

Hiding. Huge cavernous house. But we're not safe. My band of freedom fighters. The enemy is searching for us again. It's decided our group must break out of the building but we have to pretend to be wild beasts to fool the real wild beasts out there, waiting to tear us apart. The first lot to go out, failed and were eaten alive. Their performance was not convincing enough. Our lot charged down the hill, roaring, growling, becoming more dangerous with every step they took. I know the beasts (exactly who are the real beasts, anyway?) would soon turn on me if I showed any sign of weakness. My strategy was to curl up like a hedgehog and roll down the hill with my eyes closed. My monstrous friends clamber all over me as they fled from the attack. Soon I was alone unharmed. I reached the wood and climbed a rock to safety. I think I was the only survivor.

July
9 Saturday

The little dark haired lady seduces me. I know her. It is Sadie who works at CYCLOPS. She caresses and then sucks my cock. It feels great but I want to kiss her. We do and I try to put my tongue in her mouth but she rejects it.

"It's too big and thick. It makes me want to gag. Make it wafer thin and sharp. That would give me much more pleasure ".

I try but I can't. My tongue refuses to change its cumbersome, clumsy shape. She opens her mouth and shows how it should look like - flat, paper thin, like a pancake, smooth. But her tongue doesn't look sensual - it looks deadly and very alien. Like a lizard. I recoil back in horror.

It wasn't Sadie.

Phew. A narrow escape.

July
10 Sunday

Two comic characters from a 1950's Ealing comedy film, tormenting a poor animal. Then they got drunk with a third character. Me. With great inebriated joviality we fall into a boat that's unfit to sail away in dark night's treacherous sea.

In the water, I am about to drown. Swimming frantically. Then I feel her presence. I ask her to help me. She strokes my head and speaks soft words of encouragement. My confidence grows as my head is stroked upwards above the waves. Relief and joy washed over me, as I realize happily, she has saved my life. Who was she? Octavia? No. she is a dead fish. This was a mermaid. Or a sea goddess.

Hindu Mysticism

Brahman	= 3	
Maya (the Deceiver or Illusionist spell)	= 4	
Avidya (Ignorance)	= 8	
Atman	= 4	

	19	= 1

When Maya and Avidya are overcome, Atman and Brahman become One.

July
11 Monday

They were searching for Danny the Red. The Sixties should have been over a long time ago, but the Reactionaries are unforgiving. He was caught and whilst in custody he was thrown onto a slab on his stomach, stripped naked and routinely raped in the arse by officials, with a mechanical metallic implement which require two hands like a pair of shears. They said they were looking for drugs but that's just the conventional excuse for exercising their State-sanctioned perversion / sexual abuse. At the art gallery a huge topless man, covered in colourful tattoos, was being the thug he was. He wore the official moustache. The eagle's head poking out of his chest was also a giveaway. Finally, at the restaurant more police arrived to arrest people at a table but a black woman said "You can't arrest her, she's been on TV", and to prove it, the Indian woman stood up, veiled in secrecy. The police backed away, intimidated by her charm for obscurity. They tried to snatch two oriental women but they had also been on TV and were equally inscrutable. In the end a policewoman became target practice for Hollywood stardom.

Witnessing all this, made me think about the popular notion that humanity can be divided into three basic racial types, e.g. Negroid, Aryan and Mongoloid, and , of course, I wondered if these three would form a numerological "Triadic Union".

NEGROID	=	9
ARYAN	=	5
MONGOLOID	=	5
		--
		19 = 1

July
12 Tuesday

I visit Octavia in her flat. Where is Orion? Still away? I wonder. She chats pleasantly. We seem to avoid talking about our last encounter. Instead she expresses surprise to find I've cut short my stay in Ireland. "I had to," I explained, "my problems with the car and the garage."
"Really? Tell me about it."
"Every time I got in the car to drive, there was a little fellah sitting in the back seat, giving out instructions. He looked like a fairy. Or leprechaun. Or even alien."
"Alien?" she queried.
"You know, E.T. type of thing. Anyway… "
Well, I didn't get far with the story, when in walked this strange guy. A new flat mate?. He sits beside her. Tall, blond, raggedy hair, looks like he's just got out of bed. Her bed? Octavia had mentioned meeting a slightly disabled guy. This must be him, because his back seen slightly deformed (he reminds me of Coral the hunchback). Octavia massages his back. They seemed very familiar with each other. I can feel the old jealousy springing up again. I must try not to hate her this time. Then she mentions having had sex with him occasionally. Sex is such a casual affair with her. Or rather, because her friends mean so much to her, she likes to enjoy them sexually. Why can't I accept that and stop wanting to possess her?

Today, the three most widely spoken languages are Chinese, English and Hindi.

CHINES = 9
ENGLISH = 2
HINDI = 8
--
19 = 1

July
13 Wednesday

A dinner party of friends….the chat flows like a babbling brook. A rabble-babble Rabelaisian feast. Then we all burst into song, singing raucously, "Green Green Grass of Home."
"I will make the definitive TV version of "Tom Jones", I announce, rather grandly, spitting out pomegranate seeds.
Reality steps in. Thor shakes his head. "Too late mate. It's just been done," he says. For a moment, the cold shower sends the Tower of Babel crashing…..But then…
….She walks in. A longed for love. In the past I had yearned for her but she seemed unavailable. As usual my Fate twists the knife in my heart - Falling for women who never fall for me. An endless search for my soul mate. But at least she is at the dinner table, seated to my right. Dark haired, slim, her face thinner than I remembered. I was sure I was looking at Vanessa, and yet this woman also reminded me of someone else (Maria Stella Maris? Felicia? Tallulah? Laura?, Octavia? Lydia? Jesus, there are so many of them). The time came for "Vanessa" to bid us farewell. And after saying goodbye to everyone around the table, she looked at me - her cheeks flushed with emotion. Suddenly I knew. She came and hugged me, bent her lips to my ear and whispered, "I love you ". My heart pounding, knowing it had, at last, found its home. I grasped her tight in my arms and told her I loved her. She looked at me pleased and relieved.
"You heard about Jake?" she asked. I nodded. He was the reason I kept away from her, why I'd denied my love. He was her boyfriend and I'd respected their relationship and had no desire to break it. But now, they were finished with each other, and she was free and the way was clear for us to become one. She kissed me on the lips to seal the promise of our union and suddenly I became the happiest man in the world.

July
14 Thursday

Octavia was trying to lecture me on spiritual love. The implication being that that is what I should content myself with.

Sexy Sadie pursuing me. She wants to make love to me but I try to avoid her. How can I be sure she is not that reptile in disguise.

July
15 Friday

I went to two friends for help. Victor and Leonard, from university days. They understood the territory and they spoke the language. Rich capitalistic types, heavily implicated in the construction of the New Holy Order. Why they were still my friends I cannot explain. Very uncharacteristic of me to participate or acquaint myself with their corrupt world of high finance. Yet here I was visiting them in their soaring high-rise luxurious offices with panoramic views of the metropolis bedecked in shining jewels against a satin-black back-drop. It was night and the city lights shone, proving the awesome intensity of its power. I was in trouble with a double dealing shares/stock broker called Darren. He was refusing to pay me my due, by claiming extortionate expenses and demanding a greater investment than I had agreed to put out. My two friends allowed me the use of their very Special Telephone. The phone can work wonders for those with the confidence to use it. At first I was tentative in speaking, arguing, haggling with this fraudster but as I became more sure of my ground, the righteousness of my claim, the less certain he became until he agreed to send a special aircraft to drop the exact amount of what I was owed. The only point of contention left to resolve was how much I agreed to pay as investment. His figure of £600,000. was absurd. He backed down and suggested it was £6,000. I argued for £600. Suddenly a huge black plane flew over the top of our building like a flying fortress. Out of it fell the dividend I was owed. The case was now settled and I could claim a victory. Before I could rest on my laurels, the two friends reminded me that the call cost them time and money, and I should leave before they charged me. I did.

VICTOR = 33 = 6
LEONARD = 33 = 6
DARREN = 33 = 6

Just to remind myself.
NEW HOLY ORDER
6 6 6

July
16 Saturday

I meet the blond woman again. She of the elevator. You know, the one who said I'm destined to marry her. She knows Coral. I asked her who she is and she replied " I am Aquarius". We go up to the 26th Floor again.

The kisses were sumptuous, juicy, fantastic. And she chose me out of three guys.

She named us after three basic types of Triangle.... Mr Equilateral, Mr Isosceles and Mr Right.
I was Mr Right.

The Three Types of Triangle add up to One.

EQUILATERAL = 4
ISOSCELES = 7
RIGHT = 8
--
19 = 1

July
17 Sunday

The geneticist-fishermen have got what they wanted. And a voice commanded, "Destroy all Other Life in the ocean, this one has only got one defect."

OTHER LIFE = 53
HOMO SAPIENS =53

the "vesica piscis" or "vessel of the fish" is the sacred marriage of Matter on the left with the Spirit on the right.

VESICA PISCIS = 53
HOLY GRAIL = 53
WATER-BEARER = 53

The Holy Grail has been described as the Vesica Piscis, which according to Arthurian cycle was lost by the Fisher King. Is it up to the Water-Bearer to find and return it - for the cycle to be complete and rejuvenated?

Christian interpretation of the Arthurian cycle has Jesus Christ as the Fisher King.

Jesus Christ = 7
Fisher King = 7

The Water-Bearer carries the Holy Grail, which contains the Waters of Wisdom from Above, to distribute Below, thus bridging the world of Spirit with the world of Matter. Aquarius was said to be Ganymede, the cup-bearer of Zeus, pouring forth knowledge and wisdom for mankind.

July
18 Monday

Samuel Soap's new girlfriend is a real sexy little number. A seductress who knows her power, and loves to use it. She tries it on me. However, something about her reminds me of Delia Artemis. So, despite her alluring nakedness which she flaunts in my face, I reject her, and in my place comes that Hollywood film star, Jeff Golden-Bum. He ties her up, and they fuck like wild crazy animals, the sight of which gave me a gigantic hard-on. When finished, he left her trussed up on the bed, and I demanded to know why. He replied that he needed to write his book, and didn't want her distracting him. It was then I realised that Winston Churchill didn't invent the two-finger "V for Victory" salute, but St. Nintrinian.

I went to the cupboard and found that all the paracetamol and panadol had passed their "sell by" date. So I had to throw them away, leaving me without any pain killer. From hence forth, I must suffer the agonies of the world.

PAIN KILLER = 53

Another facet of the Holy Grail (53) is that it is the Pain Killer (53) that we all seek. When the world is so painful, our senses need to be numbed.

July
19 Tuesday

answer machine message from Octavia. “I’ve been away”.

I’m offered a big movie, “Solid Platonic”.

They say the film is going to do for geometry what “A Beautiful Mind” did for mathematics.

Thinking of Plato’s Ideal Forms made me investigate the Five basic regular solids....**Cube, Tetrahedron, Icosahedron, Octahedron** and **Dodecahedron**...to see if they all added up to One, since the Three basic types of Triangle.... **Equilateral, Isosceles** and **Right** add up to One.

CUBE	= 4
TETRAHEDRON	= 2
ICOSAHEDRON	= 3
OCTAHEDRON	= 4
DODECAHEDRON	= 6
	--
	19 = 1

EQUILATERAL	= 4
ISOSCELES	= 7
RIGHT	= 8
	--
	19 = 1

Again proof that everything is strung together by numbers, which create a One-ness. This is my Super String theory.

July
20 Wednesday

CYCLOPS theatre of disabled performers arrive at the venue where they are rehearse and perform. It is a huge warehouse, but looks like a junkyard, with so many obstacles, and floor levels, making access an impossible (impassable?) issue. The company complain to me. So I go in search of the organisers, a bunch of non-disabled middle-class "do-gooders", who see the disabled troupe as an opportunity to raise funds to pay themselves fat salaries, and earn the odd MBE or knighthood. I demand they make the working environment wheelchair-friendly. The chief executive, Penelope Perceval, suggests the handicap group stop being "Moaning Minnies". She says her organisation hasn't received complaints from the handicapped before. She cites Jake, "a wonderful and courageous actor", as someone who has always been satisfied with what they have offered. I reply that if Jake, who has mobility with his legs, had to walk on his fingers, would have plenty to complain about the appalling lack of access. In the end she disdainfully condescends to hold a meeting with her board of management to discuss the complaints, and she retires with her team to the office, which is a small porta-cabin in the middle of the hall. When they are all safely inside. With the door closed, I have the idea of locking the management in until they agree to our demands. I look for and find a long iron pole which I prop against the only door of the cabin, and wedge its other end against one of the walls of the hall, thus blocking the outward-opening door, and imprisoning Penelope Perceval and her team of patronising exploitative prigs inside. When they realise they are denied access to the outside world, they quickly cave in, and promise to give the theatre company everything it needs to work effectively.

July
21 Thursday

Today is the annual Earth-Sirius Synchro-mesh. Celebrations of the Dog Star begin according to Egyptian tradition.

The little oriental woman was sexy (she thinks I don't recognize her…Maria Stella Maris, I'm sure) and I enjoyed sitting close to her on the train, especially when I thought I could feel her exploring my arse and pushing her finger up my arsehole. It was exquisite until I saw with horror that both her hands were on her lap. So who was fiddling with me? The man seated on my right! The realization both thrilled me and appalled me. The sensations were erotic but I didn't want the man doing it to me. It had to be the woman. I moved away from him (he is the demon) and tried to get closer to the woman - almost on her lap - in order for her hand to take my bottom and play with it.

Later…
The builders are building a scaffold in the sky. They seem invisible but I know they are there. My friend, Thor, and I hear a droning sound about us. I suggest it is a U. F. O. - not an airplane as he seems to think. Not only am I convinced that it is a flying saucer but I will prove it by making it visible and force it to land. Thor is skeptical. But sure enough, without any effort and even to my surprise at my power, I turn the droning sound into a hat shaped U. F. O. which comes flying in from the right to left and then crash-lands to the ground. Both Thor and I are impressed at my newly discovered ability.

Talking of strange powers…
Saw this in an autobiography by this disabled actor from the 1980s and 90s "…Uri Geller, the metal bender, was frightened of handling my wheelchair, didn't want to lift it out of the car.
"It's all right! The wheelchair won't bend." I assured him.
He sheepishly laughed at his display of foolishness and took the wheelchair out. Later that day, when I returned home, I found the metal spokes of my wheelchair had buckled and snapped. I had to ring wheelchair services for new wheels…"

URI GELLER = 53

July
22 Friday

Octavia comes to visit. She tries to explain why she hasn't been in touch - but I'm not impressed. She pleads and begs forgiveness. She goes on her hands and knees in supplication, asking me to be in love with her again. She now knows what she wants. It's me. If I will desire her once more, she will reciprocate. I looked down on her with disinterested pity. Something about her makes my tongue feel heavy. I realize something is growing on the end of it. It grows quickly - fat and squidgee - filling up my mouth, suffocating. I have to get rid of it. I take a tissue and stick my tongue out and squeeze the growth which is now as big as a fist. It has the texture of a dollop of mashed potatoes. It comes off easily on to the tissue. It looks yellow as if it has been mixed with curry powder. I am relieved to have got this weight and hindrance of my tongue. Somehow I feel free of Octavia at last.

MASHED POTATOES = 53

A CYCLOPS investigation of genetic engineering (another kind of Alchemy). But Sam Soap is more preoccupied with writing an Arts Council proposal for the merger between "Vesica Theatre" and "Piscis Pictures".

The amalgamated hybrid will obviously be called "Vesica Piscis" Productions. He is hoping for an Alchemical Wedding, through the transmutation of base metal into gold.

Note: In alchemy, the transmutation of base metal into gold is a metaphor for the mystical procedure of transforming the imperfect human into the Perfect Spiritual Being. The three basic ingredients for achieving this fabulous event are **Mercury, Sulphur** and the **Philosopher's Stone.** (the Philosopher's Stone is also called the Philosopher's Egg. "Egg" and "Stone" both add up to 1).

Mercury	= 4
Sulphur	= 7
Philosopher's Stone	= 8
	---
	19 = 1

July
23 Saturday

A television quiz show with a live audience, largely made up of celebrities or other "Has-beens" from the nineteen sixties. Joy and cheers as the game progresses except in the front row, completely out of place, I recognize Mohammed Ali, and sitting next to him, Diana Ross. Both bewildered, aged and confused. Clearly not enjoying themselves amid this raucous audience. The former boxing champion looked "punch-drunk" with wild staring out eyes darting all over the place. He seemed like a frightened animal tethered to his seat during a fireworks display. Diana Ross sat small and shy, deeply unhappy. I was crying tears as the audience started to sing "How the Mighty has Fallen" to the tune of "Glory, Glory, Hallelujah" (Teacher hit me with a ruler).

We saw a UFO, which printed itself on paper. A photo which materialized lest we forget. I told them it had been seen but to convince them, I held out a sheet of photographic paper, and there was the flying saucer slowly forming as a living 3D image, like a hologram.

July
24 Sunday

The little old lady came and sat at the table next to ours, looking very pleased with herself, as she tucked in with great relish a plate of raw sausage meat
"I like my sausages rare" she exclaimed at our questioning looks. My kid sister, Fay, passing her to join us, looks with surprise and asks why are the woman's sausages uncooked? She was about to complain to the kitchen.
" No No", we shout reassuringly. "The old Crone said she likes to eat raw sausages."
But I know the little old lady is asking for trouble.

July
25 Monday

I meet Thor with my old adversary Giles - The Three of us arrive at the huge mansion. We were brought here to solve a crisis. We were allocated a large room to camp in and get ready for the mission. It was a massive sitting room with a double bed in each corner. We switched on the television to monitor our progress in the mission. The Moon had gone out of control and had become extremely unstable. Our mission was to put it back on track. I watched the three of us on the monitor as we floated into space armed with baseball bats. We were to whack the Moon into a sensible orbit. None of us knew if this would be sufficient. After all, the Moon was thousands of times bigger than us, and wooden clubs are pretty puny against such a gigantic ball! To our surprise and delight, it was ridiculously easy. The Moon responded well to our hits and moved as we wished. It felt like we were sheep-dogs with a flock of sheep. My two colleagues were beginning to enjoy themselves too much. They were hitting the Moon too hard. This should be a sensitive and subtle operation, yet they were going at it like a mallet to crack a walnut. The power had gone to their heads, and they were playing the Moon like a game of billiards or pin-ball machine, sending it out at furious speeds and in all directions. At one point the Moon just skimmed the surface of the Earth as it was batted with such force. As my irresponsible colleagues sent the Moon back and forth in ever-increasing circles I could see it would eventually be out of our reach and disappear into deep space. The Moon, meanwhile, was terribly confused and distressed and had become more unstable than ever. I sent out a plea for help. Suddenly as the Moon spun further out of control, it was blocked by a cluster of tiny, glowing crystal amoeba-like structures. The Moon was sent in a new direction into another larger and denser cluster. Its speed was reduced as it was sent into a cul-de-sac of more crystals. The Moon was under control again and felt wanted and loved. I realised the crystals were alien creatures of supreme intelligence, power and compassion. I was able to pick up one. It was the size of a cricket ball, crystal clear, glowing with a green-like entity in its centre. The love and warmth it contained made me weep, as I pressed it against my face and repeatedly thanked it for saving our Moon and ultimately, ourselves.

July
26 Tuesday

Who is Toby? Or Thoby? He came to mind. Very briefly.
Was he the mug? Poor old Muggins.
Toby? Or not Toby? Is he the question?
Are we talking Sir Toby Belch?
But I didn't think Hamlet ever knew him.
Wrong play.
Perhaps he was trying to tell me his name was "Tony", but his nose was blocked, so I heard "Toby".
I will never know because he came and went in a blink of an eye.

Ndriananahary tells me that the film is coming along but, he is being eased out. The producers didn't want him to direct. In fact, his sister is backing the producers' decisions.
"So you are being shafted by your own sister!" I said with commiseration.
"In a manner of speaking," Ndriananahary replied.
However, he is optimistic about getting a sequel to "The Jinxed Dinner" , called "Just Deserts". He also wants to produce a sequel to SLIDESHOW - with me sitting inside a dustbin, singing "Blind, Crippled and Black". The show wil! be called "See 3P Oh".

Even if I use the other spellings for the names of the three Wyrd Sisters, it still comes to a Triadic Union.

The Three Norns or Fates

URTH	= 4
VERTHANDI	= 2
SKULD	= 4
	---
	10 = 1

July
27 Wednesday

Phone message left - "The man you gave £999 to? Well, his partner has died, so they're going to be getting in touch with you."

Going into the theatre with a prospective girlfriend, Delia Artemis and hanger-on / her secret boyfriend. He made us late but we manage to get in to see the show. Unfortunately I had to sit separated from the two. Especially the girl. Very frustrating. The show looked a bit hippy-ish, people in kaftans, lotus positions, glasses of wine. More like a religious ceremony than a musical. We seem to be waiting for the guru. Then my cat, Solar Eclipse, turned up beside me. He had sneaked into my car and obviously came with us. Everyone - the audience and cast made a lot of fuss of him. I was proud that he had proved to be such a faithful friend. The question is - Will I lose him to become a theatre cat?

July
28 Thursday

Hogarth Monk, producer at FOX TV Studios, tries to hint that I write another TV play but is unable to put it in so many words.

One idea I have for Hogarth's TV play. A neurotic woman (who was sexually abused as a child) driven more insane by her sex-starved husband (because she hates sex with men), who then drowns her (now that he has found another woman who does love his cock), making it look like she committed suicide. She was found dead in a river with stones in her pockets.
I'll call the play, "Lighthouse Between the Waves"...and it will star Ella Adeliner, my favourite pop singer.

Evolution of Knowledge

Idea	=	1
Transformation	=	3
Consolidation	=	6
		---
		10 = 1

July
29 Friday

Lion prowling but lost in a maze. It can't get to me.

The Lion, the Eagle, the Bull and the Angel are the Four Creatures of the Apocalypse in the Book of Revelations. They are the same Creatures in the Book of Ezekiel. They are, in fact, the 4 Fixed "Triplicity" signs of the Zodiac....The Lion is LEO, the Eagle is SCORPIO, the Bull is TAURUS and the Angel is AQUARIUS.

Fixed	
LEO	= 5
TAURUS	= 1
AQUARIUS	= 8
SCORPIO	= 5
	--
	19 = 1

The other 2 sets of Triplicity signs of the Zodiac (Cardinal and Mutable) also follow beautifully the Three-in-One format.

Mutable	
SAGITTARIUS	= 9
VIRGO	= 8
GEMINI	= 3
PISCES	= 8
	--
	28 = 1

Cardinal	
ARIES	= 7
CAPRICORN	= 7
LIBRA	= 6
CANCER	= 8
	--
	28 = 1

July
30 Saturday

This film director, my friend Giles, so wants to be another Steven Spielberg, he has made an animated cartoon version of "Jurassic Park". I obtained a copy of this amazing comic strip magazine. Pictures from the movie are set out in frames and as I look closely at them I realize they are animated scenes from the movie, played back in each comic frame. In one I see a strange bug which works together with its brothers and sisters to form a chain stronger than steel which can lasso a dinosaur and keep it restrained. The bug is intelligent and articulate and possesses a personality. It is the sort of character you would expect to find in a Disney cartoon. The chirpy little bug explains how it works collectively to capture dinosaurs. By continuously kicking its feet against a solid mass, it increases its own mass and, bouncing off its adjacent neighbours which are also rapidly kicking, intensifies the effect so the whole line of these bugs massively increase the vibrational potential, thus giving a combined strength greater than any other creature. I watch with amazed fascination as the bugs successfully demonstrate their trapping technique on an unsuspecting T. Rex.

July
31 Sunday

I'm enclosed, trapped by walls rapidly closing in on me. My only escape is Lydia. She volunteers to stop the two sides of the walls from meeting and thus closing me in. She spreads her legs, pushing the walls aside, forming a delicious arch with her voluptuous thighs. To escape the enclosure I have to pass between her legs. She smirks as she knows my head will unavoidably touch her in her most intimate place. I'm embarrassed at the prospect and want to make myself as small as possible, so the contact with her desirable genitalia is minimized, but as I squeeze under her, my face touches her groin and she laughs, knowing that this was what I always wanted to do but never had the courage to do before in the proper context. Nonetheless, despite feelings of humiliation from her mocking and power over me, I was glad to have found freedom by passing beneath the arched gateway of her legs.

August
1 Monday LUGHNASA

In discussion with Judith Temple, the manager of the new Arnold Schwarzenegger clone (T6), who is now the US Vice-President. She is trying to work out with me the ideal movie I could co-star in, with Arnie Sequel (he continues his movie career because the President can't trust him with too many affairs of State), as he has expressed a keen interest in working with me . I told Judith I would rather work with her other client, Patrick Wolf. He'd be perfect for my next screenplay "Lighthouse Between the Waves".

The answer machine clicks on. I have two messages. The first is from Fay. She has been trying to contact me but without any success. The second is Lydia, she wants me to reach her at "Dance of Shiva" where she is working.

Suddenly I see a shadow that suggests a black cat running towards me. It seems very small and a mere flicker but as it gets closer I realize it is one of the nine lives of Solar Eclipse. The poor little thing comes up crying, looking so thin and emaciated. I quickly give my darling pussy some food. We cuddle together as I try to comfort him and welcome him back home. I ask him what happened and he replies "I was killed by a fox."

August
2 Tuesday

A racing contest across a sandy playing field. Not easy, even in an electric wheelchair. I come last and so remain an outsider.

The fox has a unique way of killing its prey. In fact, in nature, ways of dying are never obvious. The lion and other big cats, do not tear limb from limb. They quietly grip the prey by the throat, and slowly asphyxiates it. The fox has an even more "off the wall" method of inflicting death. Everyone in the room listens to me as if I was David Attenborough. "But which fox are we referring to? Surely not the fox that kills the chickens? Chickens have a banal death at the jaws of the fox." No, we are talking about the cosmic fox who is killing us all in various idiosyncratic styles. I am referring to the Fox that is numbered 666.

F O X
6 6 6

Was Rupert Murdoch and his Fox empire, preparing the way for the Big Fox? For example, why was he promoting the alien - government conspiracy TV series - "The X-Files"? Was he getting us acclimatized to the time when the Alien Overlords make themselves known? And why was Mulder named Fox? And was Dana Scully named after the Scully who in the 50s tried to tell us about crashed UFOs held in secret U.S. government bases? He was soon discredited but, was the alleged hoax admission, part of a government conspiracy to discredit his "whistle-blowing"?

The X - Files
6 6 6

Marlon is being slap happy with small shears. Slicing his nails until he takes the whole thumb nail off. He grins at me as blood spurts from his de-nailed thumb.

August
3 Wednesday

A sequence of five knocks in a wooden box. Nothing inside. It is a mysterious phenomenon which is not a good omen. Judith Temple had said that knocks on the window heralded death in the family. Does this signify my own premature doom?

Knock on or touch wood for good luck. The origin of this superstition is "Touch Wod" – Woden (Germanic god identified with the Norse Odin). And "One for Luck" originates from "One for Lok" - Loki (or Lucifer).

A knock on the door, and in walked Donald A. Light, the rotund Freemason occultist.

"You know what Lao Tzu said?" he says, giving me the Masonic eye.

"No, what did she say?" I answered.

"Excuse me?" he queried sharply.

"Loud Sue. Was she a big mouth?"

"Lao Tzu, Chinese sage from the 6th century BCE."

"Ah, another Chinaman sent to confuse us!" I replied mischievously.

Donald laughed. "You are referring to Confucius."

"I'm jesting. Of course, I know about Lao Tzu. He was said to be a contemporary of both Confucius and Buddha."

"So, you know he said - He who speaks, does not know. He who knows, does not speak."

"And?" I replied.

"You are writing a diary. Do you intend to publish it?"

"No," I reply.

"Good. But to be on the safe side, you should burn it, in case someone finds it and sends it to the printers."

"Don't you mean the cleaners?"

"I'm serious, boy. Remember the unfortunate fate of Stephen Knight for giving away secrets?"

"Yes, how exactly do you Masons assassinate at a distance? Cause people to die from brain haemorrhages, cardiac arrests, cancer and the like?" I enquired.

"Don't you already know the answer to that?" Donald replied, taking out a small musical box in the shape of a coffin, with the image of the skull and cross-bones on the lid. The melody it played reminded me of the theme tune from Kubrick's movie of The Shining.

"Be warned," said the fat Freemason, snapping the box shut, killing the music.

August
4 Thursday

I go into the news agent and ask for the Guardian newspaper. The woman looks on the shelves and says she's completely sold out. We then notice there are very few other newspapers left. In the glass cabinet I see video boxes in batches. The titles all being Disney or kiddie films. Two copies of "Lady and the Tramp" (1955), three of "Peter Pan" (1953) and four of "The Sword in the Stone" (1963), but not much else.

Found more Triadic Unions in Astrology. The 12 signs of the Zodiac are divided into three categories - **Quadruplicities, Triplicities** and **Polarities**. The Quadruplicities are the four elements; Fire, Earth, Air and Water. The Triplicities are the three states of motion; Cardinal, Fixed and Mutable. And the Polarity is the Male / Female duality. Add the constituents of each of these categories and then sum the three sub-totals, this is what you will find.

Quadruplicity			**Triplicity**			**Polarity**		
FIRE = 2			CARDINAL = 8			FEMALE = 6		
EARTH = 7			FIXED = 3			MALE = 4		
AIR = 1			MUTABLE = 2					
WATER = 4								
---			---			---		
5	+		4	+		1	=	1

And now, for my next trick - Quadruplicity, Triplicity and Polarity as three words forming a Triadic Union.

QUADRUPLICITY	= 5
TRIPLICITY	= 6
POLARITY	= 8
	--
	19 = 1

August
5 Friday

The phone rings. I wake. Nothing. Go back to sleep. I'm woken by the phone ringing.

Lydia was very unhappy. Her relationship with Gordon was at a very low point. She could no longer bear him near her. Yet she was feeling guilty about not wanting to spend a fortnight with him in an isolated, lonely cottage. The thought of such claustrophobic proximity terrified her. She cried at her increasing estrangement. I felt powerless to comfort her. I knew I could never be a good enough substitute for her, and she felt sorry for me because she knew I knew.

Lying on the beach, arms outstretched like I'm flying, as on the Cross, with a cool, refreshing breeze flowing over me. Jesus, I am flying!

The spear I bought in a junk shop, with the Masonic sword? Donald A. Light kept looking at it when he visited me the other day. Did he recognise it? The Spear of Destiny…the Spear of Odin? Otherwise known as the Spear of Longinus or the Heilige Lance. The spear of the Roman soldier that was said to have pierced the side of Christ as he hung on the Cross. Christian legend has the Roman named as Longinus, but the name is a confusion of the Greek word for lance, "longche".
In the Parsifal / Parzival / Percival legend, the spear is stolen from King Amfortas, the Keeper of the Grail, otherwise known as the Fisher King, who was crippled by the very same spear. The Fisher King is Christ who was Odin, who pierced himself with the same spear in order to obtain knowledge of all things. It is all one big allegory. To become enlightened, a true Illuminati, you must first sacrifice something of your Self. Knowledge does not come free. You must suffer for your art. You must free your soul to drink the waters of wisdom from the Holy Grail.

KING AMFORTAS = 53 = 8 KEEPER OF THE GRAIL = 89 = 8
HOLY GRAIL = 53 = 8

SPEAR OF DESTINY = 66 = 3 SPEAR OF ODIN = 57 = 3

August
6 Saturday

I keep crying all day today, it's Laura's birthday and she's dying.

UFO Abduction Case? Subject: Carmen Serena. Feb. 22 1977 near Valencia, Spain. Family of 5.
Father – Antonio Serena 45. Mother – Francisca Castellanos 42. Daughters – Carmen 15, Antonia 10, Paquita ? Time 9.30pm. The UFO incident lasted an hour. Looking at the family photo, my eye was immediately struck by Carmen. I'm convinced she was the object of the UFO's interest, partly because at age 15 she was probably at a good "reproductive" age for their human-alien hybrid fertilisation experiments. The family's encounter reminded me of "ours", so I felt an affinity for Carmen especially. I intuitively predicted that her name, if I am correct that she was the "target victim", will add up to 53. It does. I believe if she had been regressed under hypnosis she would have told a terrifying story.

Since I guessed right about Camen Serena adding up to 53, what does this tell me?

UFO photos taken by Augusto Arranda in 1967 whilest trekking in Huaylas Valley mountains near Yungay in Peru. Three years later in May 1970 massive earthquake sent avalanche down mountain destroying Yungay and its 20,000 inhabitants. It occurred to me since Arranda left Yungay just before the disaster, he had been given forewarning by UFOs. I hypothesised if I was correct, then his name will add up to 53. It does.

Augusto Arranda
1373126 1991541 = 53
More and more I am coming to the insane conclusion that the number 53 is definitely linked to UFOs.

August
7 Sunday

It is 9.53. In the morning I heard a woman call my name. It was faint as if it was outside in the corridor. I tried to open the front door but it was locked. The voice sounded like my dead mother.

Later, I look out of the window, at the cityscape stretched across the seven hills and I see a green light drop slowly from the sky. An Omen? Is the King soon to die?

Something behind me trying to have sex with me, the pressure, the pain. It was both pleasant and unpleasant. Was it a woman? I think so, yet I felt I was about to be sodomized. A woman with a penis. My breathing becomes laboured. As the pressure mounts I feel I'm unable to breath. Gasping for air, I call out "Stella Maris". Is it she? Is she trying to rape me on the astral plane? Or am I calling out her name to rescue me from this unspeakable assault? Whatever, the effect of calling her name ends the attack.
"Was it those pesky aliens with their damn anal probes?" Thor asks when I tell him about it.

Thor goes for his tea. Not long after he has gone, she arrives.
The woman touched my hair, "Ugh! What's the matter with your hair? It's all slimy."
"No, it's just greasy. I haven't washed it for days"

August
8 Monday

Today I had a smart haircut. Or was it a hard biscuit?

Start rehearsing my new play (Ella Adeliner and Patrick Wolf are playing the leads), working with some children, creating lovely scenes. I'm introduced to the man, everyone says will be the next Steven Spielberg. Hope some good will come of this and he'll make me an international star.

ELLA ADELINER = 53 PATRICK WOLF = 53 Perfectamondo!

August
9 Tuesday

Ella Adeliner takes me in her arms and carries me to the bed for a chat. I can't resist kissing her. She smiles as if to say I've been waiting for you to do that for long time. She kisses me back on the lips. The sensation is overpowering and we fall into each other's arms, holding one another tightly. She starts to cry and I caress and kiss her, saying, "it's all right, don't cry. You don't need to cry anymore." She kisses me. For some strange reason, my genitalia is nakedly exposed which heightens my emotional vulnerability. Even so, sex does not seem to be the undercurrent here, only true romance.

Gillian Terry (known as "Gilly" to her friends), probably Hollywood's greatest female film director this century, emailed me to say she loves my film treatment, **BRING ON THE DWARVES**, and wants to direct it.
The Treatment - "Freddy is a small, disabled actor, always on the lookout for leading roles to play. However, over the years, he's learnt that big parts for "little cripples" rarely happen. His line of work is just too "body fascist" for that. What film maker has the guts to cast someone like him in a romantic lead? And yet, in reality, much to his constant surprise, Freddy has never had problems picking up women. He's not called "Romeo Wheelchair" for nothing. However, maintaining love relationships is something else. Freddy has a huge inferiority complex. Well, he's as brainwashed by Hollywood as anyone. He bought the lie that people like him are simply not sexually desirable...and operating on the Groucho Marx principle of not joining any club that would have him as a member, runs away from anyone who gets too close.

Which is why he thinks he has a lot in common with the dwarf actor David Rappaport, star of "Time Bandits" and "Bride of Frankenstein" who committed suicide over a decade ago. Anyway, he personally knew Rappaport, before he went off to Yankland to pursue the "Hollywood Dream". Which is why Freddy decides to write a play to star in, about the life and death of his poor, misguided deceased friend.

Freddy has had his fill of constant rejection for his film ideas. Yet another letter arrives from Channel Four or BBC, saying a disabled Viking is just not box office or who gives a shit about cripples and dwarves being gassed in Nazi Germany. "If you make the cripple Jewish and give him a minor disability, like a small limp, but keep him physically attractive...then we could be interested."

Jesus Fucking Christ! No wonder Dave Rappaport shot himself right underneath the Hollywood sign.

As part of his research process and preparation for performing the role, Freddy incorporates a sort video diary, talking to the camera, with the idea of using some of the material for the show.

Freddy sees himself as a sort of Private Dick, investigating Hollywood's "murder" of the dwarf who thought he could be a giant. He begins his research, talking to David's family and show-biz colleagues, videotaping the interviews, discovering how David was a manic-depressive (like himself), used comedy to hide his bitterness and always on the look out for historical roles where dwarves call the shots. Not such a far-fetched idea. Elizabeth 1 had a favourite secret agent who was a swashbuckling dwarf. And there's Attila the Hun...and Walter Scott's "The Black Dwarf". David tried so hard to get film producers interested but all they would offer him are kids TV as a lovable "Munchkin" or imbecilic little sidekick with delusions of grandeur.

David had specially purchased a gun the day before to blow his brains out. He'd just got engaged. She was a tall beautiful dancer, though currently working as a waitress...like a million other Hollywood "wannabes"....and the Hollywood sign has witnessed many a suicide. Freddy puts on Dory Previn's song about Mary Cecilia Brown who hung herself "...from the second or third letter O".

Reading about David's fiancée, makes Freddy think about his own brand new relationship. Through the Internet, he's just met a woman who's twice as tall as him. It seems she's really in love with him. It doesn't matter he's disabled or "...of small stature" She's even said she'll marry him. Jesus, that's fast. What's the catch? His friends try to tell him to go with flow. "Don't fuck it up this time, you cynical prat.". One of his Ex's is really happy for him, "But for God's sake, Freddy, allow yourself to be loved this time."

It seemed David wouldn't allow himself to be loved, either. A few months earlier he had tried to gas himself with carbon-monoxide poisoning. Hose tube from exhaust pipe into car in garage. It was a botched job. People thought it was deliberately botched. Just a cry for help. Too many drugs...wacky-backy...Cokehead...natural born depressive. Freddy believed no one took David's suicide attempts seriously. Not even his agent-manager. So David bought a gun. He is in America. GUNS 'R' US. You can't go wrong with a gun. "Happiness is a warm gun" – so John Lennon sang...and he should know.

David told his fiancée he was taking the car to give the dog a walk. But the poor mutt was locked in the car, abandoned on Hollywood Hill. An irate dog-lover passer-by left an angry note on the windscreen...By then David was dead.

Freddy got deeper and deeper into the similarities and understood why David did what he did. Knew the frustrations. The disappointments. The paranoia. The rampant insecurity. Freddy was David. A man in a little boy's body. His research makes him more and more depressed. His video diary becomes more bleak as his investigation increasingly holds up a mirror of his own sense of hopelessness and disillusion.

He is haunted by David seemingly running away from apparent marital bliss. Isn't he in the same boat? He will never accept that someone could genuinely love him...want him. So, let history repeat itself. But let people see it. "They want Reality TV? Well, they can bloody have it. They wouldn't let David be an actor...or me. People like us aren't allowed to be artists."

David made a statement by topping himself beneath the Hollywood sign. Freddy will go one step better. He will make a public performance of his suicide. And he does. He shoots himself with camera and gun whilst sitting on the toilet.

The person behind the camera is heard to exclaim "Oh fuck. Oh shit. He did it. Shit. He did it. Fuck. I didn't think he was serious. Jesus. I'd better upload this on YouTube immediately......" -

The Mask of Imogen Stubbs is now being worn by Lydia. The blonde actor from "Betrayal", is in bed with her, engaging in surreptitious liaisons, whilst friendly but unsuspecting cuckolded husband, Gordon fiddles in the other room. Suddenly I am wearing the Mask of Betrayal but only permitted to go so far. The ultimate is denied, out of compassion and guilt.

August
10 Wednesday

This evening Proteus was being rough with my cat, Solar Eclipse, hitting him. This made me mad. I shouted at Proteus, telling him Solar Eclipse has never been abused and is not used to it. I get so angry I want to lash out at the boy to make him understand that violence is not a pleasant thing but so far I manage to restrain myself and move away without harming him.

August
11 Thursday

Patrick Wolf lifts Ella Adeliner by the feet and throws her in the air. She does an amazing triple somersault and lands on her head, spinning very fast like a top . However, she spins out of control and comes right off the stage and crashes to the floor. We all wait in silence- in trepidation. Has she? Hasn't she? Will she survive the fall? Then with relief, we see her get up, rubbing her belly. She quickly walks past us saying, "That fool gave my bladder such a bang, I need to go for a pee."

Chokhmah Groser, husband of Inga, and I had an argument about alien abductions. Of course, as a conservative doctor traditionally trained in the strict materialist scientific paradigm, he is totally skeptical, whereas I advance the case that what we humans perceive, can never provide us with the reality and truth for a complete understanding of the universe, Scientists, I say, must wake up and be less inflexible, otherwise they will suffer culture shock along with everyone else.

Later I went to visit Sexy Sadie, and as I drove into her street, I "saw" her pal, Netzach, hobbling down the road towards me fifteen minutes before he actually arrived.

Gilly phones me just before midnight.
"Shiram darling. I got great news. And not so great news. The good news – Hollywood absolutely loves your treatment "Bring on the Dwarves". They wanna produce the movie. But Honey, the bad news is they don't want you playing the part of Freddy. They don't think you are a big enough star for such a leading role."
"But I'm the best small actor in the business," I scream at her.
"I know, Darling," she opines sympathetically, "but they don't want a dwarf in the role. They want an A-list star. So they are going to CGI Patrick Wolf to shrink his height to pint-size. He is very keen to play Freddy because he personally knows you and is very sympatico, and is confident he will do you justice."
"Do me justice! It's an injustice," I wail. "Don't they realize that that is what my movie is all about. It is because of things like this that people like David Rappaport end up committing suicide. I tell you, if David hadn't topped himself then, he certainly would today with fucking Hollywood being more Body Fascist than ever. This is gross!"

"I know, Sweetheart. It's a shame, and I know where you are coming from, but at least you will make money on your idea. And they will probably include you in the script-writing team. So, that's good news, isn't it. Anyway, have to fly."
"Gilly, no. I'm not selling the bastards my treatment, if I can't play the lead."
"Oh don't be silly. The studios have already registered your idea and claimed ownership. Don't antagonize them otherwise, you won't get paid. I really must go."

August
12 Friday

Get woken by a sound of something dropping, clanking. I immediately look at the clock. Yes, as expected – 53 past the hour. …6.53am. I go to Solar Eclipse's food bowl. Completely empty. Stray cat? Because Solar Eclipse is in the bedroom. And the knife is on the floor. Was it the knife falling I heard? It's a weird world when stray cats go throwing knives to wake me at the 53rd minute.

The last scene in the movie "Butch Cassidy and the Sundance Kid". Surrounded, exhausted, badly wounded, they get ready for the final round. Nervously, the Colombian soldiers enter in waves to be shot down but ultimately their numbers are too great and our bandit pair cannot win. Their last words to each other as they are strung up as corpses:
Sundance "Why did we have to shoot them?"
Butch "I think because of the music."
Sundance "And why didn't we hear them coming?"
Butch "Because the music was too loud."

August
13 Saturday

My home in Ireland has got much bigger. Don't ask me how. It's a mansion. I go out into the fields.
Mewling sounds. Cows? Sheep? Creatures gamboling through grass and hedgerows. Suddenly they seem to change in the shadows to children who become aware of me. They stare at me in amazement, and call out to adults hiding in the undergrowth. I am taken by surprise as men and women emerge to look and talk to me. They're camping, holidaying on my land which then turns into a stately home.
"Who said you could do this" I ask guiltily, not wanting to ruin their holiday.
"Your Manager".
Suddenly I realize the home is no longer my own. Then I find builders inside, working and renovating. Where did they come from and who commissioned the work? Not me. The Manager, I'm told again. He is taking upon himself too much authority. The cleaners bustle past me as I check out the Grand Bedroom. One of the cleaners, a young woman, tries to answer my queries but now I'm having difficulties talking back to her. I've started to eat a beef-steak sandwich. The meat is cloying and tying up my teeth. I keep chewing but can't swallow. I feel sick and have to spit the mess out but the woman embarrasses me. I try to retreat. As I leave, I see the outline shape of a huge bird. A swan? A goose flying south, under the bed covers?

August
14 Sunday

Laura and Luther visit me in Ireland. Fay also appears. I tell them about the alleged UFO crash in western Australia and the stranded alien pilots being shot at by an irate game-keeper.

Laura made me cry because I had to remind her we can never be lovers like we were in the past, though I still love her and she is dying.

With tears in my eyes I cried out to God "Why don't you make everyone happy? Surely, that's not much to ask of an Almighty Being?"

When Einstein said God does not play dice with the Universe, does that mean he believes in God? If so, then how can he say that nothing can go faster than the speed of light? Does he want to limit God? Does he mean to say that not even God can go faster than the speed of light? If God cannot go faster than the speed of light, then light must be more powerful, more energetic than God. So, God is not All Mighty.

Anyway, I never did believe Einstein when he, a mere human, tried to put limits on what was possible in the Universe. Only a fool would do that.

August
15 Monday

Ella Adeliner, the compassionate superstar, has come back from her charity weekend in Palestine.

"How was it?" I asked

"Terrible, "she replied. "I never managed to do what I wanted to do. I couldn't find the people I needed to meet. I searched and searched and ended up getting awfully lost." She was really pleased to see me and kept kissing my hands. My once dashed hopes started to rise again.

More fool me. Because, later, Ella Adeliner didn't make me a tea or coffee. She made one for Patrick Wolf, but ignored me. Then when I try to get into the canteen, she was blocking my way - sitting on a stool. I just could not get past her. She made no effort to help me. In fact, she seemed to be deliberately making it more difficult for me. No matter how much I tried, I could not squeeze past her. It was suffocating. I couldn't breathe. My heart was pounding. It felt as if it is going to burst.

August
16 Tuesday

I attended a conference on animal experiments and vivisection. I was really shocked when sweet little Sexy Sadie wheeled herself onto the platform, and spoke in favour of the motion to continue the practice. I am totally opposed as I see it as animal torture, so from the floor, I get into a very heated argument with her, demanding to know why she supports scientific cruelty to animals? The row, of course, goes nowhere, and I leave in disgust.

I left the conference in my car, but it had got dark, so I couldn't find the proper parking place. I got lost and realized I needed to continue the rest of the way in my wheelchair through dodgy streets. As I stopped the car, a gang of black youths began to congregate around me, attracted by the novelty of my presence. I was worried about getting out of the car, worried about throwing my purse and mobile telephone onto the wheelchair like I normally do when climbing out, but I really had no choice. So I just had to trust the kids and not assume the negative stereotyping. Just because they are black teenage boys, it doesn't mean they want to rob me. They looked at the purse but they made no move to snatch it. My faith in their inherent goodness paid off. I asked them if there was a problem. The lads said yes. It was past curfew for them. They were now liable for police harassment, arrest or being shot. Suddenly they looked away in the same direction and immediately ran away. The Curfew Militia were coming.

The military armoured vehicle charged down the street after the fleeing youths. As the soldiers drove past, they threw rocks and stones at anyone who failed to hide from sight. A stone just missed me. I quickly disappeared down a side street, where a tramp told me there was an anti-capitalist protest in the financial centre, so I went to see what was happening.

Hundreds of protesters had occupied the Stock Exchange building, while others were camped outside. Some disabled people in wheelchairs complained to me that there was no access for them to join in the Occupation, so were forced to hang around at the bottom of the front steps. Then came the riot police and army with tanks and bulldozers. The commanding officer stood up in his jeep and announced with a loud-hailer that if the demonstrators didn't immediately vacate the premises and disperse, the Home Security Force will break down the walls, and crush everyone inside the building. It looked like it was going to be a massacre, so I discreetly left the scene.

August
17 Wednesday

The plastic surgeon confirmed that I had a silicon implant in my face. A small one but a real one, disrupting my health. That explains my recurring sinus problems. I go to a public swimming pool and Ella Adeliner offers to lift me in the water. Damn, I forgot my inflated arm bands, still I let her pick me up but she does it all wrong and nearly injures her back. I sit on her lap instead, and we cuddle, with her hand between my legs, caressing me. We don't seem to care that it's all very public. Doctor Penny Myer, the world-famous expert on silicone disease, is due to meet us and Ella persuades the doctor to lift me in the water, assuring her that the experience would be very erotic. Myer winks at me. Then I hear a voice of the young woman behind me. She seems foreign, slim, not very tall, dark short hair and very innocent. She reminds me of Laura. She asks if I am Shiram Labif. For a joke I say no. For some reason everyone thinks this is hilarious, especially at her total disappointment. The room is convulsed in laughter which perplexes me as I didn't think my ruse was that funny. Anyway, she realizes my little game and hands me an important note, saying the postman wants to deliver a package from Lydia. I feel the package. Crystal goblet or glass chalice? Could darling Lydia be sending me the Holy Grail? No. the numbers don't add up.

August
18 Thursday

Ella Adeliner gives out a positive feeling. She is trying to give out loving vibes, telling me that it's all right. I made a fool of myself. Just when she wasn't expecting it, I told her I loved her - she looked back at me in horror but she couldn't say anything - the audience was too big, she couldn't ruin the show. It was irresponsible of me, I know, taking advantage of her like that. But she obviously has forgiven me.

Wake up and feel restless after I had gone to bed at about 11pm. I hear a knock sound to the left of me in the room. I immediately think if I was to look at the time it would say it was 53 minutes past whatever hour. I look at my watch and sure enough it says 11. 53 pm. Well, why else would I hear an inexplicable bang in the middle of the room. The Paranormal is reminding me of its existence. The "Strange" does not want to be forgotten. "53" refuses to be ignored.

August
19 Friday

A crazy bus journey. Crowded with chickens and geese going to market. Patrick Wolf was sitting next to me, on at my left. Then Ella Adeliner came and sat next to him and giving him all her attention. So now I feel empty and lost. I fear that she will soon fade away and disappear forever from view.

The old journalist told me that when she asked a former Conservative Defence Secretary, Michael Portillo if he had been briefed about the 1980 Rendleshem UFO case and UFOs in general, he grinned and said " I know a lot but I tell a little." Smarmy, smug Tory git.
"He was born in 1953", she had said giving me a knowing look.
"53 again. Wasn't Portillo a member of the Midhurst Coven?"
All she would reply was there had been rumours that he and Michael Howard and that Labour traitor, Tony Blair, and all subsequent Prime Ministers had all been given a head start through their membership of a certain Satanic Network.

Later, I'm driving down the street, and I see a small car in front of me suddenly stop outside a sub-post office. I slow down to overtake it. As I pass to its right and parallel to it, I look into the car and see two young guys. One, the passenger, is quickly putting on some kind of balaclava to mask his face. Shit, I realize they are about to rob the post office. I stop my car alongside them to watch what they will do next. The guy in the mask as he is about to get out of the car, armed with a gun, suddenly sees me looking at them, and he quickly sits back down. He points me out to his getaway driver, and turns and gives me the "hard stare". Now we are all staring at each other, wondering what to do next. They may be thinking of getting me, but that would draw premature attention to themselves, and ruin their opportunity to rob, or they could just drive away, and come back another time. Me, I'm thinking I should stop them, or prevent them from escaping if the rob the post office. Or I could just quickly drive away, not wanting to get involved. But that isn't me. I like to imagine I am the quintessential "Have-a-go Hero". The guys eventually decide to go ahead with the robbery, and as the masked guy gets out the car, I drive in front of theirs, and then reverse hard into them, hoping to hinder their attempt. The driver panics and reverses down the street, leaving the gunman stranded, who then also quickly does a runner.

August
20 Saturday

Octavia is trying to tell me she wants me back.

Laura is searching for me. She has arrived outside my door but she doesn't believe I am there. I hear her in the corridor, pleading with a neighbour "Please I'm begging you to let me into Shiram's head."
I feel guilty because I can hear her evident distress and yet I still refuse to let my presence be known to her.
But I mustn't dwell to long on my guilty conscience…

Prisoners were taken. Hostages. One young man in a suit was being particularly victimized. The guards kept hitting him with their rifle butts. Then I heard the sentence. I didn't realize it was a trial, and that there would be a verdict. I felt sad when the man was told he was going to have his throat cut. Was it because his family and friends or the government refused to pay the ransom? Well, I will never know because I suddenly found myself in the condemned man's body. Before I could get used to this weird turn of events, I felt the knife blade slice across my throat, and warm sticky fluid pour from my throat down my chest. Then I started to choke on the blood going down my windpipe. I collapsed to the floor. After that, I quickly lost consciousness, and everything went black, and my last thought was I am dead.

August
21 Sunday

FOX TV employs me to turn my play "Lighthouse Between the Waves" into a film script. I work hard but at the end, trying to get the production manager attention, so that I may be paid, turns out to be impossible. Eventually I speak to a producer who looks embarrassed. "I'm afraid we've no money to pay you. Sorry."
I demand to see the Big Boss. I fly to Newcastle where I confront him in his high rise office but he is even more adamant and quite unapologetic. "What are you going to do? Complain to the Ministry of Culture?" he says, with a smug grin. I realize I'm defeated.

August
22 Monday

I visit this very rich, posh upper class woman. (Ok, I'll own up. It's Princess Danu) Blond and tall with a beautiful daughter in a blue nurses uniform, who is a teacher of medicine. Huge mansion stuffed with books - my kind of books - all originals, first editions - even original manuscripts e.g. George Adamski's "Flying Saucers Have Landed" (1953). The kind woman lends these priceless gems to whoever asks. I feel at home in their house - perhaps I hope to marry her daughter. I carry a plastic yellow canister of tear gas. It was leaking and I accidentally opened it even more. I tried desperately to stop the gas escaping, without avail (soon the whole world will be weeping tears). I secretly hide it in the house, under the stairs and tried to leave the premises unnoticed, feeling very guilty. But the good woman stops me with her charms. She shows me some army friends who are having an amazing visual effect being constructed for them. Thousands of feet long (millions of miles in reality) and very wide, a pulsating, star filled galaxy emanating from exhaust pipe of a car (which has crashed), reaching up into space, carrying the two "star-crossed" lovers' souls. The tall boy and his friend gather more books they can hope to read in a weekend. Almost like a student prank, giggling, as Doctor Seuss (and a biography on Diana Spencer - "Why Princess Di Dies") is finally selected from the highest inaccessible bookshelf and fired from the barrel of a tank. The owner, not realizing she will be dead next Sunday, continues to smile.

PRINCESS DI = 53

August
23 Tuesday

Erotic embrace with Judith Temple, Arnie Sequel's manager. I was sitting on her lap, resting my back against her. She stooped down over my head and we kissed exquisitely. Then she caressed my stomach and allowed her hand to touch my balls and gently stroke them. Eventually she softly fondled my penis. It was so gorgeous, I just melted into her. Which was a mistake because she turned into a succubus.

Judith Temple = 53

Putting rubbish in the fireplace, the tongs hanging from the pots and pan rail, suddenly started swinging in a pendulum manner, for fifteen minutes, swinging for no apparent reason.

Is Inga Groser trying to contact me?

Later, I am shown something, which was like watching a cartoon movie. Two characters – one tall and the other short – flat, two dimensional, more like CGI. It was me and Patrick Wolf (or Igor?), and we were disappearing into the sunset, out to sea, like we were following the sun. Across the ocean to the West, where Atlantis is laid to rest.

A few minutes later, I return, alone without Patrick Wolf, singing "There is always Hope", to the tune of "Onward Christian Soldiers".

August
24 Wednesday

Crying again. Tears in my eyes. Two friends who are now dead. One is Flora.
Hector asks "Why are we the only ones to be sad?"
I replied "We are the only ones to have lost these two people".
.....But who is the second person that died?

A loud bang. A bird has smashed against a window in the bedroom. Shit. An omen of death.

The bang causes the television to spontaneously switch on. There's a news announcement about a famous upper class man who has just died. His wife, very horsey, aloof, aristocratic type is talking to reporters at a press conference outside her mansion, about her seemingly indifferent or dispassionate response to the sudden unexpected demise of her husband. "You may think I am rather unfeeling, or show an abnormal amount of unconcern for the recent tragic death of Lord Kit McAleese Reevers, who was a super man, as well as a super husband, and a super father to our children. I have here a prepared speech, which I will now read out to you all....."

I never heard her super soupy speech because as she began to read, the picture went black and the television exploded.

August
25 Thursday

It seems Ella Adeliner is distressed and in need of my support.

Idea of the Day

I plan to infiltrate New Labour and return it into a Socialist Party. Kick out all of the Thatcherite Tory moles, put there by the CIA. As a genuine Socialist, I will be popular and easily get elected as Prime Minister. Real Labour, under my Leadership, will ***Abolish the Monarchy****, deport all aristocrats to the USA, however if anyone volunteers to relinquish their inherited peerage, they will not be deported. We will turn the House of Lords into an Upper debating Chamber consisting of past winners of TV Quiz Shows such as "University Challenge", "Mastermind" and "Who Wants To Be A Millionaire". The Head of State will be a fairy tale Honorary King or Queen, selected for a Two year reign through popular choice via TV shows "Who Wants To Be King or Queen of England?" and "Big Monarch" (a sort of "Big Brother" voyeuristic "Reality TV" show).*

Private education and private medicine will be outlawed. *All Royal Properties (palaces, castles, stately homes etc) will be Nationalised and turned into community centres or museums, galleries, National Heritage centres, with the exception of Buckingham Palace which will be turned into the International Diplomats' Centre.*

Britain will cease manufacturing and selling arms, and all Weapons of Mass Destruction will be de-commissioned. Defence budgets will be reduced to one per cent of current expenditure.

A ***steep progressive taxation system*** *will be introduced, starting with 50% tax for those earning five hundred thousand pounds a year. 99% income tax for millionaires. Anyone earning less than ten thousand pounds will be exempt from income tax. Gas, electricity, water and railways will be re-nationalised.* ***Nuclear power*** *stations will be de-commissioned and with increased investment in alternative free energy systems such as wind, solar, thermal and tidal. All films and television entertainment imported from the USA will be heavily taxed. and the revenue will be invested in British entertainment. There cannot be exceptions within U.S. film and TV imports. It is not about quality, but American domination of British entertainment. For example, 95% of British TV broadcasting output is American. This must be stopped. The British entertainment industry has been massacred because of cheap American imports.*

August
26 Friday

This morning a man introduces himself as someone who knew me when I was at Queen Charlotte's Hospital, when I was a baby barely born. This surprised me, I thought I was at least 3 years old when I first came to the hospital.

(My Real Labour manifesto…continued)

There will be massive increases in all import duties, to protect lower prices for home products and produce. All monopolies will be split up. Real Labour will take away foreign ownership of our national newspapers and national television and radio. So foreigners like Murdoch will no longer be able to own British newspapers. Our newspapers will be owned by the people who are employees of the newspaper. All of Thatcher's anti-union legislation will be repealed. Banking and all insurance will be nationalised. Britain will immediately adopt the Euro as its currency. The Real Labour will introduce a ***national rail ticket*** *of five pounds to any destination in the UK. All long distance freight transport must vacate public highways and be transported by goods trains. Trucks and lorries will not be able to exceed speeds beyond 40 miles an hour. All motor vehicles manufactured and sold with the ability to exceed the national speed limit will be banned, and contravening manufacturers and dealers will be prosecuted. All vehicles will be fitted with electronic speed limit devices, so when a vehicle enters a 30mph speed limit zone, the accelerator control will not function above 30 miles per hour. On leaving the speed limit zone, national speed limit potential will be returned. These electronic speed governing devices will not be fitted on emergency vehicles. Also on entering congested designated zones, there will be a surcharge (minimum five pounds) for every empty passenger seat in a private car. Disabled drivers who are exempt from paying road tax will be exempt from* ***Empty Passenger Seat surcharge****. This policy is aimed to encourage car-sharing and reduce traffic in metropolitan zones. With the introduction of these innovations, speed cameras and traffic wardens will be rendered obsolete, and so will be abolished.* ***The police*** *will have all their firearms removed, and the number of squad cars will be reduced by 75%. The Police Constable will be issued with bicycles and good walking boots instead.*

August
27 Saturday

Lydia was being very loving today. Can I hope for more?

(My Real Labour manifesto…continued)
Defence Not Offense. *There will not be a permanent professional army. In its place will be a volunteer militia, purely for Home Defence. No more invasions and foreign occupations. All current wars maintained by Britain will cease within three months of Real Labour becoming government.* ***Care for the Elderly*** *will be the sole responsibility of local authorities. It will be illegal for Old People's Homes and Hospitals to be privately owned. The Council Tax will be abolished. A new local income tax will be introduced. Since embassies and consulates primarily function as nest-bed of foreign espionage operatives, all such diplomatic missions will be shut down, and premises confiscated to be turned into council housing and community centres. In place of embassies, each sovereign state will be allowed one diplomat to be resident in Britain, where the national representative will be accommodated with an office and a personal bedsitting room, in the new International Diplomats Centre housed in the now vacated Buckingham Palace. There will be a works canteen for all diplomats. Who sits next to who will depend on a daily lottery allocation.* ***Adult prostitution*** *will be legalised, and community brothels will be established in every town, with a doctor and a resident priest for those who feel the need to confess their sins. The Real Labour Party believes consenting adults have the right to offer sexual services for payment.* ***Pornography*** *will be de-criminalised in the case of mutually consenting non-exploitive adults, though will remain illegal in the case of child porn, and there will remain prohibited access to those below 18 years old (as is the case with the sale of cigarettes and alcohol).* ***Recreational drugs*** *will also be decriminalised (except for those below 18 years of age) and taxed. There will be amendments to the "Smoking Ban". Wherever there are two pubs, one will be for "Smokers Only", and the other for "Non-Smokers Only". It has been found that the cost to the nation's health and economy has become greater due to a massive increase in people catching colds because they have to smoke outside in the most inclement weathers. Also the elderly are dying a lot quicker in old folks homes because they are forced to smoke outside. The laws against smoking in places of work will be amended under Real Labour.*

August
28 Sunday

They took me…and said with glee, I would burn. Throwing themselves into the waiting funeral pyre, they dragged me in with them. Holding me down, petrol and alcohol was poured over me, and then they forced me to drink some of the alcohol. I struggled hard to be free of these suicidal killers, but I couldn't escape. Then matches were struck and cigarette lighters were flicked, and I expected the blaze to erupt over my skin, but I saw no flames, and yet I still felt the burning pain. I screamed and screamed, and fought the iron grip imprisoning me within the incendiary furnace. It was to no avail. Hellish laughter accompanied more attempts by my adversaries to set the bonfire ablaze.
I began to suspect that this was my fate, to be cast into the eternal infernal damnation, to forever burn amidst the imaginary fires of Hell. However, I have also been led to believe I could turn the negative into a positive, and see this situation as a purification process, and that I will be reborn from the Phoenix womb.

And again I heard the Celestial music.

August
29 Monday

Laura has attacked her face with a knife in her anger and frustration and pain at the way her face has caused her so much misery in her life.
"the face that launched a thousand hardships"

The picture of a bird falls down behind me, just missing my head. A minute later, Sam the Legs comes in. "I just heard it on the radio. Princess Danu has been killed. Car crash, they said."

"I don't believe them. It was murder," I replied thinking about the falling picture just now as an omen of death. "The princess told me that the secret powers were out to kill her. She was assassinated by her Royal in-laws."

August
30 Tuesday

Lydia and I visit Laura in hospital. Whilst there, I fall out of my wheelchair and a break some bones. We have difficulties finding help. Eventually, I am rushed off to another hospital.

Lydia holds me in her arms and caresses me. And my bones are healed. The power of love.

I have a new vehicle. A transit van which is evolving into a motorized caravan. I invite Ferdinand and Delilah aboard but find some "Boyz from the 'Hood" have already taken over the passenger seats. They are threatening in a friendly way and allow me to take command of my vehicle. But I am so put out that I have difficulty climbing into the driver's seat, until Ferdinand, trying to put me at my ease, points out that I'm in the middle section, not the front cabin. So I go to the proper place and have less trouble climbing into the driver's position.

We drive pass two young men with long black hair running amok in a complex of buildings. Ferdinand said they were brothers. Twins in fact. One was a commander of the police. The other was some kind of leader of revolutionaries. They police claim he is nothing but a gangster. Well, they would, wouldn't they. We pause as we see that the guerrilla leader and his band of militants are under siege by the special police combat group. He stood on the roof, with a Kalashnikov, firing rapidly at the police below, determined not to give them a breathing space. I heard him shouting as he fired, "I'd rather have a Kalashnikov than the sham freedom of speech! Britain is a nation of Nazis. Death to all Nazis!"
"Isn't he gorgeous! Doesn't he remind you of Malcolm McDowell in the final scene of 'If'?" said Delilah.
"I doubt he will survive long," I said sadly.

August
31 Wednesday

Nights of Nano Technology with the Stars. It's amazing seeing how a huge lorry can be created in a clear crystal box no bigger than a CD case. Same shape. I watch aghast at the real world of magic, as each small box opens out to form an individual lorry. The audience applauds as I move from the back of the stage to the auditorium, but I've left my wheelchair. A Star from the audience volunteers and rushes to my aid. "I know you," I exclaim. "Have you forgiven me?" I jest as he smilingly picks me up to carry me.
"No, I'm wrong, you're not Jonathan Dimple-prix," I said looking at his face. "You're David, aren't you?"
He nods resignedly. I suppose the brothers get used to the constant confusion from the public.

The sky turned purple which was a warning that the UFOs were coming, and landing.

Next, I find myself on board an alien space craft, and we are taking off. I'm presuming to their planet. But we could be entering a different dimension. Their dimension? They refuse to tell me anything. I just have to accept being abducted, and taken I know not where.

Later, back at home, there is an irritating sore on the inside of my right nostril. Typical result of alien intervention. I read that extra-terrestrials use nasal probes on their abductees, to place implants inside the sinus cavities near the right hemisphere of the brain, which is the location of imaginative – spatial – creative activity. I believe the right cerebral hemisphere is where dreams are located, and therefore ideal as a centre for alien communication.

September
1 Thursday

Octavia visits me in hospital. Made love and we climaxed and I came inside her. Afterwards, she said, "You realize you could have made me pregnant?"
I nodded and smiled. "How do you feel about that?" I asked.
"I'm very pleased at the prospect," Octavia replied.
"So am I," I said.

It has occurred to me that it wasn't really Octavia, and I was not in hospital. In fact, I have a suspicion I never left the alien space craft. I was still aboard, and held in their medical examination room, where a female ET seduced me. I was made to make "love" to her because she wanted to extract my sperm, capture my DNA. I believe the woman extra-terrestrial is now pregnant, and will give birth to a human-alien hybrid. I suspect this is just one of many "space-rapes" that has gone on in the history of Mankind. The Sons of Heaven raping the Daughters of Earth, and the Daughters of Heaven seducing the Sons of Earth.

Laura came to say goodbye. She and Luther are joining a Hippy Commune.

According to Gnostic Tradition, the Universe is created by the evolution of Mind, Thought and Word.

MIND = 4
THOUGHT = 9
WORD = 6
--
19 = 1

September
2 Friday

Sitting opposite Lord Harvey Christian, multi-billionaire media emperor, at a meal table, I give him a hard time for being a member of the global ruling elite. But then I break down and tell him how grateful I am to him for helping Laura with airline tickets on his Woolf Atlantic Airbus, to go to the USA, to find a cure for the Hades disease. I choked back the tears and Lord Harvey kindly wipes my eyes.

After I had recovered my revolutionary's self-respect, I handed him my proposal for a Global Tax System, which immediately gave him a heart attack.

"What the world needs is a Global Tax system. If I "Ruled the World", I mean, if I was Leader of a World Government, I would institute such a system. I believe it is the only way we as a civilization can survive, and would be a vital way of ending all wars between nations and races. However, for it to work effectively, we would need global single currency, which would prevent currency speculation which today consistently undermines the economic integrity of Nation-States. The global single currency unit will be known as the UNO (based on the Euro, as opposed to the US Dollar or British Pound sterling or Japanese Yen).

My global tax system would equitably discriminate between the Rich and the Poor. By making the tax system global, to be administered by an international fiscal and revenue authority, neither individuals nor businesses will be able to evade or avoid payment of due taxes by seeking tax havens as there will not be any. So, for example, British mega-high earners cannot move to the USA to benefit from lower taxation rates, because all countries will be subject to identical taxation rates.

My Global Taxation system would have the following progressive rates of taxation.

The first 10,000 Unos of annual income will be tax free. This means the poor and lowest income margins do not get taxed.

Anyone in the world earning between 10,000 and 30,000 Unos will be taxed at 25%.

If annual earnings are between 30,000 and 70,000 Unos, a supplementary tax of 50% is imposed on the additional income beyond the first 30,000 Unos.

If income is between 70k and 100k, then this additional 30k will be taxed at 80%.

So, an individual earning 70k will have to pay 5k (25%) on 20k, plus 20k (50% of 40k), giving a total annual tax bill of 25k Unos, leaving the individual with net income of 45k Unos.

An individual earning up to 100k will have to pay 5k (25%) on 30k, plus 20k (50% of 40k), plus 24k (80% of 30k), giving a total annual tax bill of 49k Unos, leaving the individual with net income of 51k Unos.

Under my taxation system, there will be a ceiling to what an individual can earn. Anyone in the world earning more than 100k Unos, will be taxed at a 100%, and will receive a tax rebate of 52k Unos.

To illustrate for the stupid or Conservative

Example: earnings 70K

range	earnings	rate	tax	net income
10k	10k	tax free	0	
10-30k	20k	25%	5k	
30-70k	40k	50%	20k	
Total	70k		25k	45k

And where will all these taxes go? 60% will go to fund your local/regional council budgets responsible for local education, health, social services, arts, community, local housing, policing and emergency services, and local government admin.

30% will go to the national treasury to finance national government, and supplementary financing of regional budgetary imbalances (usually the product of regional differences in population densities). Notice that I do not include any national defense budgeting. No Nation state will be permitted expenditure on arms/defense/offense.

Finally, 10% of your taxes will go to the International Government Agency, to fund the International Peace Keeping Militia, to fund planetary advancement, protection and maintenance projects, and to re-distribute economic resources according to individual Nation-State needs.

The headquarters and parliament of the International Government Agency will be located on a tropical island that is currently uninhabited, and can be rendered neutral, with no national partisanship.

September
3 Saturday

I'm in the bath, when a stranger enters the bathroom. How the fuck did he get in? I can't see him properly because I don't have my glasses on. I see his dark outline as he approaches the bath tub. He moves my wheelchair away from the bath, which is not good. I feel vulnerable and loss of independence. I ask the Intruder not to move my chair but he just mocks me plea by moving it further away. I still can't see him properly but he vaguely reminds me of someone with learning difficulties I once knew. As he moved towards me I knew he had come to kill me. He leaned forward and grabbed my head, pushing my face in the water. The Assassin is trying to drown me. I fight back but he has all the advantages, and I cannot stop him. I try to grab his hair, and stick my fingers in his eyes, to pull his head in the water but I don't have the leverage or strength. He manages to keep my head submerged, and I am drowning. In a few more seconds, I will be dead. Again. As I lost consciousness, I surmised THEY probably didn't like my idea for a global tax system.

September
4 Sunday

Laura tells me everything is alright with her now. Luther agrees.

The Secret Agent pretends to be my friend whilst sending his spying reports on me to our fascist regime. I try to tell him I know everything, that the secret police have already tried to recruit me, implicate me in their dirty games. He shrugs at me, suggesting I am simply being paranoid.

A massed gang of Hells Angel bikers ride rough shod over a queue of traffic. Many motorbikes ride over the top of cars, boots, roofs, bonnets. One young guy rides over a police car but fails to do it cleanly and his wheel knocks the police light off. As a consequence he and his bike slips off the side and gets crushed by the traffic. When the vehicles have cleared, we find he has broken his back, with his head twisted back to front. He is still alive but we know he hasn't got long to live.

September
5 Monday

Go to Ireland house for weekend.

Unexpected guests, Laura, Lavinia and Proteus, ask if they can use the washing machine. I reply, "Of course". But then to my surprise, I find they have brought along one of their own.

It was beautiful. A small multicoloured UFO. When I saw it, I was with Lavinia, Laura's daughter. I saw it first and just assumed it was plane lights coming towards me. I point it out to Lavinia, who agreed that it was an airplane. But then as it got closer, I realized it was a miniature flying saucer, covered in spinning coloured lights. It was about 5ft. in diameter. The funny thing is, it seemed more like a living entity than a machine of metal and bits. And it seemed very playful. We were both delighted as it flew around us, demonstrating its aerobatic virtuosity. I just have to show it to Laura and Proteus, so I tell Lavinia to fetch them.
"Get back quickly," I urged, "because- Look! The UFO is losing its shape and power!"

Sadly, by the time Laura and Proteus arrive, it had collapsed into a silvery-type bird made of the metal plates. It lay slumped on the ground, gasping for its last breath. When it finally expired, it evaporated into thin air.

Saw a bright light to the north, shone brighter than the star, then just blinked out as I tried to look at it. Thought a cloud may have obscured it but after half an hour, it remained vanished, even though clouds had moved on and the sky was clear. Where did it go?

CCTV Camera monitoring the faery fort is on the blink. But a lot of interference. It takes a while for the picture to stabilize. Unlike the camera looking down the lane. Is it because there is a disturbing presence out there?

During the night....
nocturnal intruders. Visitors in car, sounding horn up the lane. I tried to hide.

September
6 Tuesday

What I saw next was like an epic historical drama movie. A walled city was under siege. The despotic King Amfortas was fighting for his life, as our armies successfully breached the walls, and I was the first to gain entry. I was given the job of emissary, sent to offer terms of peace. I inform the doomed tyrant that he must voluntarily give himself up for execution, and all his people will be spared, otherwise every man, woman and child will be put to the sword, and the city razed to the ground. The King agrees and marches ahead of me to the gates, to meet with his conquerors waiting outside, and offer his life to them. I feel sad that such a brave man should have to sacrifice his life. There was something Christ-like in his demeanor, dying that others may live. However, just as the martyr King reaches the gates, a great crowd of his citizens rush up to him, pleading with him not to leave. They forgive his tyranny, and will accept him once again as their ruler. They would rather the devil they know than the devil they don't know. The King, very much heartened by this new found support, agrees and turns back to renew the struggle against the invaders. With his confidence returned, convinced that this time they will win, he looks at me, and declares that Malcolm / Klingsor / Parzival will now suffer for the treachery. I quake in terror, as I wonder if he means me. Does he think I am Malcolm / Klingsor / Parzival? With trepidation, I follow him to the huge banqueting hall where victory celebrations are being prepared. I hang around expecting at any moment to be executed, but instead I find I am ignored. Eventually I realize the whole set-up was a ruse by the tyrant. The siege was a sham. He had organized a fake attack by "foreign" forces and his proposed "self-sacrifice" to trick his own rebellious people into returning to the fold, and allow him to continue his cruel oppression. With this revelation, I realize I had outstayed my welcome, and quickly left the city.

MALCOLM = 24 = 6
KLINGSOR = 33 = 6
PARZIVAL = 42 = 6

September
7 Wednesday

This afternoon a group of us are marooned on a traffic light island. We are trapped in the middle of the road because of a power failure and no one dares cross without the green light giving the go-ahead. I don't understand why we have to wait for technology to function properly. We can all see the way is clear. Why don't we all just cross? Just as I am about to persuade - the power returns and everyone is relieved that they can continue with authority. As we say our goodbyes to each other, I see her, Delia Artemis, the one I have fallen in love with. Everyone smiles knowingly as she makes her rounds, kissing all goodbye, with complete abandon. I await her kiss excitedly, an older woman grins, sensing my rapid heartbeat and pulse racing madly as Delia Artemis approaches me with loving eyes. Much as I relish her succulent farewell kiss I don't relish the farewell. To my surprise, she suggests that I go with her for a tea or coffee. Happily I realize she has no plans for us to part company just yet.

All day…. Delia Artemis kissing me passionately.

Damn – one can have too much of a good thing…

I see on my left, a plant-like object about the size of a stick of celery - green, slender with vertical grooves. Now that shouldn't be there. So I try to remove it. But I don't do it properly. I cut it at the trunk whereas warning bells in my head tell me I should have pulled it out at the roots. As I examined the roots of the strange plant embedded in the ground, I felt a stabbing pain on my right big toe. I'd put the main stem down by my foot, not realizing it was alive or animate. But the creature, for so it turned out to be, seemed more like a sea cucumber as it held fast to my toe, pumping itself into my flesh. To my horror, I saw millions of tiny worms swarm under my skin. Within minutes my whole foot was infected by these glowing subcutaneous wriggling parasites. I sought help but as usual no one believed me. After a few hours, the whole of my right side, the leg, the hip, my right arm lost to billions of squirming filaments of bright red, green, purple. I tried to prove to Thor the danger I was in by peeling away some skin from my tongue to reveal the wriggling mass, but to no avail.

September
8 Thursday

One a.m. Returning from the Taverna. Flashes in the sky - lightning but no thunder and no clouds. Starry night was crystal clear. The flashes continued through to two a.m.
I remember something similar way back in a different decade. I think it was the eleventh of March.

Ataoko Loinona and I meet up for the first time in ages. I was pleased to see him but he wasn't a overly enthusiastic. In fact, he told me he had never liked me, despite me telling him I liked him (even though he occasionally got on my nerves).

Ataoko Loinona = 53

A blond sex kitten in tight blue trousers and a fluffy white woollen jumper with a roll neck, comes to me and sits on my chair, pressing her buttocks against my legs. I didn't know her but she acts with a seductive familiarity, and flirts with her eyes, chatting me up, her hands all over me.
I am astonished but mightily pleased with her attentions.

Later, I am back on stage, in a play about this swashbuckling hero called Kato Kaelin, who is ready to elope with the beautiful girl. Her family and friends object to the union. In character, I draw my sword, wave it about and shout, "I will kill. Kill to marry her."

Midnight. I wake up because of the hotel phone ringing. I answer but there's no one. Then the alarm rings. Funny that, it was set for 7am.

Then the phone rings again. "Hello. Who is it?" I demand.
"Shiram Labif?" came back a voice.
"Yes. Who is it?"
"Kato Kaelin. You wanted to know the history of the Spear of Destiny?" asked the Hero's voice.
"Did I?"
"Yes, you did. The Spear of Destiny was the spear Odin used on himself to gain complete knowledge of the Universe, which was subsequently passed down to his descendants, until it fell into the hands of the Germanic kings. Then when the Romans under Tiberius conquered Germania, the Spear of

Odin was stolen by a Roman centurion, Gaius Cassius Longinus who later became a jurist and politician. He was great grandson, Gaius Cassius, one of Caesar's assassins. After stabbing Jesus Christ with Odin's spear, Longinus quickly rose to great power, eventually becoming proconsul of Asia minor in 40–41 during Caligula's rule, and legate of Syria in 41-49., exiled by Nero to Sardinia in 65 and returned to Rome under Vespasian. While proconsul, Longinus sold the Spear to a wealthy follower of Jesus, who was collecting relics of the Cruci-fiction – nails, fragments of cross, crown of thorns, all of which were unearthed in the 4th century by Constantine's mother, Helena, which she returned to the Empire. In 328, Helena gave the Spear to her Emperor son, thus consolidating and strengthening his power."

"All very interesting, I'm sure, but what has that to do with me?"

"You have the Spear." Kato whispered.

"Do I?"

"You do. Hold on to it. You will need it when the Invasion starts." The phone goes dead.

September
9 Friday

Traveling on a plane to Babylon, I'm sitting on the right side of the aisle. Two people in seats at my right. Delia Artemis arrives and wants to sit next to me. She climbs over the back of the seats, as she does so, she reveals a lovely silky thigh. I press my lips against her soft skin and lick her. She smiles in acknowledgement of my heartfelt attention. She slips in beside me but over the lap of a handsome black guy who helps her to pass, with his huge crutch touching her bottom

After Babylon, I fly to Jerusalem. Lydia is there somewhere on board the aeroplane, probably sitting at the back, wanting to get a bit of breathing space, probably sad about something. Probably disappointed with the birthday present I gave her. Maybe it was because I sat with this guy who had been irritating her, which drove her away. A woman comes and sits on my left, very friendly, almost American, asks if she met me before. In fact, she asks me whatever became of the trip to the moon. I ask her if she knows where Lydia is - she replies, at the back, she's been crying. It wasn't clear why. I thought Lydia and Delia Artemis had got over their moment of tension and were now friends. Lydia had told me they were hugging each other last night.

September
10 Saturday

A conference in Rome. Thor was there. A major event in the disability arts scene. Thor informs me that Lord Richard Atthegrove has arrived. Good. Now the film project could get moving. Thor goes and tells Dickie I am here and with a smile of benign greeting, the patron comes over with his usual promises of a meeting to get the production going. In the meantime, he offers me a choice of some fruit from a tray. To my annoyance, I pick the prickly pear, knowing I haven't the skill to skin and eat it without being stung. As usual, I seemed to be biting off more than I can chew. Suddenly the hall empties. The main events have started and I feel abandoned, left out. Eventually, at an interval, some people emerge and I inquire what have I been missing.
"Two disability films," they inform me. "A very good French one, and one the usual Hollywood slush". With this, I decide not to miss the next screening. However, it comes as a shock to all of us in the audience, to find that this film turns out to be a vortex, a space-time portal. The screen pulls us into the picture and we find ourselves in Nazi Germany, hiding behind a wall. We watch some SS soldiers lined up on a road to block a protest march of gypsy men, women and children. With horror, we realize the soldiers are going to massacre them. But I lead a rush of cinema goers onto the startled guards, who had no idea where we'd come from. We just appeared from nowhere. I go straight to one young Nazi and ask him to hand me his machine gun. I am scared that he will simply point it at me and shoot. But he turns out to be more petrified of me - a little man, in alien clothing, in a wheelchair. He meekly gives me his gun. The other soldiers give theirs to others in our group. Suddenly we realize we had better scarper. The element of surprise only lasts so long. We disperse in all directions. I reach a house, where a woman offers to hide me but somehow I feel there is no escape. The damage has been done. Time has been interfered with. We from the future, by going back to the past have altered the course of history .

Ominous rolling thunder approaches.

September
11 Sunday

The three great cities supposedly referred to in the Book of Revelations are Babylon, Jerusalem and Rome.

BABYLON	= 8	
JERUSALEM	= 5	
ROME	= 6	
	--	
	19	= 1

Well, I was complaining to my friend, Cynthia, that I hadn't seen a UFO for several days, when suddenly we looked out the window and there was a flying saucer hovering nearby. The next thing we knew, the light bulb in the sitting room starts to flicker and finally blew. The room was plunged into darkness except that it was morning.

I tell Cynthia about my suspicions concerning Laura's illness being created by other dimensional entities (O.D.E.) when she may have been abducted. Her doctor thought she might be suffering from "Lupus". The name interested me because it means "wolf". Well, we saw a pack of wolves at the time we saw the Green UFO. Native Americans believe the wolf originates from Sirius and came to teach humans. So, I wonder if some wolves are alien shape shifters. In other words are werewolves really E.T.? It was in the 19th century that French doctors first gave the name "Lupus" to a condition which looked like the patient had been bitten on the face. According to certain studies, people (especially women) who have been abducted by ET, often suffer from "Lupus" type symptoms.

Cynthia tells me that one night last week, she woke up to find light pouring in through the window from outside. She was so scared, she starts to pray. The instant she did that, the lights went out.

I have now noticed that on occasions when I have been pissing blood or nose-bleeding, it has followed a UFO or intruder experience.

September
12 Monday

I sneaked into a hospital and found a consultant who started to tell me what was medically wrong with me and the treatment that was necessary. He called a colleague in to give further advice. Then a dentist arrived and told me I needed work on my teeth. Then another doctor, followed by another. All with a remedy for my ills. Just when I thought I was going to be made into a new man, a clerk came in and said that before they went any further, a credit check was required to see if I was capable of paying such a huge bill. Then I realized I had been sucked into a bloody Blooper hospital. When they discovered I didn't have the financial resources to pay for the consultancy I'd received to date (which I'd not asked for in the first place) never mind what was to come - everyone disappeared and I was left stranded. My clothes were taken and I found I could not leave the hospital until I paid off the debts. Confined to a ward full of screaming children I knew was destined to go insane. Then the children vanished, and various adult patients who spoke and looked like they'd received lobotomies came, and showed me what my future was likely to be. Then the place became empty and I was totally abandoned.

September
13 Tuesday

Worked on my film script "Lighthouse Between the Waves" in Belgium, and Dionysus appears unexpectedly to distract me.

He suggested looking at the tripartite psychological structure based on the Freudian psychoanalysis theory….. this is what we found;

CONSCIENCE	=	9
SELF	=	6
ID	=	4
		--
		19 = 1

Later…
Laura rings, crying. Begging me to get an ambulance for her. Luther has beaten her up.

September
14 Wednesday

Laura is really very ill. Her voice (she's talking on the telephone) is fading fast, she is so weak. she ends the conversation by telling me she tried to commit suicide last night and "...it was bloody awful". She had the "baby voice" when she told me this - a sign of her desire to revert to the safety and innocence of her childhood .

Later. A little child was kidnapped by gangsters, and held for ransom. For some reason, I was also snatched. Probably because I was the child's guardian. We were taken to their hideout, and the child was put under tight guard in one room. However, the gang seemed to be ignoring me, either because they were thinking I was irrelevant or harmless, or they were not really aware of me. Could they actually see me? I began to think I was somehow invisible, because I was able to move about their domain without attracting adverse attention. Their leader reminded me of a black female pop singer (Diana Ross? Donna Summer? Whitney Houston?). Who was the victim? An English little girl abducted from a hotel in Spain. Later I hear the kidnappers say that when they receive the ransom money, they will still kill the child, as they plan to sell her off organs in the organ donor black market. This was horrific. I had to do something to save the little girl. Suddenly I felt I was sitting on a small object. I put my hand underneath me, and found a mobile phone. The gangsters must have overlooked it when I was grabbed. Now, I must try to ring the police without anyone noticing. I went into an empty room, and planned to dial 999 (or 112 or 911 or whatever fucking emergency number works in this place), but I noticed someone in the kitchen area rummaging in the cupboards. I waited for him to leave but instead, someone else arrived. Judging by the gang members' behaviour, I realised he was the supreme boss – a young white executive in a suit. I suspect this is another Corporate crime...which means government ministers will be implicated...and the guilty will go unpunished...and whistle-blowers sacrificed...and I won't be able to save the little girl.

September
15 Thursday

I am in a large open plan hut in a forest, a jungle in some tropical land. Various friends (Lydia, Igor, Kyles etc) are with me. Things seem aimless. I am at a loose end. Thor, who is also there, decides I should be given something to do - to get me out of a rut, away from apathy and lethargy. He gives me this puzzle he has been unable to solve, a sort of bagatelle. I have to slide six balls into six boxes down a maze. The game that requires subtle balancing and tilting maneuvers. No one has yet succeeded in getting the six balls in their proper places in the correct sequence. The feeling comes over me that this is too impossible a task. But I hear some music and realize I can be in control. Nothing can defeat me. So I concentrate and apply all my patience, determination and skill. Finally I manipulate all the balls in their correct goals, including the last and sixth one. I shout in exhilaration, "I've done it!"
Everyone looks at me in amazement. I'd achieved the seemingly impossible. Suddenly, Kyles cries out, "I've done it too". Then Thor, then Lydia and so on. It appears that my triumph incites the success in my companions. I am feeling happy and positive.

When the Intellect is coupled with the Heart, then we have the Will, a packet of three that knows no bounds!

INTELLECT = 1
HEART = 7
WILL = 2
---
10 = 1

September
16 Friday

I catch myself crying huge tears. The grief was intense. I was weeping for black Africa. It seemed so doomed. I was in some African village. Had there been one of the many wars that keeps the black nations from ever achieving stability? There was certainly a depressed atmosphere. I expected to find the place littered with corpses. And I found one. A young man lying on the hospital floor. The building was otherwise deserted. As I bent over him to see if he was dead, I saw movements in his chest and fluttering in his eyelids. He was breathing but in a very a bad way. I have to find medical help for him urgently. He seemed so helpless. I picked him up in my arms and held him tight, trying to feed him my warmth and life blood. He was fading fast. I called for help. I wanted desperately to save this man's life. I had found him so he was my responsibility. Eventually, some people came but they were useless. All they did was argue and complain that Africa was finished. "The people hate each other more than they hate the whites. They are deliberately killing themselves. You are wasting your time. You can't stop this self-inflicted genocide."
I screamed at them to shut up. They were wrong- even if they were African . How could they talk so negatively about themselves. I refuse to believe, to accept that African people are dying out. We must save them. That was when I started crying and crying. The pain of the tears soaked my soul.

September
17 Saturday

Delia Artemis and I have a serious conversation. Unbelievable.

Friends of Gordon Waters, including the novelist, Tahlia Paige, are cartoon characters on television. The thought just popped into my head that I would see Gordon as a cartoon figure and sure enough he was. I rang Gordon to tell him he was at last famous - albeit, as an animated "Toon".

September
18 Sunday

Delia Artemis is going to dump me.
I was warned by friends (and by the tarot cards which said she was the Queen of Swords) that Delia Artemis would be a terrible disappointment for me.

The Tarot said I must not give her too much of my heart and soul. Protect myself.

DEPRESSED! How can anyone want to be with me when I have such an indiscrete arsehole! I fart loud, long and continuously in front of Delia Artemis. I simply cannot control the wind factory. It is so embarrassing. In the end, Delia Artemis insists that I see a doctor about this severe case of flatulence. It doesn't help that Felicia in the other room is giving me a hard time with her constant shouting, accusing me of continuing to be such a wanker.

6pm Maslum and I discuss the possibility that Satan fucked Mary, in the guise of the archangel Gabriel, and so, was the real father of Jesus. This thought brings a stinging sensation to my arm.

Later, I was really fucked in the arse - raped- by a demon or supernatural entity during the night. I was lying on my stomach and found I was being mounted and felt my anus penetrated and then violently shagged repeatedly as I was pinned to the bed, paralyzed. It was painful, frightening and I could barely breath. It felt like I was being repeatedly raped by an unseen vicious being which didn't care if I lived or died. In fact, each time it entered me I thought I was going to die.

The more I reflect upon this, the more I suspect there are hostile entities out there, who exploit their powers of invisibility and their ability to pass through walls, to sexually abuse us humans.

September
19 Monday

College reunion? Anyway, a gathering of past disabled friends, Associates, colleagues. At first, I am an outsider (not unusual) and remain aloof, and so, I am ignored. Then the dancing begins and suddenly a disabled woman in a wheelchair who I remember as having long brown hair, looking like a hippie child of the nineteen sixties - a sort of Ali McGraw .... who had a fiancé called Luther (a different Luther) he was also in a wheelchair back in the Beowulf College days.... smiles at me, recognizing me and offers herself for a dance. I take her hand as the name comes back to me, Sue. Our wheelchairs swirl around one another, held by hands clasped fast . Then the centrifugal force pulls her out of her wheelchair and she falls towards me. I catch her and cushion her fall. She smiles in gratitude as her body relaxes into mine. The look in her eyes tell me she has been dreaming of doing this for 26 years.

Rumblings. Distant. The approach is relentless. The earthquakes are coming.

September
20 Tuesday

The man (I knew him from somewhere...an old friend perhaps) has some taboo information which kills anyone who sees it. It is Forbidden Knowledge. Knowledge for the Select only. He is on the run from those who seek to punish him, both for glimpsing the Secret, and for stealing the Sacred Object. Now at a strange rendezvous, a derelict building in the middle of nowhere, he meets up with me, and dooms me by revealing the Prohibited Sight to me. A small square stone with strange mysterious symbols engraved on it. He says the object was at least 5000 years old. He also, with a sly smile, tells me I am now an Unauthorised Initiate. I film an interview with him. “Until now,” he said, “these symbols have never been deciphered. If we meet again, I will tell the meaning. Meanwhile, meditate upon what I have shown you, because I feel you will intuitively discover the truth. I suspect you have the gift.” After telling me his name, Glen Kilmarten, we go our separate ways, hoping we can escape the Assassins that are now in pursuit of us both.

September
21 Wednesday

My agent, Joshua Samba, phones me to say it's all are going to pot, disaster everywhere, in showbiz-land and he will ring me later with the full details of the catastrophe.

I accidentally ring my girlfriend. She answers by giving her name as "Kushdie Rushdie". However, on hearing it's me, she hangs up. I am mortified - especially when I realize she didn't use her usual name, Delia Artemis. Is it over between us?

I add up the letters of Kushdie = 5
And Rushdie = 3.
so this is after all, a hopeful sign? She said a name meaning five and three. 53. Which is her number. On the other hand, experience has shown me that 53 can be a double edged sword, cutting both ways. For good, and for ill. What the Lord giveth, the Lord taketh away. 53 is Janus-faced.

September
22 Thursday

I keep getting into the lift with the same woman. We even talk to each other, but I was getting quite embarrassed about this repetition. I was worried she might think I was following her, stalking her. She was blonde. Anyway, the next time we met at the elevator, I decided not to go in with her, but go in the second one, the doors of which were opening at same time. On seeing this, she addressed me with a sarcastic comment that we might as well go separately since I was so cool, aloof and uncommunicative. But before I could reply that I didn't want to seem to be harassing her, she was gone. Then my problems began. Every time I tried to get into my elevator, the doors would close too quickly and I could never make it in time. Finally, I jammed the door, but a single plank of wood on the door got caught up in the spokes of the wheels of my wheelchair, and the more I tried to disentangled myself, the more trouble I got into. I now see I should not have been so paranoid, and gone into the other lift with the woman.

September
23 Friday

A lion tries to jump on me as I turn my back to him. My Enemy threw me into the circus ring, trying to get me killed, but I quickly picked up a stick and defend myself, forcing the big cat to return to his pedestal.

It was the blond woman I kept meeting in the elevator. She wanted me to do some riding but I was nervous that with my disability I couldn't sit safely, and if I can't do it properly, I don't want to do it at all. Then along comes this donkey offering itself as my transport. I asked the girl if she would help me on and stay with me to make sure I didn't fall off. But the donkey without any prompting got down on its knees and lay low, so that I could get on by myself. Then it slowly and gently raised itself with me sitting comfortably on its back.

September
24 Saturday

My little pussy, Solar Eclipse appears, looking very ill, lack-lustre eyes, very depressed as if he feels I have abandoned him. Then as he settles onto my lap and senses that I have welcomed him back, he turns into a delightful little girl with big happy brown eyes, laughing and giggling.

Alone in the Withdrawing Room, I look out in the night sky. A red light amongst the stars moves swiftly across, I realize it's a U. F. O. The sudden realization draws an attack. Tiny flying objects, like little metal birds, shaped like bullets, missiles, shuttlecocks, fly at me… but I am a magician juggler and I keep catching them. I cannot be hit and I am pleased that I'm able to contain them in my hand and hold them as evidence.
My friends in the other room burst in to tell me that they too have seen the red light in the sky, and to prove their point we all see it travel across the ceiling. However, the sudden interruption by my friends, cause the miniature flying objects to vanish… even the ones in my hands. All but one disappear. With relief, I endeavour to present the last scrap of evidence that we are about to be invaded.

I deliver a great, mind-blowing speech to the People's Assembly, but on leaving my mouth, the words evaporate into forgetful hot air. Nothing remains of it at all. Except the fear I have said too much.

Within minutes, I receive word that a pair of assassins have been sent to kill me. Well, we know this isn't the first time.

September
25 Sunday

Speaking with Wolf Light on the phone one minute, then the next minute she is beside me in my sitting room. Delia Artemis is also with me.

The Integrated Theatre Company had become an institution. The premises big, airy, full of corridors, cavernous performance halls and toilet cubicles. It was like being back at the Dump in the old days, with all the fun and frivolity of the immature inmates. Even the non-disabled actors had become infected. Professional artistic production values were no longer the premium. Games and occupational therapy was the name of the aim. Two girls on either side of me, flirted with me. Nothing was serious any more. It was like old times. Then I was caught in the toilet with another girl. We were French kissing and promising each other "bum rubs". Samuel wasn't even angry, merely amused when he found out.

I think Leo Tolstoy knew a thing or two about nocturnal alien visitations, though he talks about them as nightmares, and in terms of incubus. In "Anna Karenina", on page 753 (Plato-puss Classics 1987 edition), he writes "At dawn a nasty nightmare, which Anna had had several times even before her involvement with Vronsky, repeated itself and woke her. A little old man with unkempt beard was leaning over a rod of iron, doing something and muttering meaningless words in French (alien Tongues?), and – this was what always the nightmare so dreadful – she felt though this peasant seemed to be paying no attention to her he was doing something horrible to her with the rod of iron (the Rod of Aaron?), doing something obscene to her. She awoke in a cold sweat." Alien entity in the guise of a peasant (this is probably how a 19th century Russian "Posh-o" like Anna Karenina would interpret a fearsome creature) with the ubiquitous anal probe?

September
26 Monday

The snows again.
I have to get somewhere before I am stranded.
Then a bungalow appears and I think I found sanctuary. I'm not supposed to enter but I go in. I feel like a burglar. Getting in is easy. The place is very accessible except I have to creep around the rooms very carefully, trying not to knock anything. Her home is very cluttered. She's in there somewhere. Perhaps she's asleep in the bedroom. She doesn't know me and she will certainly raise the alarm if I'm discovered.
I decide to leave. There's nothing there for me.
Suddenly I can't find my way about. Doors have changed positions. Exits have become inaccessible. The interior geography has become alienable and obstructive. Awkward steps and difficult inclines appear to bar my escape route. Her paintings, with the paint still wet on the canvas, reminding me she can't be far away and liable to catch me at any moment. Her house and all its contents, conspire to keep me prisoner. I should never have had the audacity to have gone there in the first place.

September
27 Tuesday

Octavia criticizes me for being nasty to her. just because I mentioned Greenpeace. I blame Graham Greene and the not so Quiet American peace.

Lydia is not happy. I am not very nice to her. I will get my cum-uppence.

Later…much later…..very much later…

A Visitation…I didn't want to have sex with him but he insisted that I fuck him in the arse.
It was horrible.
He was ghastly….skinny, blotchy
….and the sex was disgusting.
I think he had HADES and now I fear he's made me have it.
How many times must I be doomed?

September
28 Wednesday

Lying in bed and woken up by an intruder. It's Solar Eclipse, my lovely black cat. He's come home. But I was supposed to collect him tomorrow. At first I thought he had made his own way back. But no, Argentum Silver brought him. Her head pops around the bedroom door. I smile and thank her. Solar Eclipse and me cuddle, glad to be back together.

It all changes, or does Solar Eclipse change? His face seems to take on human form.

Next thing I know, Laura is lying beside me on my right, snuggling up to me, pleased to be back in my arms, laughing at my astonishment to find her there,
"I bet you're wondering how I got here? I've been near you several days. You haven't seen me but I've been with you"
Suddenly it felt good to have the old Laura back. The mad carefree Jokey Laura. Then the prospect of having Laura back makes me nervous, anxious. The stress, tensions, fights will return and it will all become a nightmare again.

September
29 Thursday

I wake up to a noise outside the front door. Intruders.
But I see him through the frosted glass. He tries to duck down.
Then as if to punish me for spotting him, he grabs my cat, Solar Eclipse, as my baby tries to run in through the cat flap. The look of fear on poor Solar Eclipse's face as he is snatched.
Later I realize the intruder has gained entry because the front door is slightly open. Something tells me the burglar or whatever, is hiding on my left in the sitting room. I warn my friend, Geburah, in whispers. "There's an intruder in the house. Don't move. Pretend you haven't noticed," I tell her in hushed tones.

Later this morning I've not surprised to find blood on the tissue when I blow my nose. Proof I was visited by aliens again.

Leonie, my past dog died several years ago, comes back.
The golden Chow wants to be with me. I see her walking along the road.
I stop the car, and she runs up to me. I open the door and my lovely Bear-Lion with the Purple Tongue leaps in.
We are together again.

The blond woman of the elevator, comes to stay in my cottage. She tells me her name is Geburah.

Did the crystal ball under the left pillow and the amethyst purple under the right pillow bring her to me?

A little fart, and out pops a little turd. Fuck, I've shit my pants. Quick, must go to the toilet and clean up, before this new woman, Geburah, discovers my smelly bottom.

September
30 Friday

I could not sleep. Coughing. Spasms in my breathing. Tossing and turning. The long night dragged on, and I was getting more knackered. I looked around me in the bedroom, Geburah lay sleeping beside me on my right. The atmosphere changed. Became very different. A kind of transparency – a shimmering veil, beyond which was a different dimension. It was the bedroom but it was "see-through". I was detecting an alien world hiding behind the fabric of our "reality". It seemed alluring and yet at the same time threatening. I didn't trust what was on the other side. Or maybe I just wasn't ready to pass over.

However, as I began to resist the attraction, I felt powerful hands grip both my wrists, holding them together. I struggled to break free of them, but there were too many of them. Two or three pairs of hands like thick ropes binding my arms. They were determined, ruthless. I couldn't defeat them. There was no escape as I felt them pull me by my hands towards the boundary between this world and the next.
I panicked.
Trying to scream.
Finally, I attempted to call out Geburah's name, but it was garbled as if my lips were glued together. Nonetheless, my calling her, albeit telepathically, worked. The iron-like hands released me, and scuttled away into the darkness like five-legged demonic crabs.

October
1 Saturday

A good chin wag was anticipated by all. Friends had returned and I'd ordered traditional English takeaway TV dinners. I was dishing up the plates of the mashed potatoes, veggies and sausages and ham and spam.

Then Igor arrived and I asked him which plate he wants. He's not that bothered. What he has come to talk about is too pressing to be concerned with such trivia as eating.
Like an ignored and underrated housewife, I insist he makes a decision, so that we can all start to eat. He picks spam and mash, then he and everyone else go off to another room and start the chin wag without me because I have to stay doing the kitchen chores.
I tut away in the kitchen. Look at all those half eaten food? When are the boys going to finish their dinners? I can't eat until they come back, I grumble to myself as I put an extra portion of cocktail sausages on to Igor's plate.
Then Delia Artemis comes in, chattering away to me about her mum. Suddenly, half way through the conversation, everything goes dead as if the phone has been cut off.

Tsunami is coming. A giant wave heading straight for us. Is this The Last Wave I have been expecting since I saw that movie while a student at the University of Sorry?

Geburah and I went to the seaside this afternoon, and strolled near the promenade. Then I saw the huge tidal wave racing towards the shoreline. The tide was in, so I could see the wave was going to sweep over us if we lingered any longer. I urged Geburah to get me up the steps quickly. She pulls the wheelchair up but the stone steps are a little slippery and at first she has problems. However, she finally manages to pull me to higher ground, and away from the seafront in time.

October
2 Sunday

Laura singing “Don’t forget me in your dreams,” or “Don’t forget to dream of me,” to the tune of a Stevie Wonder song, “Isn’t she lovely made from love.”

So I go visit her... and Luther. I apologize for not getting in touch for months.
She laughed. “Months? Don’t you mean days?” That’s a relief. She seems OK. I tell her about how I cannot make any TV shows anymore. Producers are simply not interested in what I have to say. I complained about Idealism having a shelf life. Just as I tell her that, we are interrupted by the arrival of a little fluffy white kitten which makes Laura go all gooey. And I go all gooey too, of course.

Later in the evening, Geburah and I visit what we thought was a museum, but all the lights are out. We are quickly lost in the cavernous darkness. Geburah complains that there are no light switches. Quite right, too. The inexplicable darkness spooks her, and I don’t see her again.
Eventually, the rods take over and I begin to feel at home, now being able to see a little.
There are black silhouettes of waxworks manikins…or the sleeping undead.
I jump out of my skin when I notice a man sitting in an armchair, wearing an old sea captain’s cap.
“Are we in a sunken ship at the bottom of the ocean?” I jokingly ask him. Getting no answer, I turn to a door which creakingly opens, throwing out a shaft of light, and I see sitting in another armchair a Zombie-fied Igor, my old buddy. I walk cautiously toward him and he suddenly moves.
“How’s it going, pal?” I nervously ask, hoping he has not become one of those flesh-eating Zombies, because Igor always had a huge appetite.
“It’s a fuck up,” he replied. “I’ve been trying to pull that bloody light switch but it keeps swinging out of my arm’s reach. Watch.” Igor leans forward to grab the light cord, but it immediately whips away, and he is left grasping at thin air. I wondered why he didn’t just get up from his sitting posture and walk up to the light switch, but I guess he liked to stay in the comfy armchair. Anyway, the good news is that with the help of my encouraging presence, Igor manages to catch the annoying wayward light string, and thus, there was Light.

October
3 Monday

I'm in my back garden in Wellingtonia, and unbelievably, the garden is not a mess. There's a patio with benches and tables. Then I find that the Pikey neighbours upstairs, Chrissy Naim and her boyfriend, had taken over it in my absence. I can't begrudge them it really, because they did something decent and useful with it, and they are willing to share it.
Or are they? As they prepare to have a barbecue, I get the feeling that I am outstaying my welcome in my own back yard.
Or is it that I find their new friendship too disconcerting?
I quickly mutter my apologies and after some clumsy moves in my wheelchair I beat a hasty retreat indoors - but not before noticing how splendid their own garden is, with a pool and beautifully laid out beds of flowers.
Inside, my sitting room window looks out at the family eating. So that they cannot pry on me and I can give them privacy, I draw the curtains. Besides, I didn't want them to see me masturbating.
Then, I stop, realizing the pointlessness of this sterile activity, and as soon as I do, a woman enters the room which is immediately transformed into a sort of laboratory. Suddenly, I am to undergo new tests to see if I'm still fit to fly. The woman, stern in a compassionate sort of way, gives me a hearing test which I pass.
Then a girl enters who seems attracted to me which surprises me. More people enter and I lay on the lab table which becomes a comfortable bed. The Examiner gives me an apple which becomes an orange.
The girl gets close to me and presses her arm against mine and whispers.
Meanwhile, Delia Artemis comes in, and feels the need to announce to everyone how much she loves me, something she has always been too scared to do in the past. Still, the girl snuggles more into me which keeps me wondering. The Examiner then peels the orange which becomes a lemon, Or was it a yellow orange?, I imagine the girl is going to blindfold me and test my sense of taste. Everyone leaves except for the girl who suddenly caresses my thigh and penis, telling me she loves me.
I suspect she is softening me for another of those intrusive explorations and experiments.
Must be Aliens.

October
4 Tuesday

I am in a group of people. I am being chatted up by this woman with short blond hair. She flaunts her Nordic-ness and names herself Hilda. She tells me she's going to fuck me and the next thing I know she takes my clothes off and strips herself naked. Hilda is not very tall but her body is very voluptuous. She pushes me on my back and straddles me. Gets my cock very hard and puts it in her vagina and fucks me senseless. The screwing transports me to another place where someone is giving a lecture on the life and death of John Lennon. I'm given a special ticket to commemorate the fact that I was there, and I am invited to a banquet where I find myself sitting next to Paul McCartney. We get on like a house on fire. Hey man, it looks like we gonna be everlasting pals. He tells me about his charity to provide music therapy for people with learning difficulties and other disabilities. He explains that for the purposes and practices of the work the charity has to use the medical model. He knows my opinions on that – Rather than ruin a promising relationship, we agree to disagree. However, I secretly plan to get Jungle Jim McBurger to put Paul straight.
Meanwhile "The Walrus" offers to give me his contact details and phone numbers. I look for my Serious Pictures business card to give him in return but I can't find any that are not dog-eared and mouldy. I daren't give him ones that suggest I'm just a has-been. Trouble is, until I give him my card, he won't give me his.
So Paul turns from me and starts to sweep the floor with a broom. As he does, I softly start singing his best hit single "Yesterday". I suddenly feel shy and nerdy. He must get sick of hearing people trying to sing that song in front of him. But I can't stop singing it.
The only thing that can stop me singing "Yesterday", is to do the sums… which I do.

Paul		McCartney = 53
14	+	39
(5)		(3)

I knew it! John Lennon knew it.
Paul McCartney had something to do with Extraterrestrials.
Was he one of Them? *Them?* "Them" were ants. Paul was a beetle.

Well, according to "Abductees"/"Contactees", there are three races of aliens…"Hominids", "Reptilians" and "Insectoids".

October
5 Wednesday

Mali Roo as I remember her (I was 20 and still a virgin), when she seduced me to her bed - young, slimmer, energetic and hopeful. I failed as a lover that time but she forgave me. Now she gives me her new address and phone number, and hints that as I'm now a little more experienced, I am more than welcome to give it another try.

Some small slant-eyed people were trying to catch me. Japanese? Oriental-looking, anyway. I don't know why they were chasing me, but they pursue me for many miles, and finally trap me in a building. As they approach me, I throw everything I can lay my hands on, bombarding them with cutlery, crockery, chairs and tables, and other pieces of furniture. It must have seemed like they were in another earthquake, so much shit was falling on their heads. I ran into a dark room, but more "Japanese" were waiting, and made a grab for me. But they weren't quick enough. I escaped their clutches, and raced out of the house.

Hours later, I am travelling along the road in my wheelchair, and I meet this posh middle aged woman. She sort of reminded me of my lovely friend, Cecilia Francesca, who died last year from a brain haemorrhage brought on by a broken heart. This woman, however, was not an American, very English and aristocratic. A snob really. She condescended to give my chair a push. We chatted as we made slow progress through the desolate wasted countryside. Did either of us know where we were going? As she was beginning to fatigue of pushing me, and about to abandon me, a large white car arrived. The lady hailed it as if it were a taxi-cab, but it turned out to be her own urban tank, i.e. a range-rover type "people carrier" 4x4 thingy. Her chauffeur was a young severe looking, closely cropped hair woman – probably a man-hating lesbian, who was not happy about the lady suggesting I get into the vehicle. A young boy was in the front passenger seat, so I had to go to the back, but on opening the rear door, I found the seat blocked by a young girl of about 7 years old. At first she refused to move over to the other side of the seat, until the lady ordered her to make room for me. "Move over, child," she barked. "The little man doesn't want to have to crawl all over you. He is not a pervert, you know."

October
6 Thursday

Leonnie, my past died dog (a lovely golden Chow Chow she was), is being forced to stand precariously on the roof of a tall building. Fucking Gordon, pretending to be Igor, is torturing the poor darling purple tongued lady Bear-Lion.

Laura is trying to get me back, and attempts to seduce me. Almost rapes me in her demon desperation. I struggle against her wishes, not because I hate her. I don't - but because we cannot turn the clock back. We can never trust each other like we use to as lovers.
As friends - yes, as soul-mates, as "brother" and "sister" - yes.
Besides, there will always be the danger of Luther.
He has taken another woman in the other room.
We hear her scream. She staggers out into our room and collapses to the floor. She is about to die. Laura and I look at each other in horror. We realise we are witnesses to murder. Luther will not allow us to escape, leave the premises alive.
He storms in, sees us and smashes his fist into the side of my head.
I am instantly killed.

I know I am dead, even though I am conscious.
I fear Laura will be next for the chop...
There is nothing I can do to save her.
Corpses never make good saviours.

October
7 Friday

On the Ship of Fools, being rowed out to sea, escaping from sin and guilt - or merely life? Is it me? Or is it someone I despise? Probably both.
A shoreline appears. Hope of a happy landing. A brave new world awaits.
But horror. Horror upon horror.
It's a coastline of death. Thousands of rotting corpses. A massacre.
Who is responsible? Him or me? Probably both.
We must not disembark. The scavengers are more than just crows and ravens. There are also humans, on their hands and knees, picking the flesh and bones. Leprous creatures with all their bodily parts in rapid putrescent decay. They wait in brittle silence for the Traveller to come ashore.
We scream at the disease-ridden cannibals to stop. They are becoming what they eat.
But neither they nor we, will ever pay heed, for the Ferry Man has already been bought and the crossing is one way.
The Isle of the Undead must now be my eternal home.
The voyage was a gamble and it didn't pay off.

My friend, Lydia rang me. How does a ghost pick up the phone?
Lydia told me her daughter, Gwen was in a panic…. she had seen me through a glass door, and I was dead in my wheelchair. She feared I had topped myself… i.e. committed suicide.
Surprisingly I was able to tell Lydia that Gwen was mistaken. I wasn't as dead as I thought I was.

October
8 Saturday

I am on trial for Laura.

But it doesn't end there.
The Enemy has more charges against me.
No sooner do I leave one trial (it still isn't clear if I have been acquitted or whether there's an adjournment) than they snatch me outside the Caught House for another one.

3.53pm. The prison is full. Hundreds of people are being persecuted for being or having been Beatles fans or admirers. Arrested and held for questioning. Evidence was being planted on us to incriminate us. Such as Hippy drawings of cannabis leaves and sketches of the Beatles. The brutality shown the spastic fans was particularly appalling. I turn to Ringo and tried to get him to plead our case but discover he has become one of the prosecutors. He has completely forgotten his past- who or what he was. He is now part of the establishment locking us up for being "nutters". Ringo doesn't even recognize an old sketch of John Lennon or himself, or he refuses to. The ex-drummer is obviously in denial now that he has jumped on a new bandwagon.

Eventually my protests in the overcrowded cell sparks off a resistance movement. One guy gets very angry and threatens to tear the walls down. A guard comes in to try to placate us. She takes the angry aged hippie away and tells us we are all held in custody at the Press Secretary's pleasure. I incite everyone to riot at once. The prison will not be able to contain our struggle. The mob gathers for the big one.

Damn. It turned out to be a damp squib.

They captured us, all of us. How many? A hundred, two hundred. Thrown into a room and then knocked out and tied up. But why wasn't I put to sleep and bound? A cover was put over my fellow prisoners and a small furry animal released into the room. I looked at how cute and sweet it was but then realized it was a baby and that it would in a very short while grow into a huge ferocious bear, which would kill and eat all of us. When our captors had left us to the mercy of the furry time bomb, I ceased pretending to be helpless and quickly caught the innocent but deadly creature and was able to get the prison door open and let it loose into the corridors of our persecutors.
The bear happily wandered off, free to eat a more natural food.
Meanwhile, I was left wondering how to wake and free my fellow captives.
However, it turned out to be very easy.

October
9 Sunday

The phone rang. It was Hilda. Screaming at me for dumping her. "No one has ever dumped me before. It has always been me doing the dumping. Every man I ever had, I dumped first. And then along comes a little pip-squeak like you. A cripple who should be flattered, honoured, grateful that I should even look at you, never mind let you shag me, and you have the audacity to dump me. Such ingratitude! How dare you!"

Delia Artemis and a black man down in the basement having fun and games. She looks so much happier with him than she ever did with me, leaping and laughing (she did warn me once that she preferred black guys). I watched them through a big glass petition which gives me a bird's eye view. The stairs down, of course, prohibit me access, so I have to suffer in silence. Typically, she ignores my presence despite my making a special journey to visit to see her. I decide that I'd better go and announce loudly my intention. Her flat mates all apologetically rush to attend me, and the couple downstairs stop fooling around.
As I am about to leave, Delia Artemis comes up the stairs, talking on the mobile phone, typical of her. Those bloody things must have wrecked so many relationships. People don't talk face to face any more, only electronically.

I'll be glad when there's no more electricity.

October
10 Monday

Woken early this morning by strange dragging noise, then I saw Jingle Bells, a notorious stray cat, peering at me through the cat flap. Got up to see what could be causing the weird sound. Perhaps the plastic rubbish bag been split open? No .
I go back to sleep but am woken again by the same sound, and again I see the cat looking mischievously back at me through the cat size hole in the door. Are they really cat's eyes? Or something more sinister? Something more alien?

During the day my guts feel all wrong, keep wanting to piss and am headachey and groggy, lacking in energy. This is symptomatic of alien intervention. Plus, my nostrils have a blood clots. Small but evident. Clearly, another sign... Of what? Me going nuts?

Later in the afternoon, I'm driving a van with three companions, Ferdinand, Delilah and Geburah. Suddenly I see a big posh golden car coming up behind me. I'm sure it's my Enemy. I decide to try and stop him, and crash my vehicle into him, but he dodges me, and the chase is on. I pursue him across a wide variety of terrain, along hazardous roads, and then along river banks But who is chasing who? I have the feeling that somehow the roles have been reversed. Or are they just doing that to confuse me, so that they can escape? Finally we crash in the water. It looks like I deliberately hit his car – the golden machine. Yes, I stopped him but I damaged myself in the process. Both my legs are broken. My supposed enemy comes out of his vehicle, and suddenly seems friendly, and wants to help. The police are summoned, and I realize they mustn't know I was driving the van and had deliberately caused the accident. Ferdinand agrees with Delilah's suggestion that he would say he was the driver and I the passenger. Even my Enemy wants to keep the truth from the police. "This is a private affair between you and me," I seem to hear from his mind.

On my right I glimpse a woman trying to look into the van. Is it Delia Artemis. Someone with big brown eyes. The foxy lady is trying to find out who is in the van with me. Is she jealous of another woman? But there isn't a woman with me. Where is Delilah? And where is Geburah? I thought she was sitting on my left in the passenger seat. And now she's gone. Are the women companions being hidden from me? Or have they been abducted? Was I trying to rescue them from the golden machine?

A black guy, all smiles, comes up on the left. He could be a cop. Looking a laid-back Hippy, he greets and kisses me – but I think this is just a ruse – to get physically close to me. He is smelling me – trying to sniff out the truth. He suspects I was the driver, and that I was behaving dangerously. However, he continues acting like a long lost friend, rather than the Smokey Bear I believe him to be.

As I am pulled from the wreckage I notice my legs are no longer hurting me as much. Perhaps they are not broken after all.

October
11 Tuesday

Something was in the room…
Something on the bed with me.
Something bad, trying to sexually abuse me while I lay on my stomach.
Some Thing evil about to rape me in the arse.
I shake it off momentarily, but the demon, might even be the Devil itself, is persistent and is attempting to take possession. In the end I have to forget my pride and independence, and turned to God, just like last time, and pray for His help.
God drove the evil away from me and saves my arsehole from a brutal demonic buggering.

Sound, light and smell are necessary for an Exorcism

SOUND = 1
LIGHT = 2
SMELL = 7
--
10 = 1

October
12 Wednesday

Octavia visits me. I just can't seem to shake her off. But I must admit she was rather erotic. Loving in her distant detached gimlet-eyed way, almost blissful. But so very faint, transparent. She was always more ghost than girl. A chimera.

Later…
I create huge bubbles, bigger than anybody else's. Besides, once produced my bubbles…MY BUBBLES… continue to grow of their own accord. They also constantly change shape at the slightest touch . They are very strong. I feel they could last forever.

11.53pm. Damn! The bedside lamp's new light bulb blows. The second in two days. Shit! Seems I'm leaking too much energy.

October
13 Thursday

Some kind of surgery being done to the left side of my back. Hilda was there, dressed in nurse's uniform. Two surgeons at work on me. One old… the other young, more like a trainee. The older one, the Professor, gave me a kiss on the lips and then sliced some skin from the left hip, he then gave his young colleague the freedom to take whatever he fancied. The enthusiastic young man chose the left buttock as it was nice and juicy- A painful choice for me because I was going to have to sit on the wound for some time. Doctors are such sadistic bastards, I thought, as he eagerly massage my bum, preparing the flesh for his scalpel.

If only I could see through the veil. I know I would glimpse their true identities. The doctors are aliens in disguise, I'm convinced of it.

But no avail. Their smoke-screen, as always, is too thick.

October
14 Friday

Isis burns my denim waist coat. She seems overjoyed and grateful to me for having allowed her the privilege. She thinks it's liberating me.

I have this idea to make a movie, set in medieval England where the main aspect of the story surrounds the wild isolation of the people, where wolves play an important focus and function in their lives. The film is concerned not so much with town dwellers but country drummers. Realizing I would need vast tracts of unadulterated forests, I decide we will need to film in Europe, Scandinavia perhaps, where virgin forests, complete with wolves still exist. Thinking of writing to the various national film institutes, Norway comes to mind but that worries me because I may have to involve Hilda the Nordic Sex-Goddess. And she makes for a dangerous bed-fellow. She has this urge to kill me….for a crime she believes she committed in a previous life.
If she has killed me once, why does she need to kill me again?

October
15 Saturday

Another Black Friday. Stock Market Crash synchronised with winds of hurricane status. Millions of trees felled throughout Britain. At 2.53 this morning the electricity was cut off. The top of my roof blown, and all the roads out of Wellingtonia are blocked by fallen trees and other windswept debris. And just like 1987, the almighty storm sends the financial and stock markets tumbling from a great height, smashing the bricks of Wall Street to smithereens. Well, I'm not sorry for the Capitalist bastards, serve the greedy fuckers right. Hope they all throw themselves from the tallest buildings. But I do weep for the loss of so many forests.

Delia Artemis is pissing me off again, so I tell her THIS IS IT. It will be over between us by November, I'm moving permanently to Ireland.
The postman delivers and she gets up to go, leaving me stranded on the sofa with my wheelchair seemingly out of reach. She refuses to pass me the wheelchair, "Since you have dumped me, you Mong, why should I?" she teases. However, somehow, I succeed in getting into my chair. I'm too late, of course. Always too late.
Delia Artemis reads from the hall. "Isis," she sneers.
Damn! The interfering little bitch is opening and reading my mail. I snatch the letter from her and we both leave.

Workmen outside are building new gates with house numbers. I can't find my car. It's not where I left it.... or is it buried under the workers rubble? Do I report it missing? Whatever happened, I nonetheless find I am climbing down in the subway, searching for a train on a deserted platform- But not quite deserted....There he is, my arch enemy. And he is now in disguise as a railway architect. Ha! He thinks I think he is the train inspector. He tells me no one can help me.... "There are no trains," he smirks, twirling his mustang. I call out his name as I recognize him, "Barry Maysbury."
Is the escape possible now that we have confronted each other?
Barry Maysbury (= 62 = 8)

I meditate upon his name, trying to work out why he is my arch enemy. "Barry Maysbury". Maysbury, wasn't he a Ripper suspect?

Ripper Jack = 53 = 8

October
16 Sunday

Go for a shit… and find blood - coming out of my arse - Lots of red bloody blood-blood (the bill had been nabbed). FUCK. A burst hemorrhoid?
Or something much worse? A ruptured rectum? Cancer of the colon? What is happening to my insides?
This morning lots of blood coming out of my mouth after I cleaned my teeth. I am rotting away.
Oh well, never mind. You gotta go sometime. Did I have intruders last night? I think so. Was it them again? "They That Interfere"? Was I abused in my sleep? Is that the reason I am bleeding today?
Or is my body simply reacting to the content of my mind?
The Walrus who believed he was the real killer of John Lennon (and not Mark Chapman), was sexually abused by his mother when he was a little boy. She would savagely rape him with her fingers when she was giving him a bath. Her excuse was she was checking he didn't have any worms. Her long sharp nails made him bleed. He was four years old.
And the one "worm" he did have, she would beat with a hair brush whenever she caught him at it. He was eight years old.

October
17 Monday

Another argument with Delia Artemis. Details have evaporated. Probably inconsequential.
But the blazing row was interrupted by me receiving a text message on the mobile.

"Thank you for discovering in your dream I have been murdered and covered in mud. Much love. V"

Who is "V"? And when did I dream that she had been murdered?

And how do I know that "V" is a she?

October
18 Tuesday

I looked in my library of serial killers, and see that the Ripper suspect was called James Maybrick, not Maysbury. So that's not the answer as to the real identity of my Enemy.

The beautiful woman gazing at me with such innocence, leaning across the wall, with the coastline bathed in bright sunlight behind her. Who does she remind me of? Apart from Helen of Troy.
I tell her she must have many men coming on to her with the flattering cliché that she has a face that launched a thousand ships. She laughs and says "No. You are the first". She bends forward to give me a sweet kiss. As she does I can see in her eyes that I have won her.

Later, I realise she reminds me of Lydia.

Still later I get the strongest impression that Cecilia, the blind singer, using her telepathic powers, is trying to communicate with me. Perhaps, she wanted to tell me she has been seeing UFOs again. However, I forgot to consume Magic Mushrooms, so her messages must be flying way over my head, missing the mark and plunging into watery depths. Still, she can always text me.

Driving out of town, heading towards the gothic city, a little bird collided with my windscreen. The poor thing must have been killed even though I was driving no more than 20 mph. Sadly, I couldn't have avoided the defenseless creature as it seemed to come at me out of nowhere. It left an impression of dust and fluff on the glass from its impact. Does this signify anything? Someone I know going to die soon? Sadly, I know a few candidates – Batty Betty, President of the Irish UFO Society has been diagnosed with cancer of the brain...Thor with lymphatic cancer, and my old Welsh school friend, Horus, has just been rushed into hospital with pneumonia.

October
19 Wednesday

Go with Delia Artemis to the video club to watch "If...." But a different version, although Malcolm McDowell was still the young rebel.
The doors jammed, but we gain access around the door because the wall is missing.
Suddenly the door seemed pointless.
Felicia was there, but Delia Artemis and she acted like they had never met before. It all seemed so unlikely and yet here I was with the big question "if...", with two women who never delivered the love affair I thought was coming to me.

I go to the American Embassy. The US President asked me to meet the new Director of the CIA, Bob Wisdom Morris. The new man is a Hippified big black American with dreadlocks, wearing a tee-shirt in the Rasta colours, who I took an immediate liking to. He knew all about the Illuminatus, Crowley, Strieber, Steiner, Icke, Castaneda etc. "Shiram," he growled, "you know why the weather of the world is behaving strangely? What is causing this build-up of natural disasters, earthquakes, floods, droughts, tempests etc.? And the build-up of international tensions, urban unrest, riots, civil wars? And the recent international economic crash?"
"You – the CIA, with the Illuminati?" I suggested.
"Hey Man, can't you see with my appointment, the Company is gonna be a reformed agency. The bad old days are over. I'll tell you the reason. The Earth is tilting on its axis, and the polar caps are melting. Why? A new planet at the edge of the Solar System is coming fast. NASA tells us it is disrupting the planetary orbits."
"Someone told me earlier this year that something is coming to planet Earth unannounced," I said.
"Oh? Who was that? I've only just learned this from NASA."
"I can't remember. Just how bad will it all eventually be?"
"Bad," the CIA Director replied. "Very bad."
"Many Messianists hope Rescuers from the Skies will come in the nick of time to save Life on Earth," I said. "Are these just hollow dreams?"
"Perhaps you know the answer better than I do," Bob Wisdom replied, wrapping up the meeting.

October
20 Thursday

I meet Anne Karenin, star of "Happy Birthday, Mr President" at a party. She vaguely remembers bumping into me at Stage Door at the royal National Theatre. She is behaving very extrovert and manic, just as I imagined she would. In fact, I could see many people avoiding her because they fear she's a little crazy. But I like her. She reminds me of Laura. I ask Anne Karenin if she would read my script "The Vertigo", as there is a part I would love her to play. She says, "Yes, of course, darling," but she may be just saying that as she doesn't want to hurt my feelings. Meanwhile, her agent or manager arrives, and escorts her from me, as if Anne Karenin was a psychiatric patient. Both the agent and assistant behave like nurses. The agent returns and tells me off for breaking professional protocol by appealing directly to her client, and not going through the proper channels, i.e. herself, Anne Karenin's agent / minder / carer. She has taken the script from the star, and hands it back to me. "You should be ashamed of yourself," the agent tuts, "for attempting to take advantage Ms Karenin's current vulnerable state. If you wish to re-submit your script through the proper manner, that is, through my office, you may do so, but I cannot guarantee that my client will see it."

I sheepishly try to hand her the script, but she refuses to accept it, saying, "Excuse me, I am not at work. I'm partying. Post it or email it. Goodbye." And with that, she walks briskly away, leaving me with the feeling I never get my film produced.

I meet Clint Eastwood and we have enjoyable, entertaining adventures together. He seems to genuinely like my company. Perhaps he will cast me in his next movie. What are you thinking, Shiram? That old cowboy hung up his gun a long time ago.

Later, I go visit an old friend, Mae Groser, a respectable university lecturer. I find that she is upstairs. "I will be with you in a minute," she shouts down. Just then the phone rings and I pick it up. It's the manager of the local community radio station, who offers me a job which allows me to select the programming, and produce my own work. I was about to accept the job when Mae walks downstairs, stark naked. She asks if I mind if she exploits my disability for a moment, and then leans on my wheelchair, kneeling in front of me. She proceeds with her left hand to smear and rub red jam around her crotch, and into her vagina, as if she were treating thrush with yoghurt.

October
21 Friday

I come back to my flat in Wellingtonia, and find that my front door key will not open the lock. It's been changed. I cannot get into my home. I bang on the door. I try forcing it open. But to no avail. The noise brings out the next door neighbour. Mrs. Ashdown.
She used to live above me, but now she lives on the side.
Anyway, she died several years ago.
But her presence did not seem to surprise me.
"Where is my home?" I cried. "Why have I been locked out?"
Blessed Mrs. Ashdown tries to comfort me. She tells me the council have given my place to new tenants whilst I was a way.
"But dare they? Without warning me? Informing me? What a bloody liberty! Now I am homeless," I wailed.
"No you are not. They built you a little room to the side. Here." She opens a door and reveals a pure white room, white bed, white carpet. All my things and furniture covered in white dust sheets. I am horrified. I cannot live in this single room. Some police arrive asking me to fill out a questionnaire on how to improve the service. I asked them If they could sort out to my problem But they weren't a very helpful. We have an old saying. "There's never a policeman when you need one. And when there is one, he is good for nothing."

I discover a dry piece of shit clinging to my bottom, somewhere between the cheeks. It was long, crusty and wormlike. I quickly picked it from my hairy buttocks and dropped it down the toilet before Delia Artemis found it.

Later….Delia Artemis complains about the mess on my bed. "You've let that bloody cat of yours sleep on the bed. If you expect me to sleep with you, you had better keep that animal out of the bedroom."

October
22 Saturday

Lydia and her teenage daughter Gwen are fighting. Lydia is abandoning her, or is it the other way round? I can't remember but there is a terrible crisis, and lots of sadness. Some sort of loss is taking place. Then the pair become transformed into Laura and her daughter Lavinia. I'm trying to reconcile the two but without much a success. I plead with Lavinia not to forsake her mum, even if she is probably a ghost. I am crying my eyes out. Mothers and daughters.

Four hours later, I am crying my eyes out again. Two of the three terminally ill friends died today – Batty Betty and Horus. The bird smashing into my car windscreen four days ago, was an omen of death as I feared.

Haley, she's a PR woman, who has taken an interest in one of my movie projects, greets me, and takes my hand to kiss it, but then wrinkles her nose, sniffing my fingers.
"Are you going blind?" she asks. I reply I didn't think so. "Why?"
"Because your fingers smell shitty. Usually the first sign of blindness," she says.
I feel acutely embarrassed as I have recently been sticking my fingers up my arse, but only because I need to push back the piles that keep popping out. I thought had been very diligent in washing my hands afterwards. Clearly, I need to use more soap.

Later, just when I'm about to sleep…
Delia Artemis in bed with me, slaps my bottom twice. This is unusual that she should be in my bed again. I thought it was over. Still, I do like having my bottom spanked.

Delia Artemis publicly wipes my bottom, as I sit on the commode. We are surrounded by glass walls. I try to object as people watch aghast, but she insists I am no longer capable of looking after myself. She claims I have Alf Zimmer's disease.

October
23 Sunday

Hephaistos' wife, Aphrodite is trying to seduce me.
She is moaning that I am not carrying out my promises to make love to her.
But Hephaistos is my oldest school-friend. Okay, he is cheating on her. He even touched Delia Artemis, stroking her bottom, pretending he was admiring her long hair, but that doesn't give me the license to grab a tit for tat.

Later a knock on the door…
The little girl couldn't find anyone to repair her doll. "She has lost her head," said the weeping child.
"What is her name?" I asked.
"Alice," she replied.
I call out "Alice! Alice!" and in no time we hear a little squeaky voice, "Yes?", and I find the doll's head.
I tell the girl that I know the most effective method of stitching the head back on the body, because I can see the insides are made of hay. This will enable me to weave the threads of the neck. The girl didn't believe me at first until I showed her the repaired doll. As the girl happily departed with her precious doll in her arms, "Alice" turned her head and said "Thank you."

October
24 Monday

Paddy "Blue Lips" O'Hara, a blast from the past, visits me.
Why did he stick the dart in Sandy's breast?
He claimed not to know what I was talking about.

Suddenly a TV screen appears in front of me, showing images of a futuristic Sci-Fi cityscape. The colours very saturated like a European 1970s movie. A voice-over announces that "...the Intergalactic Co-operative of Advanced Beings have decided the rogue planet needs to be punished and quarantined. The combined irresponsible behaviour of this chaotic mindless world is soon becoming a threat to the safety and security of neighbouring star systems.
"We have no choice but to send an invasion, occupation and disciplinary force to Clancarty before the intergalactic situation spirals out all control."

Reports of the Sun changing. Massive solar flares reaching across, and striking the Earth. The electro-magnetic field is buzzing. The Auroras are spectacularly beautiful. Some expect the poles to switch at any moment, and the axis to shift. No one is sure what the overall effect will be. But our brains are nests of electrical activity, and such intense electro-magnetic interference may blow our minds.

Clancarty? I only know of one Clancarty – Lord Clancarty (Brinsley Le Poer Trench), a leading spokesman on the UFO phenomena. He once famously organised a House of Lords debate in the 1970s on the subject of UFOs. His theory was that the earth was hollow and contained underground bases for the UFOs, which emerged above ground via a hole at the South Pole in Antarctica.

CLANCARTY = 7
3 31 5 3 1 92 7 = 43

EARTH = 7
5 19 2 8 =25

CLANCARTY = EARTH ? If so, why call our earth "Clancarty"? Is it because ICAB regarded him as the natural representative or ambassador for Earth?

October
25 Tuesday

WEREWOLVES!
Something was making them come out into the open. But they were getting captured as a consequence. It looked like one had been brought in. Was he dead? I think it was male. Anyway, it was laid out on its front, unconscious. Perhaps, tranquillized by its hunter. Or was it the medico-lab technicians/doctor-vets? How do you treat a werewolf? As an animal? Or human? A doctor or vet? Geburah suggests either a "Vector", or a "Dot". The creature looks like it was caught halfway through metamorphosis. The bottom half seemed more wolf than human. A Lycanthropologist said a good protection against werewolves was lemon and lime. Does he mean protection against attack from werewolves, or prevention of becoming one?

To stop the spread of werewolves, the US Federal government has ordered the total extermination of all wolves. They are offering $1,000 reward for every wolf killed. Bastards. Cowardly murdering bastards.

October
26 Wednesday

I am working on a Rolling Land Jaffa Cake movie, but I'm not playing a significant part. Jake is in the lead and Jaffa Cake is trying to get him hooked up with some new young starlet. Meanwhile, discussion is being made around Jaffa's next big project about the American war of Independence. Hollywood bosses are grumbling about a British director depicting a crucial period in the U.S. history. I think it's a good idea. "Then, it'll have a more detached historical truth." No sooner do I say this, I notice to my right, battle scenes between the redcoats and colonials already being staged. No sooner said than done.

Meet this American actor who tells me Harry Oddfellow sends his best wishes. Did I ever work with Harry, the Yank asks, impressed, thinking I must be bigger than I looked.
"No," I said, "but he probably knows, and respects my work."
How smug can you get.
Sometimes I hate myself.

October
27 Thursday

Delia Artemis and her family. They know about our relationship, and are furious. Very threatening. Delia Artemis has abandoned me anyway. So it's all history. Nonetheless, retribution seems to be on the cards. Her Dad has a baseball bat under the shop counter for just such an eventuality. It will be tragic really, if I end up getting my head bashed in, because we never even got to fuck.

I escape Wellingtonia and travel abroad to Greece, and at the end of the day, a woman appears before me. It is Sophia, the Wise Girl, reminding me that I am still in her thoughts. "I hope you have not forgotten me," she says.

We look up and see a bright lightning flash coming from the Moon. A Full Moon. Is the Moon exploding?

"That reminds me," she says, "I dreamed last week that my husband, Ronny and I, together with you and A. Nother are to live on a meteor. It was a huge stone. A sort of cosmic egg."
"The Philosopher's Stone…the Philosopher's Egg?" I enquired.
"That would make sense. I am Sophia, after all." she coyly smiled.
"Are you Sophia or are you Isis?" I asked.
"That's like asking if I am the Stone or the Egg." she replied.
"Who is this A. Nother that lives with us on the meteor cosmic egg?" I ask.
"An Unknown Woman. Never seen her before…but she clearly belonged to you."
"What did she look like?"
"Tall. Long blond hair. Slim."

I wondered if Sophia (a.k.a. Isis) was talking about a planetary object that is hollowed out and turned into a s spaceship that the four of us were going to be living on. The mythical Nibiru?

October
28 Friday

I'd overslept. It was now 1.45 in the afternoon and I was going to have to ring Marty, the Director, to apologise for missing half the day. Just as I got into a panic, the alarm went and the police come knocking on my door, suspecting me of committing a murder. I'm to go to the station to be charged. I ask if I can continue to do the rehearsals until I am convicted in court or should I ring Marty, the director, and give her the bad news now. The copper thought I could probably carry on as normal. This gives me hope that they might not have much of a case against me or on the contrary that it's such an open and shut, cast iron case, that out of pity they are allowing me to make the most of my last days of freedom.

I have to go in a cage with two tigers.
Will they be friendly? Or even if friendly, will they accidentally hurt me?
Or will they just simply eat me?
They approach me with eager interest, their golden-green eyes alight with fire, their breath stinking of rotten meat, and deep sub-sonic purrings that turn my bowels into liquid mush.
But still I think it will be okay.

October
29 Saturday

I arrive at what seems to be a café/restaurant. It's run by this old man.
I sit at the table, wondering whether to stay and try and eat something. I'm hungry but I have very little money (unsurprisingly, if I'm dead. Who ever heard of a ghost needing cash?). And I'm not sure if the place is open or just closing or if it is really a café.
A family group arrive, dominated by the mother, and suddenly the place is bustling. It dawns on me that I am in a Mediterranean country – am I in still Greece? Did I ever leave Elysium?
At first, the mother starts to prepare the table I'm sitting at for her family to eat.
She looks at me as if to say "Please move to another table", but I feel I have a right to stay. I was there first, after all. Then she seems to accept me and continues the preparations.
I notice one of her beautiful daughters talking to the owner at the counter. She smiles at me.
Then the mother starts moving tables together at the far side. She has decided her family will eat separated from me. Everyone praises her for her ingenuity in rearranging the tables and making them into one big banqueting table.
The girl comes to me and asks if I would like to eat something. I shrug, not sure if I'm allowed. She smiles and says she will make a plate up for me.
The old man comes over, welcomes me and sits at my table. Then the daughter hands me a plate of food and makes me feel at home. Romantic music begins and I know I am in Greece.

(Greece = 7. "Seven" rhymes with "Heaven")

October
30 Satanday

I was going down the street, and I saw in a shop window various interesting items for sale, such as a banjo and other musical instruments. I enter, thinking I will buy the banjo or something. I have always wanted to play the banjo since I was a child. Inside, the shop is like an emporium, full of fascinating bric-a-brac. I browse the shelves in the waiting area. Finally the owner, an old man with a long straggly beard, comes to welcome me. With him are two young boys – okay, one is a young man of about 18 years old, and the other is between 8 and 12. The older of the two quickly takes his leave of us, while the younger one, a dark hair, olive complexion kid, stands around looking depressed or moody or angry. I can't really tell…but I get the impression that he is suspicious of me, or resents my presence in some way. Maybe he is trying to tell me something, but can't because the old man is watching him. Well, I look at the owner who acts very friendly towards me. Wearing a small colourful embroidered round hat on his balding head, he reminds me of a Jew or Muslim or an aged Hippy.
"What can I do you for?" he asks beaming broadly.
"I'm interested in that musical instrument in the window," I said, thinking of the banjo.
"I know exactly what you need," he replied, scuttling off to the back of the shop, and immediately returns with a beautifully carved ornate lute type instrument. "Play it," he suggests.
I tentatively pluck a couple of strings, and instantly it plays by itself, sounding a bit like a zither. The tune is "Greensleeves". I play another two opening chords, and the instrument goes on to continue that melody. I am enthralled. What a magical instrument. I want it, and ask the shop-keeper if this is a Pawnshop. He smiles and nods. I ask if the instrument is available for purchase. He says he will go and see. He comes back with the good news it is still unredeemed. "How much?" I ask.
"Sixty-five pounds. Special price to you." I am crestfallen. The magic lute is certainly worth the price, and more, but I do not have that much cash in my pocket. The kindly old man sees my bitter disappointment, and strokes my hands in a lascivious fashion, his eyes suggesting there are other ways I can pay him. I look at the young boy who seems even more miserable. I sense he was trying to warn me. But I really would like to possess the magic lute. Perhaps I am going to have to sell my body to this dirty old man, for it. Or is it my soul he really wants?

Suddenly I realise what the boy was trying to tell me. It is the Devil I am about to make a bargain with.

October
31 Sunday SAMHAIN EVE

I woke this morning and there was something in the room, a threatening menace. It scuttled away in the corner. I felt powerless.

Later I was being pursued by gangster. I thought I had a gun on me, but it turned into a pair of scissors. My car was parked in a car park viewing point, overlooking a grand vista. I needed to get there to escape from the thugs and crooks who were annoyed with me for messing up their plans to rob the world. I thought at first it was Geburah who was with me, but it was Sadie. And I was shocked to see she is pushing me. "Can Sadie walk now?" I wondered. I looked questioningly at her, but she just shrugged her shoulders. We got to the car park, but found to our horror, a huge problem. It was full of sleeping lions. How the hell are we to get pass them and into the car without waking them? I signed to Sadie to carefully open the car door just wide enough to allow me to slide from the wheelchair onto the car seat. But Sadie didn't do it right, and she allowed too much of a gap for one of the lions to slip by, and into the car. It climbed on to the back seat and lay down. There was nothing for it but to take the lion with us. At least the gangsters if they catch up with us will have a bit of a shock.

The wail of the banshee was heard on stage tonight. Everyone else heard her but I didn't. They said it was very freaky sounding. The funeral march haunts my restless mind.

The strange woman moved her face up to mine and kissed me. After she had gone, I thought she might have been Death.

Is Galadriel / Leannan Shee the Angel of Death?

Unbeknownst to me, on this day, he died, of a brain haemorrhage. He was my best friend amongst the adults when I was a child, and it was he who introduced me to "The Hobbit" and "Lord of the Rings"...and "The Magus" (where Chapter 53 is "Freedom")....and "Rock Machine: I Love You."

November
1 Monday SAMHAIN – SEASON OF THE DEAD

Delia Artemis has been trying to phone me all day, but I am reluctant to converse with her. She's merely toying with me. When I finally picked up the phone to speak to her, it was 12.53

I am about to drive off in the car, Delia Artemis wasn't going to come with me until she saw two girls getting in the car instead. When I told her I had no more room for her, she made room on the dashboard. The two hitchhikers showed off their sexuality, giving me views of their naked breasts and thighs. This was making Delia Artemis very jealous. Finally when the girls gave me glimpses of their vaginas, Delia Artemis, refusing to be upstaged, did so also. I was surprised at how fleshy and full her vagina looked.

Later, I have to drive across this really high in the sky bridge over a deep river. The bridge is barely wide enough to take the car, and there are no safety barriers on either side. Also for some reason, I can't see the way properly because the view from the windscreen is restricted and I can't drive accurately. The next thing I know, I'm looking at the Water and realize I've just driven off the side of the road bridge. The car and I plummet downwards and I know I am doomed. When the car smashes into the Water, I am instantly killed. The moment of pain is brief and soon passes, and the Water changes from being a deadly medium to a soothing, calming, cleansing one.

November
2 Tuesday

I was telling a bunch of friends of how I heard on live radio, Jesus being crucified on the Cross. "How was this so?" asked Thor.
"Must have been a play on Radio 4," suggested Kyles.
"No. Wrong time of the year. Don't forget, Friday is Guy Fawkes Night," said Lydia.
"Same difference," quips Isis. "Burning at the stake, hanging on the cross. It's all a Celebration of Death".
"No, listen," I said. "It's a new kind of radio which picks up real events at any point in time. It's a sort of Time Machine receiving signals and allows you to listen in the present what occurred in the past, which in terms of the Space-Time Nexus, is, in fact, ever-present. What has occurred, is occurring, and will occur. So when I heard Jesus being tortured on the Cross, he was screaming in real time, and it wasn't some actor. Christ's death was live, and painful for me. I felt for him, and I wept buckets for him, and I'm no Christian. But I cared about the man suffering a horrible death."
"And where is this amazing Radio Time Machine now?" asks Thor.
"It disappeared with the tide," I replied.

I understood how this Time Machine worked because of my Great Big Ball of String Theory of the Universe. The Space-Time Net is one long infinitesimally thin string, of an infinite length with both ends joined forming a loop. This thin string with a width, as I said, infinitesimally smaller than any sub-atomic particle, rolled into a tight ball, which means that time is not just linear (one-dimensional), but parallel in all directions, spiralling around itself in ever decreasing or increasing circles. In other words, if SpaceTime is structured as a ball of string, then Time will have a minimum of three dimensions, and if you know the x,y,z coordinates, you can home in on any Time location in the Universe.

November
3 Wednesday

An artist known as Blues Lee has an exhibition – a sort of installation, with plenty of performing arts, Situationist-type exhibits, living art. Wearing these crash helmets, we listen to his voice-over as it guides us through the various displays. Some are in tents (very intense), and sideshow booths. One I remember seeing, he titled "Beauty and the Beast". I am shocked to see it is a cage with a young semi-clad woman dancing and shadow boxing a ferocious angry lion, which keeps leaping around her, trying to swipe and claw her frail and vulnerable naked flesh. But she is very nimble and easily dodges his bestial lethal lunges.
However, despite her seeming complacency in her adroitness, for a brief moment, I catch a look of fear and uncertainty in her eyes. Is she really in control? How long can she keep up this dance in the jaws of death? Will they let her out of the cage before she tires?
Even so, the image reminds me of the eleventh tarot card - "Strength" or "Victory". Hebrew letter Lamed. Astrological sign Libra…though we are in the month of Scorpio.

(Blues day for road shirts and Mary game these best to old Lee fort lunches I learned by island island island island island islander and Beilin I learned I learned I learned I learned our own arena in dairy diary and reading during Ireland).

Back in Ireland at the cottage, I look out of the window of the bunk bedroom, and see five black circular dots in the sky, slowly moving from right to left, diagonally downwards. At the same time I hear the "Chicken Kiev" groaning sounds reverberating in the atmosphere. The call of the spacecraft it seems. Geburah has just come in the room, and comments on the strange sounds. I tell her to come to the window and see the strange apparitions or meteorological effect in the sky, but by the time she is at my side, the black dots have spread like clouds, dissipating, losing the precise circular shape. Now they no longer look impressive and alien.

November
4 Thursday

The cloud cover has lingered too long. There has been no sunlight for months. If this continues for much longer, things are going to start dying.

Isis in trouble? Ill? Sad! Trying to contact me.

So, is the new myth of human origins, as advanced by the supporters of the extra-terrestrial hypothesis, confirmed by my numerological discovery of another trinity?

APE = 4
ALIEN = 5
MAN = 1
--
10 = 1

Geburah saw a tiny streak of blue light dancing in my hair, as we were making love.

She wondered if we were being watched.

A large spider, bigger than my hand, with big brown eyes, looking mischievously at me, in preparation for an attack. Out of the corner of my eye I see another creature that seems less threatening. I shout "Go Away" at the spider, and as it leaps for my throat, Geburah gets out of bed and accidentally steps on it, crushing it into a slimy sluggy mess on the floor.
"I think you may have just killed Delia Artemis," I said

Later, while lying in bed, relaxing, cuddling, we hear a loud bang beneath the bed. The noise shakes the bed. I look at the time – 11.53pm.

November
5 Friday

My friend, Inga Groser, who is a maths teacher, appears from nowhere and tells me history was never her strong point at school. I laugh because we are going to the cinema to see Disney's "Darby O'Gill and the Little People", which has nothing to do with either history or maths.

Is this a viable trinity?

```
TRUTH   = 6
BEAUTY  = 2
LIGHT   = 2
         --
         10 = 1
```

Oh no, I fell out of my wheelchair again. What damage have I done to myself this time?

I find myself in a hospital bed. The cavernous ward is empty, save for myself. I'm told the hospital will soon be demolished (now that I'm no longer a child, they said). A short fat woman enters and waddles towards me, talking nineteen-to-the-dozen. I immediately think she is an American, although her black hair (probably a wig), and pink chubby cheeks remind me of the late Batty Betty, ex-President of the Irish UFO Society. However, I have a suspicion this woman wants to supplant my girlfriend, who has just wandered off somewhere else in the huge medical complex. The chattering Yank ministers to my eyes which are glued together by a thick viscous slime, scraping away with careful attention and affection. A dangerous activity if she is caught at it by my girlfriend. Luckily she clears my eyes before Geburah returns, but hold on….I am shocked to see it is not who I thought. My girlfriend who is tall, blond and in her late thirties, is now a short fat woman in her early sixties, in a white nurse's / medical outfit. The grey haired matron persuades the American would-be usurper to position herself under a suspended skull above, which is grinning and ready to drop on the unsuspecting. Then the skull weeps an even smaller skull from one of its empty eye sockets, which plummets down towards the Yank's head, but she catches it in her hand, and waves it about, exclaiming, "That's Funny, ha ha."

November
6 Saturday

Isis tells me that her friend, Selene, whispered to her the other day that the Moon was not natural. I asked, "What on earth could she mean - the Moon was not natural?"
I took out my imaginary telescope to check on the Moon's appearance.... It looked normal to me.... A shining lump of rock, pitted with craters, Perfectly natural.
But even as I tried to reassure Isis, I had a nagging feeling she and her friend, Selene, knew something ....
In fact, I have just found out they were right, and I was wrong, deluded .....that we all were... Latest calculations and diagnoses have shown that the Moon was no longer what she seemed.
For thousands of years we thought we could depend on La Luna's luminous companionship, feel her soothing caresses on our oceans, And in our blood, play with our emotions .....
But now, we must ask - has something happened? Unbeknownst to us earthlings? Has there been a transformation? Has our Moon been hijacked? Has it metamorphose into something more alien and dangerous? But still, as I gaze upon her radiant lunatic smile in the milky white heavens above, I insist the Moon is still natural.

Later I read that a 53 year old woman, called Whitney Streaba, was told by grey extra-terrestrials that in the next 20 years the Earth will tip on its axis. According to these aliens, which she calls Zetas, this will be caused by an alignment of the planets, during which the combination of their gravitational pull, together with that of the Sun, will displace the Earth from its orbit. The ETs have reassured her that they are doing the necessary measurements and calculations that will allow them to save Life on Earth when the time come comes. Didn't that CIA director, Bob Wisdom Morris, recently tell me something similar?

(Hip known kabuki..... a pro cheese..... one small to Mike in a beating (of the fall))

November
7 Sunday

Bambi has died and is met at the gates of Disney Heaven by his old friends who died before him, Thumper, Flower etc. They are so pleased he has finally come to join them. Now the fun can really begin.

Just before falling asleep. Was it that hypnogogic state? Usually I get these sensations lying on my back. But with my back still hurting from Friday's accident, I have to sleep on my front. I am becoming paralyzed, and I can see my soul as a separate entity suspended in an increasingly darkened space as a terrible evil approaches. Something coming to possess me. Turn me into a demon and there's nothing I can do about it. I am helplessly immobilized and I cannot call for help or scream. My voice is Frozen, or soon will be. A web like numbing is tightening its grip on my vocal chords. My jaws, tongue and lips are seizing up.
I must call help before it is too late, before I have no power left of self-determination. Before my Free Will is stripped from me.
I have been in this situation before, when something wicked was trying to abduct me or kill me. Now, It is injecting itself into my soul. I am slowly being penetrated….raped.
My soul is changing its apparent shape, getting uglier and uglier in front of my very eyes.
Soon I will be a Monster, out of control.
I must call out while I have a little power left. But to whom? In the past I cried out "Help Me" to an unseen Greater Benign Power but I can't keep relying on something I refuse to name "God". If I Believe I am on my own, then I have no right to ask for help. That is just taking the piss. This is My sole soul Responsibility.
What are the magic words to evict the swelling menace Within. What new simple phrase formula must I scream out to jettison the evil entity seeking possession?
"Help Me" no longer has a sincere potency. I need something new and fresh that has a greater authoritative charge.
Suddenly, the right words spring from my mouth. "Be Gone" I command, and It, the Foul Soul-Eating Devil, is expelled. Banished to the Nether Regions - and sweetness and light returns once more to my inner being.

"Help Me" = 5
"Be Gone" = 3

November
8 Monday

Fifth Street and Eighth Street. All lit up.
Some American city.
New York?
San Francisco?
LA?
Every day the street names are swapped. I consider this to be weird and wonder how all the locals cope with one day living on Fifth Street, and then the next day, their address is Eighth Street, and Vice Versa…..and Versa Vice
"The Nurse was Nicer when the Vice was Worser".

They sent me out on a separate mission, a diversion to keep me from discovering their own evil activity. Major Tom Odin, the commander, was supposed to be my friend. They were all friends and colleagues and yet, he led them into the gang rape and subsequent murder of the woman I loved. Had I known what was afoot, then that I could have stopped them by wiping them out.
But in my innocence I went off in the opposite direction on a wild goose chase.
Then later, I caught a clairvoyant vision of their own destruction, which made me grieve at the time as I did not know of their atrocious act, which I now know.
The troops were marching down a ravine in a jungle clearing. I saw the natives in ambush, about to attack them. It was a vision where I could not intervene. All I could do was watch helplessly as my erstwhile companions were quickly, mercilessly slaughtered. It happened so fast that I could barely witness the details.

Billy Meier meets a pair of Ufonauts in 1978, "Erra" and "Lyra".
Or should their names be spelt "Error" and "Liar"?

Erra was a Sumerian / Babylonian deity of Pestilence and Rebellion….
What does this possibly tell us about the E.T.s?

November
9 Tuesday

Wolves. There are always wolves somewhere. In my blood.

A woman-friend comes to a gathering. Another party. Always a party. She came with people. Fair weather friends, as usual. Anyway, she and I have a good time together. I think I help her. Before she arrived, she was depressed and confused.
As I study this woman closely, I realise it is Ella Adeliner, who I thought I was madly in love with, once upon a time. Well, soon it's time for her to go, and she does the rounds, saying goodbye to everyone. First, she seems to ignore me and I'm wondering if she'll give me a special recognition of our history together.
Suddenly she comes to me and gives me a gorgeous kiss on the lips, pushing her tongue into my mouth. Then she is gone. I amazed. Why did she kiss me, and on the lips, and more astonishingly, her tongue in my mouth? That is so untypical of her. She always was an exotic and refined lady.

Magnetism, electricity and gravity as a Triad do not add up to one, but change "magnetism" to "magnety", so it has the same suffix as the other two, and we have the desired union, which could be the first step to the Grand Unified Field theory!

Electricity = 3
Gravity = 3
Magnety = 4
--
10 = 1

Watching "The Grapes of Wrath" gave me an idea for another Triad.

Apple = 5 (Apple the fruit of knowledge)
Tomato = 3 (Tomato the fruit of love)
Grape = 2 (Grape the fruit of anger)
--
10 = 1

He he he CRANK!!! You can say anything with numbers...he he he.

November
10 Wednesday

Shadey the cat met me on the road. She was well pleased to see me, even though I locked her out all the time I was away.

Another party of dead stars. I see some of the guests are British celebrities of the 1950s and 60s. Adam Faith (died 8th March 2003)...Norman Wisdom (died 4th Oct. 2010)...Roy Castle (died 2nd Sept 1994). Didn't Roy Castle once play the Artful Dodger in "Oliver Twist"?
I chat with Norman Wisdom about his past greatness. He is pleased he is still fondly remembered. Perhaps there were some differences of opinion and, maybe I did upset him a little with a few tactless remarks, but I have to speak my mind and he understands. So we end up still feeling conviviality towards each other.
Then Roy Castle (disguised as the Artful Dodger) comes bustling in, full of energy, bringing with him an artefact from the ancient Mayan culture – it is a clay mask. He hangs it on the wall, next to an interesting Time piece. Is it a clock? The Dodger sees Norman sitting depressed at the dining table and decides to act the clown. In fact, he puts on a performance very similar to what Norman was famous for in his comedy films. The Dodger stands behind Wisdom and over his shoulder mimics all the strange faces and pathetic looks Wisdom use to pull in his heyday. In fact, the Dodger (Roy Castle) impersonations are so perfect that Norman Wisdom becomes even more despondent – realising that anyone can be him – so where did his uniqueness go? The Dodger is so pleased with himself, he leaps around all over the room....until he accidentally knocks the Mayan Mask off the wall, breaking it.
Suddenly we all sense disaster has struck. The Time piece rings and stops. We realise Time has Run Out. The End has come. What the Mayans predicted will shortly come to pass...but I know the real date. It is not what they all think. That's just a red herring.
"Remember Maya in Hinduism refers to Illusion," I say.
As I ask, "Is the Age of Illusion soon to close?", we all hear rumblings and the ground begins to shake. The Apocalypse Approaches. The Cycle is reaching its Full Circle.

November
11 Thursday

Somehow, I manage to accidentally eat my own shit.

The cats are fighting.

War never seems to end.

Magnus is in trouble. He's going about into the city streets. Dark and foreboding with alley ways harbouring lurking muggers and rapists. My friend is warned not to go walking but his usual bravado gets the better of him. As he leaves I see two Pakistani yobs look at each other, give the signal, which I interpret to mean "let's get the gang together and attack this Hindu bastard."

I decide to go out and come to his assistance. I grab one of my swords and search the urban nightscape. I spot my friend as he goes down a cul-de-sac. Then, I see the ambushers. Three groups of ten or thereabouts. I rush to warn him, drawing my sword. As I approach the gang, I become confused. They are mostly white. It's not a religious war.
Secondly, they all look pathetic, not threatening at all. I only need to attack one and the rest will run without a fight. I go from one group to another, trying to make up my mind who to attack, waving my sword about meaninglessly. I finally target a dark-haired woman, slim built. As I try to slash her face, she mutters mockingly, "How typical of you to pick the weakest of us. A woman. I bet you think I'm ugly. Just because I've got freckles all over my face".
I tried my damnedest to cut her up but the blade never goes near the skin. My heart simply isn't in it. I can't bring myself to kill or hurt her. I'm no Jack the Ripper. I just make lots of threatening gestures instead. Everyone laughs at me. Even my friend, Magnus, finds me embarrassing.

Clearly, I'm deluding myself, into thinking I've got the killer-warrior instinct.

November
12 Friday

Two assassins, civil servant types, come to kill Kyles and me. We know too much. Seen things we should not have seen. I am reminded of that UFO we both witnessed.
Now we must pay with our lives. We wait in the basement for their arrival. We wait meekly like lambs waiting for the butcher's knife.
They materialise before us in black suits. I can't decide if they look like a pair of undertakers or bank managers.
Kyles' big brown eyes look up beseechingly, pleading with his killer.
But the Man in Black is totally dispassionate, a bureaucrat just doing his job - nothing personal - and wraps a towel around Kyles's neck to throttle him.
The second MIB approaches me… but I have a razor blade hidden in the blanket on my lap. I will slice him if I have to. But I'd rather talk him out of it. I don't want any bloodshed.
I start to reason with him but slowly realise I have made a blunder. I should have acted, not talked. The opportunity has been lost.
I will die because the Assassin (Hash Ishim) is a ruthless killer…. And I am not.

At three minute past eight,
I drive into a dark tunnel through a mountain. And come out the other side into the light.

There are little bits of blood in my right nostril. I think I got off lightly. Poor Kyles.

However, "Tomorrow," as Scarlett O'Hara once famously said, "is another day."

I fear it is a game of cat and mouse. Perhaps they haven't got all they want from me yet.

I mean, just how many times must I die before I finally die?

And how many times must I ask this damn foolish question?

November
13 Saturday

I meet this Yank, Buster Alldrink, who tells me NASA has published a magazine article, warning us of “The After Shock”. I asked him if the space agency were referring to the expected Betelgeuse supernovae, which could happen today or in a million years’ time?
“No,” he replied that NASA were warning of mass population aftershock on having it officially confirmed that the extraterrestrials are here and have been for a long time.

I looked up at the sky. It was still very cloudy, but burning its way through the greyness came a shining white circle / ring cloud, the same as was seen over Moscow, and Rumania. It was definitely a giant flying saucer hidden in the clouds. But I saw more. The cloud formation was made up of three concentric rings, but only the outer one was circular. The two inner ones were elongated ellipses. This also told me this was no natural meteorological phenomena. I took a special photo based on X-ray radiography, and developed film showed the middle ellipse was the end of a long tube, pointing out at an angle of 45 degrees into space. The inner smaller ellipse was at an angle of 90 degrees, again reaching out into the cosmos beyond. This suggests that the phenomena or UFO is the product of three universes meeting or intersecting. The tube could be a vortex, leading to the portal, which is in fact, the space-craft. Maybe we have got it wrong – UFOs are the round doorways to and from Other Dimensions. I mean, they are not travelling through portals but are the portals whereby the non-terrestrial or “other-dimensional” entities pass through.

“Interesting idea,” says the Yank. “Sounds similar to my theory that we humans are portals through which flying saucers enter our world from planets too many light years away. They can travel faster than the speed of light, because they travel as thought-forms. “
“You believe Extra-terrestrials are using human brain wave activity to enter our space? Using our minds like film projectors?”
“Something along those lines,” the former astronaut replied with a smile.

November
14 Sunday

I was given an electric guitar belonging to one of Franz Kafka's Beetles. They told me to keep it in safe-keeping. "If you take care of it, keep it hidden, you just might save the lives of the last two remaining Franz Kafka's Beetles," they told me. They said that eventually I will have to give it back to the original owner. But which one? Ringo Franz Kafka Beetle or Paul Franz Kafka Beetle?

Now I have to do a runner, escape because the possession of their Guitar has made me a target. I mustn't be found with it, because that would put their lives in greater jeopardy. It appears that if the FK Beetles have their Guitar, they are doomed, and if they don't, they are also doomed, Or am I totally confused? Anyway, as the concert ended and the walls came tumbling down, the Fab Two fled down a secret tunnel to avoid the dangerous murderous tide of public disaffection. To my surprise, the Lovable Mop-Top Duo popped up in my hideaway cell, carrying the Holy Guitar I was supposed to be looking after. In addition, I am even more amazed to discover that one of the FKBs was, in fact, my old friend, Ferdinand. "Which Franz Kafka Beetle are you?" I asked.
Instead of answering, Ferdinand shook his head, and put a finger to his lips. "Are you one of the living FKBs, or squashed one?" I continued to quiz him, determined to ignore his frantic sign language to keep silent. "And another thing," I demanded. "How the hell did the Holy Guitar slip my grasp, and find its way back to you?" Now Ferdinand felt impelled to speak. "That's the reason neither us, nor you were killed."

I went home and started up my laptop computer, and immediately it began to send a spray of water at my face. I tried to turn the computer off but the jet became more powerful. And the more I tried to turn my face away from the curtain of liquid, the harder and more torrential the deluge. I found the watery assault was so intense, it felt like I was drowning. I struggled to breath, but I couldn't. Did I once say that death by drowning can be quite peaceful? It doesn't feel that way today.

November
15 Monday

I am drowning but am rescued. Then Babs Paradiso, the Indigo film director, lures me back into the water and I begin to drown again.
I gulp in water.... but I don't think it's water because I am not choking.
I exhale and inhale... and discover I can breathe underwater. Go with the flow. It is never as bad as you imagine.
What a relief.

A crime was committed. A bomb explosion with many casualties. The Government, of course, blamed foreign terrorists. The State is always inventing some new menace. Muslims, Arabs, Jews, Chinese, Gypsies, Hippies, Whovians. Needless to say, I suspect the Government. Our own secret police are normally behind so-called "terrorist" outrages, because the perpetuation of the fascist police state needs indiscriminate civilian massacres or murders of state officials. Consequently, the Government needs to round up suspects for public consumption, and as I am their most famous and vocal critic, I have been targeted, and labelled as the perpetrator of these bomb attacks. I know someone overhead me accusing Special Branch of sabotaging the railway with bombs, and reported me. So now the police have listed me as "Britain's Most Wanted", and I have been forewarned they are coming to get me.

Today's night, Geburah and I are about to sleep when they arrive, intruding into the bedroom. Two of them go to Geburah, telling her they are taking her to a beauty salon for a makeover. Shit, what kind of euphemism is that? "We will transform you into a Perfect Being," they alluringly whisper. To my horror, I see Geburah is believing them. I protest and shout that they are masquerading. "They are the Gestapo," I scream. The Third intruder comes to my side of the bed, puts a hand on my head to keep me calm, and tries to shut me up. But without any success because I continue to scream, "It's a trick," though I am having difficulties breathing. The bedroom invaders fan and waft Geburah, so she floats out of the window. It was then I realise we are not dealing with the normal State Security. These are Psi Cops with abnormal powers.

November
16 Tuesday

I am in serious trouble. I have committed a terrible sin. A crime. At least, it seems I stand accused. The Grosers have discovered my wickedness - especially Hecate who had admired and respected me, now damns and disapproves of me.
I await trial and verdict in their country mansion.
My last supper is prepared. We sit at a long banqueting table, waiting for some very important people to arrive, to deal with this suspicion that I am a murderer or rapist. The charges against me seem uncertain. But definitely trumped up.

At last, as the recriminations mount up against me, the V. I. Ps. arrive in their black saloon. It is Ella Adeliner the singer, and her family. With their arrival comes the snow. Winter is upon us and the ground is thick with glistening crisp whiteness.

Ella Adeliner and her brothers joyfully get out of the car to play in the snow, throwing balls at each other, seemingly oblivious of the seriousness of my situation. However, I want them to continue their games as it prolongs the final judgment because I don't know if Ella Adeliner has come as my liberator or my jailer.

After they have thrown all the snowballs they can muster, and plastered each other from top to toe, she is asked to testify. My heart drops as she enters the witness box, giving me one of her ambiguous looks. She stands erect and proud like Royalty, and creates a mind blowing speech, which successfully acquits me of all charges. The Court tells me I am free to go….for the time being.

They are still searching for the Great Un-nameable Guilt which constantly pursues me like an immense lumbering beast down endless corridors and tunnels.

November
17 Wednesday

I wake up to find myself submerged in water.
Not right, somehow.
I struggle to surface but discover that I am being prevented from doing so. I look up and see I am in a bath and two men are holding me down. They are drowning me. I cannot resist them and soon I am dead.
DEAD.

Later my body is discovered by another man, who pulls me out and talks to me. I have now become a bodiless spirit but am able to communicate with him.
The trauma of my death is still with me. I'm exhausted and in pain… which surprises me. I thought through death came relief from suffering but I'm in agony partly because I hate having died in such a humiliating helpless way.
I see a dead woman who is also in distress. She begs me to sexually assault her, ravish her. At first, I'm tempted but then I decide I have to forgo my baser instincts and refuse. Instead I decide to record in my diary that I have been murdered by two men. As I feebly scrawl the words. It dawns on me that the dead cannot write in physically real diaries. Something is wrong. I must be mistaken.
I cannot be dead after all.

November
18 Thursday

I meet the wolf, who immediately grabs my left arm in his jaws and tries to drag me out of my wheelchair. It seems very frightening and I am disappointed that the wolf takes such a negative and aggressive reaction to me. However, I refuse to be intimidated and soon the wolf releases me and I feel it is going to be all right between us.

The Wolf turned out to be the very same Golden Wolf who guarded the head of the martyred King Edmund, sacrificed to Odin by Ivarr the Boneless. The Wolf whose name was Luna gave me the gift of another Triad, with the words, "The Divine Victim must have this Trinity of Qualities…or so they say," she added with a wink. "We call them the

Three Crowns of St. Edmund,"

CELIBACY	= 6
KINGSHIP	= 3
MARTYRDOM	= 1
	--
	10 = 1

The German cinematographer, Lukas Herzog, was trying to persuade me to take part in his experiment. It was very important, and it involved me in having to die. But he made it sound very attractive and worthwhile…that my death would be a great contribution to humanity, to the advancement of civilisation. Geburah was with me as he talked, and she didn't seem to object to my volunteering to be killed off with his lethal injection. The artist-scientist had two other colleagues with him as support, and one in particular was rather thuggish. It was as if the brute was there to make sure I honoured the agreement. The two leave me to get ready after I finally signed the "Buy Out" forms, saying they will return to conduct the experiment on me. Geburah and I go into another room, the laboratory where I am to be killed, and I am surprised to find there is already an audience waiting to observe and witness the event of my transition, my transformation from one state of being to another. As I begin to reconcile myself to my fate, I notice Geburah is busily texting her ex-husband, Daath, telling him I will soon be dead, and she will be free to return to him. I am outraged, accuse her of betrayal and infidelity. Suddenly I decide not to take part in the experiment of death, and break the contract. Lukas Herzog returns and is furious, and warns me that I cannot go back on my word. "You have signed a pact with me," he hisses. His two henchmen advance towards me in a most threatening manner, making it clear they will not allow me to escape the deal. Geburah steps in between us, and quickly reminds the German that the experiment will lose all validity if the subject does not participate willingly. The audience voice their agreement, and Lukas Herzog has no choice but to let me go free. As Geburah and I speedily exit the amphitheatre I whisper "Were you texting your Ex. to goad me into changing my mind?"
She smiles enigmatically at me.   LUKAS HERZOG = 53

November
19 Friday

Big fight with Babs Paradiso. I criticize her TV documentary, accuse her of a shambolic creation.

Geburah and I visit the Cheshire Home for Incurables where Icarus once stayed. We are accommodated in one of the dormitories, and I end up sharing a bed with two girls, one being that sexy little minx, Sadie. Nothing happens, though. I just want to sleep but my naked bottom could be provocative. Geburah covers it with a sheet. Sadie isn't interested, anyway. She's moaning about something as usual. Geburah and I can't sleep, so we go to the canteen.

The canteen food is like a delicate-essence. Exquisite and refined.
But the canteen staff refuse to give me any. They say they have run out. Then, the famous Yank Hollywood movie star, John Malkovitch, arrives (I thought he was dead but he's probably one of the Patrons of the charity), and I see him at a table eating from a large plate of exotica. I go over to him and ask him (I mean, he was supposed to be some sort of Liberal, wasn't he?) what does he think of the fact that he can have this meal and we can't. He doesn't answer. He just shrugs and looks embarrassed that he has been blessed and we haven't. And he carries on eating – regardless of our exclusion.

So, I get a coffee, and Geburah and I go down a country lane. But it is guarded by two ferocious hounds. We have to pass through their snapping jaws. I decide their bark is probably worse than their bite. I hand the cup of coffee to Geburah, and I go and brave the canine barrier. As I came up to the dogs, they fell silent and stood aside to let me pass. They turned out to be very friendly. This is what I am beginning to learn. If you approach potential danger without fear, and assume there is a positive in all things, you will invariably come away unharmed. I turned and saw the Keeper of the hounds in a field nearby, attended by two other dogs. He was watching me intensely, checking to see if I would succeed in pacifying his guard dogs. I looked behind me, and saw a third dog had joined the two sentinels. The bodies of the hounds merged into one body, but retained the three individual heads. At once I knew I had just encountered Cerberus, the three-headed guardian of the Gates to Hades the Underworld. I look back and I see on the other side Geburah weeping. The Keeper of the Hound shouts out assurances to her that my time hasn't come yet, and immediately, I find I am standing beside her.

November
20 Saturday

Jonah, my old Jewish kabbalah mystic friend, who always reminds of an emaciated Father Christmas with his long white hair and white beard, has discovered another God Number - 137.

Jonah also knew that the meaning and number for the ancient Semitic word "Magon" was "shield" and Hebrew gematria = 734. I asked because I wanted to learn more about "Magonia", the magical land in the clouds, from hence came great Cloudships, which raised tempests and storms, creating crop-circles. In the old days, peasants blamed the Devil or demons or fairies, and thought they were stealing grain. Now, we know it is extra-terrestrial or "other-dimensional" entities in UFOs producing the signs and wonders in the cereal fields. My etymological research showed that "Magonia" is derived from the Punic or Carthagian word "magon", meaning "give" (as in "the father gives his son"), but the older Hebrew meaning was "protector" or "shield". Ike points out the full meaning of "magon" refers to "David's Shield" ("David's Star" as originally believed). Also "magon" comes from "mag", i.e. "magic", or "mage" or "magi". I also wondered if the Magonia was so named because the UFOs looked like flying shields.

MAGON = 5
DAVID'S SHIELD = 53

Geburah is now being harassed by a strange man – one of many bedroom intruders. I catch the man in the act of forcing my new friend on top of him, clearly about to rape her. I leap to her defense, reaching for one of my many swords, determined to teach the dirty rotten scoundrel a lesson. He must realize I mean business and quite capable of being utterly ruthless. I have one nagging thought – all my swords are fake. Can they do him any real harm?
Will he just laugh at me?

November
21 Sunday

1.17 am Back of my head and neck ache...
Suddenly the CD player comes on and starts to play music.... one of the tracks seems to be of me singing a well-known popular rock song, and it sounds really good.
But I have a few niggling questions.
First of all, there is no CD player in that part of the room where the music is coming from. All I have are computers which play CD's in the bedroom.
Secondly, why isn't the music disturbing my sleeping neighbours upstairs?
Even though the music isn't a very loud, it's loud enough to penetrate the wafer thin ceiling and annoy the normally belligerent upper level occupants.
Thirdly, I don't remember ever singing or recording that particular song.
So where did that track come from?
Before I could dwell on any of these questions I heard the most beautiful music ever. It seemed to come straight from Heaven itself . In fact, it was celestial cosmic music.
Suddenly a voice seemed to ask me, "Now, do you want to die?"
Without hesitation I replied, "Oh yes!"
At that moment I heard a door slam. The buzzing and ringing in my ears got louder and fluctuated in waves, rising and falling but continuing to increase in a crescendo.
My body started to freeze and a paralysis began squeezing the life out of me. Beginning first at my feet, and then progressing up my legs, to my hips...
Suddenly I became petrified and realized it still wasn't time for me to die and I struggled against the creeping blackness - forcing my body to shake off the paralysis.
I succeeded.

November
22 Monday

Hecate and I being sexual. Kissing, cuddling, caressing, being very physically intimate.
We didn't quite get to make love though. She backed off at the last minute. I seem to be plagued by prick-teasers.

It took my family a long time to finally tell me that my Mother had died. Several months in fact. And would they have ever told me if I had not first got in touch with my younger sister, Fay? The relations were embarrassed that Mama had left me nothing in her will, but they needn't have been. I don't care. I have never expected anything from that woman, described as my Mother. I didn't exist in her life, so why should I exist in her death? However, they were particularly embarrassed because my Mother had left a small package for Fay whom we all thought was hated more than anyone, but then there were so many of us she hated or despised or ignored, we could never be too sure who was on the lowest rung of her ladder of regrets.

Geburah ignores me when we arrive at the big convention. Suddenly we seem to be swallowed up by all the hustle and bustle of the huge house. Then I ask her if she will go with me to a particular meeting but she doesn't answer me. Instead she goes off with a little girl who seems to have bewitched her. I go looking for Geburah and find her playing a board game…looks like chess to me. I try to talk to her again, but she continues to pretend I don't exist. I decide to knock the chess table, upsetting the pieces, to stop their game in an attempt to gain her attention. Instead, she just gets up and walks off with the strange girl. After that I spend the time searching all over the mansion for Geburah but she seems to have completely disappeared. No one has seen her – or they have been instructed not to tell me where she is hiding.

A much younger Igor comes to visit me. It can only mean my best friend has, in fact, died.
"Igor, are you dead?" He smiles enigmatically, and rolls himself a joint, offers me a puff, and we relax back into the old squat ways of sitting cross-legged, drinking pots of sweet milky tea, smoking pot and chewing the fat.

And then much much later, Geburah reappears and orders me and Igor to get into bed together and fuck each other. I don't want to – but during the night Igor tries to rape me in the arse.

November
23 Tuesday

Is that another piece (or peace?) God is going to have to now pay for?

Geburah and I still at the Summer Holiday Camp (where it is always Summer), staying in the huge mansion with out-buildings on a large estate. Geburah is flirting with every man at the Fun-seeker's Paradise, including the party vicar, who reminds me of David McCallum (Illya Kuryakin, a man from UNCLE). Later in the evening I catch a glimpse of Geburah running naked across the park being pursued by the randy vicar, who finally catches her and spanks her bare bottom.

So I spent the evening talking with Lydia. We were discussing shape-shifting, metamorphosing, transformations from human to animal or whatever. I explained it was all a matter of liquid. Everything is fluid. All in the universe is capable of becoming liquid, and shape coalesces from a program giving co-ordinates for solidification. So, to transform into a different shape, one must become liquid and then congeal in the desired animal or mineral. With this understanding, I can quickly metamorphose from me into an eagle or wolf or woman. As I explained these basic principles, I knew I would soon be rewarded for giving the correct answer by a visitation of flying saucers….and sure enough, within minutes, a formation of silver discs came winging into view. Possibly ten in number, dancing and flowing in the sky like fish swimming in the sea. And as if to reiterate my point, they flew into a large roadside advertising hoarding, merging themselves into the picture, becoming one with its two-dimensionality, and yet constantly moving in and out, like ripples erupting and sinking into the poster, shooting around in all directions, skating on the surface.

I suddenly thought I should take a photo of these incredible UFOs but then I remembered Geburah had my camera in her bag.

November
24 Wednesday

This morning it occurred to me that 53 was crucial to the Super String Theory.

This afternoon I was telling Geburah how one time earlier I heard something fall and I expected the time to register 53 past the hour but I was uneasy about checking it, and sure enough when I did, I saw it was 14:53. I found the confirmation rather unsettling. Geburah smiled and said "Oh, don't worry they are just trying to communicate with you."

Then later this evening Geburah was working on her "Name day calendar" on the computer and found that 53 had been typed several times. "Where has this 53 come from?" she asked surprised, "I didn't put it there." Looks like someone was trying to communicate with her now. Then she wondered if there was any name that added up to 53. We saw that there was just one - Virginia.

Geburah finding "Virginia" adding to 53, made me remember the time when an unknown woman who called herself "V", text me to thank me for telling the world that she had been murdered. Well, I haven't done that yet. So I need to find out if there are any stories of Virginia murder.

I search on internet and, of course in the Land of Homicide, find plenty of murders in Virginia, USA. But what about a woman called Virginia, was such a named person murdered?

This evening I found a Virginia, Virginia Woolf who allegedly committed suicide by drowning herself. She put stones in her pocket to weigh her down. However, the mysterious text message I received has made me wonder whether it was suicide or was it murder? Did Virginia Woolf's husband, Leonard, kill her? He had enough of her mental illness, and was tired of her constantly refusing him sex (Virginia hated sex with men, probably because her half-brother sexually abused her when she was a child)? In addition, Leonard Woolf had fallen in love with another woman almost half his age, Trekkie, who promised him much sexual gratification. Leonard now had the motives for doing away with Virginia, and because she was already known as a "head-case" and habitual suicidist, it would be easy to drown her and make it look like suicide. The more I think about it, the more I am convinced that it was Virginia Woolf trying to communicate with me from beyond the watery grave. She knew that I, of all people, with experience of assassins trying to drown me (remember, I have already died, at least once, through drowning), would be sympathetic to her cause, and I would tell the world she had indeed been murdered.

November
25 Thursday

A dual onto Death. He was a supreme Master and utterly without mercy. By challenging him I didn't stand a chance. How could I imagine I could defeat him in a sword fight? I may be a talented amateur but he was an experienced professional killer. It's not just losing one's life at the hands of this cold-blooded relentless tyrant. It's the shame of stupidly biting off more than one can chew.

How did this happen?

I think I was fitted up. Falsely accused of a drugs related crime. Someone set me up, then I had to prove my innocence through trial by combat.

But the dice was loaded against me.

The weapons I was offered were made of plastic and blunt. So my persecutors were not even giving me a fighting chance with the champion duellist. He had that smug smile of an executioner eating his dinner before sharpening his blade.

And I had not eaten anything yet. If I am to have any possibility of squaring up to him. I must first obtain some energy input and build my strength up.

I have a few hours to find some food and perhaps a lethally real sword, and not the toy I was being offered.

I left the building whilst my intended nemesis was engaged in a prior contest.

Going down the street, I came across a carnival and behind some chain wire fencing I see the drug pusher lurking in the shadows, waiting for another innocent to prey on. I am sure he is the one who set me up. But how do I prove he is more than he appears. No one believed me in the past so why should anyone believe me now?

Then I spot the girl with the little fluffy dog in her arms, creeping up behind him. She's an undercover cop, and the dog is a narco sniffer. Then I see the plain clothes DEA officers hiding around corners and with a wag of the puppy dog's tail, they pounce on the unsuspecting Slanderer. But will his capture facilitate proof of my innocence? Vindicate and acquit me? Cancel the duel, indefinitely postponing my date with death? Or will the police simply remove the only witness I have to a miscarriage of justice?

My salvation seems to depend on the girl with the little fluffy dog. We've met before.

November
26 Friday

I attempted a reconciliation with Sheela na Ghee, the Israeli Mossad agent who tried to seduce me with her crap plays many years ago. But she wasn't having any of it. She will neither forgive nor forget. However, and this is most unlike her, because she knew of my interest in secret occult societies, Sheela gave me a gift of another Triad....

Trinity of rival occult systems
Mason = 8
Witch = 9
Shaman = 2
--
19 = 1

A flying saucer was heading straight for the house where I was staying. It was night, and the huge machine flew right up to the large window. Its grey and solid mass hung out there like a benevolent great whale. An intense feeling of empathy passed between us.

This evening when I took Geburah for a ride, she told me that I drive like a Mongolian warrior riding his horse. This fills me with pride, and encouraged me to drive even more recklessly down the A3 highway, heading towards London, going faster and faster as I approach the Robin Hood junction. Suddenly I lose control of the car and it spins around, facing the wrong direction on the dual carriageway. In panic I try to turn the car in the correct direction before the rush of oncoming vehicles collide into me, but with steam from my sweating eyes misting up the windscreen, I am not immediately able to. Eventually, gaining control of my breathing, I have the car pointing the right way, and I slowly exit the speedway, taking a thin ribbon of a slip road that arches high over the city. I am very nervous as I steer the car on the narrow bridge. Finally, I succeed in reaching suburbia, and try to find someone to help me, as I can no longer drive with my nerves all shaken up. Just by thinking about it, I find myself in someone's house, in the middle of their sitting-room.

November
27 Saturday

I visit a garden party / fete at my old school, Duckwood Hill. Lots of small children playing around me. Big appealing eyes. Innocent looking but ultimately untrustworthy. (Little Greys?) In one of the rooms I leave my mobile phone and purse full of money on a table unattended.
I go across to the other side and end up putting my sunglasses and car keys on another table. I am surrounded by cheerful chattering children who distract me with their charming attention. Then I sense a foreboding, and look for my glasses and keys. They're gone. Fool. I realize my money and moby will also have disappeared by now. I rush to the other side of the crowded room and sure enough, that table is also bare. Of course, no one knows a thing. I am admonished with clucking pity. "You must expect things to vanish, if you are not entirely vigilant," the Old Dears chirp around me.

In the school hall, I attend a drama workshop. A Master Class in screen acting, led by the great Irish-Italian movie director, Bert O'Loochie. I wouldn't normally bother going. Such workshops bore me. They are admissions of failure, i.e. you're not getting work, so you spend time attending classes to keep your skills honed and up to speed. However, I decided to attend this workshop because I had a bone to pick with Bert O'Loochie. I wanna ask him why did he refuse to cast me in his movie "Little Butter"? He had seen me perform on stage, playing a despotic emperor, and had said I was an excellent actor, so why didn't he want me? He also saw me in the movie "The Settee of Joy", playing an Indian leper begging in the streets of Calcutta. Did he think I would give the same performance in his movie set in India? I wondered if he would remember me as I joined the group, which was mainly made up of women. I was not very cooperative, thinking too much about my own agenda. I pulled the black polo neck up to cover the lower part of my face, not wanting too much involvement with the other class members. It made me look like a suspect character. People start whispering behind my back. Insinuations. Aspersions cast. Soon there was talk of someone being the Antichrist. He was present among us. Which one of us was this Enemy of Christ? One woman looked at me and suggested that it was me. Everyone decided to have a vote to decide who was the Antichrist, or were they simply electing the One who would be the Scapegoat for starting the Apocalypse? I chose not to hang around to find out who was selected or accused…accursed, and quickly beat the drum of a hasty retreat.

November
28 Sunday

6.53 am. Got awoken by Solar Eclipse, my lovely black cat, crying for me. He was obviously in great distress because he had not seen me for nearly two months. But Solar Eclipse is over 500 miles from me. Was my baby really communicating his upset to me?

I am being pursued by a monster truck. I have to pass through a gate into a field before it catches me. I reached the gate and pull an upright plank away but to pass through the gate I must shed my trousers and pants and leave my lower half exposed. An old proverb – "To survive, one must first suffer indignities." I do so as the truck is about to breathe down my neck. I slide into the field and, discover the wonderful sensation of hovering over the ground - I realize I am able to fly and soon make my escape.

Later…
The animals are loose, roaming free. They had escaped from the private zoo. I heard the owner committed suicide, and let them out because he thought October 21st was the End of the World.

Wild and wandering in the back yard. I see lions and tigers hoping to get into the house. The large glass sliding doors are not closed properly. They are prowling and getting ready to sneak inside. If they succeed, we will be trapped, and easy meat. Geburah sees the problem and immediately slams the partition shut. But our little children think the beasts are lovable fluffy playthings, and sit at the glass, talking to them. Our little boy is looking at the door handle, trying to work out how he can let the tiger in to the sitting room. Geburah quickly snatches up our son, and feeds him a plate of worms, which immediately reminds me I should tell her that the number 53 is crucial to Super String Theory.

November
29 Monday

Samuel Artli, "Why Are The Homeless?" film director, has given me huge speeches to learn for the pickup shots just before filming. It is so unfair of him to load all this on me at the very last moment. Now everyone is having to hang around whilst I struggle to learn the lines before the camera can roll. Samuel walks away impatiently, giving me accusing looks at my floundering, not imagining that his demands are unreasonable.

Revelations

13:11 And I beheld another of the Nine coming up out of the earth; and he had two horns like a lamb, and he spake as a dragon....he appeared as a Peacemaker but was in truth a Warmonger, and he was the Devil Incarnate...the Antichrist...Dictator of the New World Order.
13:12 And he exercises all the power of the first beast before him, and causes the earth and them which dwell therein to worship the first beast, whose deadly wound was healed.
13:13 And he does great wonders, so that he makes flying saucers come down from outer space on the earth in the sight of men,
13:14 And deceives them that dwell on the earth by (the means of) those miracles which he had power to do in the sight of the beast; saying to them that dwell on the earth, that they should make an image to the beast, which had the wound...to his genitalia...by a sword, and did live....the extra-terrestrials, "Sons of Heaven", will show allegiance to the Antichrist, and perform miraculous feats in his name, and raise from the dead the first great dictator who did die violently and had been placed in cold storage for future resuscitation.
13:15 And he had power to give life unto the image of the beast, that the image of the beast should both speak, and cause that as many as would not worship the image of the beast should be killed....thus, he created the movies and television and the Internet so that the Antichrist may appear to all the world, and those who refuse to watch his broadcasts will be executed.
13:16 And he causes all, both small and great, rich and poor, free and bond, to receive a mark in their right hand, or in their foreheads: all world citizens must have an implanted microchip with an identity number.
13:17 And that no man might buy or sell, save he that had the mark, or the name of the beast, or the number of his name on a social security identity credit card.
13:18 Here is Norman Wisdom. Let him that hath understanding count the

number of the beast: for it is the number of a man, who is a comic gibbering entertainer who distracts and deceives, a bewitching charming enchanting orator who cloaks the sinister corporate ruling party of venomous vile reptiles that molests, bullies, whips, lashes, devours, slays, shatters, scatters, ruins, destroys, burns up, lays waste; and his number - Six hundred threescore six.

It was not an easy speech to learn at such short notice.

November
30 Tuesday

Gangsters. Black gangsters. White gangsters. The black are my allies.
The Gang War spirals into Civil War, and the entire nation is momentarily convulsed. But CNN and FOX News loses interest, and so everything returns to normal.

Meanwhile…
The UFOs zooming around a criss-cross matrix, set against a black sky and because they were very high up, they appeared two dimensional. Actually, the neon brightness of their colours made me think of animated computer graphics. Whilst at the same time their behaviour unfolded like a spectacular firework display. What delighted us most was the playful quality of this vision.

Geburah and I visit a peaceful and chilled out commune in the country.
Laura, Proteus and Luther arrive. Laura is looking well and fit, considering she is supposed to be dead. It is grand to see her so relaxed and contented. Pleased to have found the commune.

Solar Eclipse, my black cat is also there - except he has turned it into a big black Labrador dog. A crystal hanging in the window, projects a rainbow onto the dog's black coat. I decide to rename my metamorphosed animal friend, Rainbow.

Does this mean there is going to be a big change coming with the Mayan predicted Solar Eclipse in two weeks' time?

SOLAR ECLIPSE = 53

December
1 Wednesday

Little Sadie, bad girl, tries to seduce me. She lays on my bed and with her innocent wide-eyed expression removes all her clothes, and endeavours to give herself to me in all her fragile nakedness.
But before anything can come of this I start picking a spot on the end of my nose which turns out to be a great lump of pink fat which is so embarrassing I try to hide it in the palm of my hand. Every time I rolled the lump between my fingers, it just gets bigger and bigger.

I add a new gold coin to the collection of commemorative medallions. It's a £15 coin, celebrating the 1953 coronation. Elizabeth is looking more and more like the ancient Queen Victoria.
Later I see a group of young archeologists digging up the past at the site of a fairy fort. My fairy fort? No, the field adjacent. Then on closer inspection I find they are oil prospectors or looking for a gold mine....The Doors come to mind..."Weird scenes inside a gold mine"....They have a mechanical device making small bores, a "nodding donkey", hoping to strike it rich.
I am dismayed. If they discover oil, then everything will be ruined. The landscape, the beauty, the environment, the peace and quiet – the splendid isolation.
Then I hear a shout of joy. One of the young men rushes over to me, pleased as punch.
"We've struck oil. The farmer is going to be very happy. Your field is next. Maybe your fairy fort is another money pot," he suggests excitedly. I am about to reply "I hope not", when we feel the rumble. The ground shakes. Everyone turns to see if the black liquid gold comes spurting out of the ground. But I wonder if instead, the foolish prospectors have disturbed and woken an angry subterranean beast...the Behometh that was best left sleeping.

Again this evening, Sadie offers herself to me for sexual intimacies. I go deeper into my exploration. Suddenly I feel suspicious. Is she really Sadie? We are going too far too quickly. I offer my apologies and beat a hasty retreat from her enticing presence and find myself back at home, in the bathroom, where I decide to clean my teeth. I pick up the tin mug and before I fill it with water, I hear faint music coming from the mug. I hold it to my left ear as if to listen to waves breaking on a distant shore in a sea shell. The music is like church organ music but better, as it is in tune with

my soul and flows to the rhythm of my breath.
I tap on the side of the mug, and a tribal drum beat accompanies the celestial sounds.
Geburah comes from the bedroom to find out what's keeping me and doesn't understand me when I try to explain why I have the coffee mug to my ear. So I am left to be entranced on my own.

December
2 Thursday

Geburah has turned out to be something of a guru, and was teaching us all this method of singing that would become separated from us and crystalize into a three-dimensional form, with an identity of its own.
I'm a bit dubious and not sure if I want to take part. The theatre space is darkened as we meditate and she leads the singing which has a wave-like breathing quality. Everyone joins in except me. The melody is dreamy and sleepy and begins to take us out of ourselves. I struggle not to succumb. I have a fear of becoming a part of the whole, of losing myself. The singing detaches itself from us and drifts away, taking the souls of the singers with it. It feels like a Song of Death.
As the music fades into the Heavens, I feel an isolation, a deep bottomless regret. But had I allowed myself to fully participate I could be dead by now.

The Egyptians believe a person is protected during his life by three spiritual entities –
KA, alter ego or double, the ghost?
BA, The Sun's companion into the nocturnal journey into the Underworld
KHAT, the astral body

And so we have another Triadic Union

Ka = 3
Ba = 3
Khat = 13 = 4
----
10 = 1

And then as if rewarded, I see a beautiful UFO in the night sky.

December
3 Friday

I visited another Gathering.
The Man was full of himself. He obviously believed he was born to lead. He told us he was Aquarian, and therefore one of the Elite. "Aquarians," he arrogantly announced, "are the Elect of Humanity, and destined to govern the world, especially as we are now entering the Age of Aquarians." I silently snorted. I don't like fascism of any kind, even if it is to be based on the signs of the Zodiac. In fact, Zodiacism is probably the most pernicious form, so I didn't bother to tell this would be ruler that I was also Aquarian, as I didn't want to be part of his club. I asked the woman seated beside him, if she was also an Aquarian. "No," she replied. "Try to guess."
She looked strong, assertive, energetic. "Aries?" I suggested.
"Nope. Have another guess."
I looked at her again, and thought she had a seductive but deadly quality about her. A sensual darkness hiding many secrets. "Scorpio?"
"Wrong. Try again, Honey."
"One more but if I get it wrong, you will have to tell me," I said."
I still thought she seemed a positive strong assertive optimistic passionate sort of person, so I chose another Fire sign. "Sagittarius."
"Correct," she exclaimed with joy. "What made you think so?"
"Maybe, because our Solar System, on the edge of the Milky Way galaxy, is revolving towards the constellation of Sagittarius."

Later, I was with the Boys from D.A.R.E. (Disabled Anarchist Revolutionary Enclave) in a tower block. It's dark outside, and we are looking out into the night through a huge window. Then I see it coming towards us, luminous flying object. I was so pleased to see a UFO again. It's been a few days since I last saw them, and I was beginning to think they had forgotten me. I looked at my companions but they seemed unaware of the flying machine as it hovered in front of us, on the other side of the glass. I was surprised to realise that this UFO may not be metallic at all, but in fact organic, a living creature like a manta ray, slowly undulating its wing-like sides. Flapping to keep it airborne, suspended in the thick viscous ether of the night. I felt that I could be at the bottom of the sea. The sentient UFO had a pair of huge eyes (windows?) that looked wistfully straight into me, giving me its undiluted attention, trying to communicate something to me, but I was missing the message, too intent on trying to get my pals to see this extraordinary visitation. Sadly, they remained oblivious to its presence, babbling away among themselves with their chat room trivia. As I sat in my isolated lonely awareness, I sense also the aerial messenger becoming depressed as it knew it was tragically failing to convey its earth-shattering meaning.

December
4 Saturday

This afternoon I was directing my film. Poor Sadie (the real Sadie this time) had to suffer my mad schemes. I wanted her to roll down a steep road in her wheelchair for a dramatic shot. Unfortunately it turned out she was unable to control the chair as would be travelling too fast. At the bottom of the road, was a precipitous drop down an even steeper road – almost vertical. The only safe way was to put the wheelchair on a very long rope, about the length of the road. As director, I took responsibility for controlling the rope. Big mistake. Because I cocked up. As the totally trusting Sadie hurtled down the hill, I slipped and accidentally let go of the rope. With horror I watched my end disappearing fast down the road. We all tried to catch it but failed. The look of terror in Sadie's eyes as she realised nothing could save her, was heart-wrenching. She glanced back at me, pleading, hoping I could work some magic which would rescue her, but this was no movie, and I couldn't. As she disappeared over the edge, she gave me one final look, wondering how I could have so fatally let her down. "I really believed in you," she cried. Her last words as she plummeted down, were "You have destroyed meeeeeeeee."

Evening. Visiting Duckwood Hill School. It seems deserted, which is becoming quite normal nowadays. Not the noisy vibrant place of my childhood. I am searching for something. A book. I go across the playground, to the school buildings, to see if the library is locked. The new Headmaster is lurking somewhere in the corridors. Or is it that batty old Headmistress, Nellie, who would appear sometimes as a green witch? No, it is the young Headmaster. He looks haunted as he waits in the dismal shadows for ghosts.
As I search, I realise I am not looking properly. Everything is blurred – out of focus. How am I going to find the book if my eyes are rebelling? A moment of panic. Then, suddenly, it dawns on me, I have forgotten my spectacles.

December
5 Sunday

The night sky was full of throbbing clouds. Then as this cover of luminous cumulus began to break up, I could see in the beyond straight lines of incandescent red slicing up the heavens.

This rather reminded me of a previous experience, years ago, where the sky was filled with clusters of glowing cosmological icons which raced at great speed from one end of the panoramic vista to the other. I felt as if I was at some sensational celestial disco or rave party.
On this occasion, the display above me was evolving differently. The red lines were growing into an elaborate network of lattice (lettuce?) like matrices, which like a spider's web, blew back the dust of the clouds. But the feelings of ecstasy were just as intensely profound as I watched the sky being criss-crossed with intricate neon structures.

Like the parting of the red sea, the clouds were being shredded and whisked up into a vortex reminiscent of a plug-hole. The psychedelic filigree moved about the burning vaulted space like UFOs. And beyond this radiant scaffold was a pulsating organic-looking dome which tapered upwards into a seemingly infinite intestinal tunnel.

At such a moment of visionary bliss, I could not help but ask, "Was our world inside someone's head... or their bowels ? And was God's head really full of shit?"

Lying in bed with Geburah asleep beside me on my left. Suddenly I hear a snort-like sound. Was it a pig in the bedroom? Just as I realised it couldn't be, I tried to sit up and saw between the bed and radiator on the left by the window – a dog. It must have made the weird noise. I immediately think of our new dog, Rainbow but I realise "no", because it had red glowing eyes, glaring menacingly at me. A Demon! It goes straight for me. A hand grabs my face, fingers shutting off my nostrils, palm pressed tight against my mouth, stopping me from breathing. I try to struggle against the attack but the Demon restrains my arms above me. Or are they paralysed? Just when I think I am going to be suffocated to death, I hear a sound. Rainbow the dog. He is lying on the floor, to the right of me. Also Geburah moans in her sleep. The two sounds startle the Demon, especially when Rainbow begins to growl, and it quickly vanishes into thin air. My two new friends had rescued me.

December
6 Sunday

I cannot believe it. The date has changed, but it is still SUNDAY!!! How did that happen? By rights, the 6th December should be a Monday, but it isn't. It is still Sunday, and I hate Sundays. Must be something to do with fluctuations in the electro-magnetic field. The temperature reading on the weather station said one degree centigrade and frost warning, but the displayed report only lasted 3 seconds, then returned to 14 degrees C. Or was it a ghost passing? But a ghost doesn't explain how come it is Sunday immediately following Sunday.

Geburah and I attend a Summer camp commune to study Climate Change (the fact that it is a Summer camp during winter just shows how pertinent the subject matter is), Anti-Capitalism and other New Age topics. Geburah is loving it, and making many new friends of a kindred spirit, whereas I am feeling the usual Outsider. Then the time comes for everyone to move on and vehicles arrive to transport us. Crowds of students board, I refuse because Geburah is nowhere to be seen, and I am reluctant to leave without her. But waiting around and seeing the place becoming more and more empty, I begin to fear Geburah has disappeared. Did she go without me? As the hours pass and I am all alone in the deserted camp, my feeling gets stronger…my paranoia…that she forgot me, or couldn't care less about me, and went with the others, abandoning me to the sudden chilling onset of Winter.

December
7 Sunday

No, no, No! Not another Sunday! I just can't believe it! Has the Earth stopped spinning on its axis or what? Did the poles shift, and the NASA bastards never told us? That would be typical of them. Or is this a punishment from God because I was always trying to get out of going to church as a kid? Well, three times on Sunday was a bit much. Once, in the morning, I thought was fair enough. Even Sunday School in the afternoon I tolerated, especially if it was my turn to play preacher…but having to go to the boring evening service as well! I started a small rebellion, and soon all the kids followed my protest, and the staff capitulated and evening chapel was no longer obligatory. And now I have been cursed with three Sundays in a row for my sins.

This afternoon I was invited to an airfield to witness the test flight of a new drone or UAV (Unmanned Aerial Vehicle). When I arrived the craft was already in the air, demonstrating its aerobatic capabilities. However, there was something odd about it. I saw a man on the ground who seemed to be controlling it by talking instructions to it. Whatever he commanded, the drone performed. The aircraft was five foot long and missile-shape, though there seemed to be very small wings on either side of the fuselage. The big shock came when the remote controller brought the UAV in to land, very slow and at a walking pace so he could walk beside as it flopped gently on the runway, and the craft was opened up to reveal, lying inside, completely cocooned in blankets, a small man paralysed from neck down, with only muscle movement in his eyebrows, which were electronically wired to the drone's guidance mechanism. So the missile was not unmanned after all, but piloted by an expendable cripple, who was telepathically controlled from the ground.

December
8 Monday

The lion is hunting me. I must hide but I cannot run or the even wheel. I can only crawl.
It is searching through the labyrinth of huts dotted about. I see its shadow seeking, sniffing me out. The only place I can find in time is the toilet but I have no confidence, as I crouch in the cubicle, that it will conceal or protect me. Suddenly the lion is startled by a man's cough, and runs away.

The kind old man, very wise, wants to teach me everything he knows. He has been watching over me from afar. But why is he in bed with me? Does the imparting of the Ancient Wisdom involve him having sex with me? He seems too nice to want to ravish me (savage me? Or salvage me?)
Perhaps we are just sharing the bed for the sake of companionship.
Anyway, as he talks, I came to realise he was Doctor Khenti Amenti visiting me from the Dead.

And he said to me, "When you are a ghost, you can either like white ice cream or green ice cream. If you like green, then you are a happy ghost, at one with yourself. But if you prefer white ice cream, then you are disturbed and liable to be a nuisance."

He also told me the Freemason's Supreme Deity is known as
The Great Architect
6 6 6

I asked if that meant the Freemasons were disciples of the Antichrist?

He replied, "Read the Book of Revelations." I told him I already had. Six hundred and sixty-six times. He laughed, patted me on the head, and said, "That's my boy."

666 is the number of Ommo Satan: the 'Evil Triad' of Satan -Typhon, Apophras, and Besz

Typhon = 8
Apophras = 4
Besz = 7
--
19 = 1

December
9 Tuesday

Darkened bedroom - about to make love with Sadie but intense feelings of guilt. The shades of Laura and her children are in the other room. Laura's ghost is hurt that I am ignoring her and about to make love to another woman- even though she knows it has been over between us long ago. Then Sadie is transformed into Laura - but an alien copy - not the real person . Suddenly the atmosphere becomes much more ominous and I realize nothing is what I thought.

This morning when blowing my nose, it didn't surprise me to find tiny flecks of blood from my right nostril on my tissue. A symptom of a bedroom invader incident?

The theatre bar and café. Lunch break in the rehearsals. Samuel, my old long lost colleague, lifts my wheelchair up onto the servery, and orders food for me. I ask for sausage and chips. Then he leaves me stranded on the narrow platform. One false move backwards and I will topple over. I am precariously balanced. I can't ask for help off the ledge until I've had lunch, and I must wait for my orders to be delivered because I cannot continue rehearsing without food.

I wait impatiently as the food keeps avoiding me. The bar begins to fill up and I worry that everyone else is going getting sorted while I am made to wait. The more people arrive the longer it will take for my service. Many of the newcomers are disabled, some old acquaintances of years back. I see Annie, still looking as miserable as ever. I would have thought she would have been dead by now.

The servery bar is circular in the middle of a large round hall. Someone, a disabled limping girl, sits next to me, wearing the fashionable tight jeans, barely hanging on to her hips, almost falling down with her waist naked to the four winds. She smiles, as the tattoos on her back flash an over familiar welcome. I barely grunt, I am so annoyed.

The food has finally arrived but it's not what I ordered. The barman apologizes and promises the sausage and chips as soon as possible.

"I will be late for rehearsals," I snarl through salivating teeth.

"Tell them to wait," he replies. "Send them a note explaining the delay"

"I cannot. They can't re- write the schedule for my convenience, or for your incompetence"

My anger and frustration unsettles me as it may edge my wheelchair off the ledge. Too much anger can lead to a fall.

December
10 Wednesday

There were six of us – me, Geburah, Lydia, Thor, Ferdinand and Delilah. We were on a picnic in the woods, near Guildford. We were all nicely seated on the ground in a clearing, enjoying the camaraderie and delicious food of cucumber and tomato sandwiches, cake and strawberries and lashings of cream…when suddenly I heard a wolf howl. I was astonished and looked at the others to see if they had heard it too. They had and were clearly anxious. But there are no wolves at large in the British countryside. The howl sounded rather close…too close for my companions' comfort, though I wasn't worried as I love wolves. I turned and looked behind me, and I saw them. Grey wolves. Very large. Three of them. I didn't think they were too threatening as they seemed uninterested in us. I looked at my friends, and saw they were paralysed with fear. Then, I suddenly thought of Rainbow, our dog. He had wandered off, and I worried that the wolves will attack and kill him if they encounter him. I called out his name, "Rainbow. Rainbow. Here, boy." Nothing. No sign of him. I shouted at Geburah to find him and put him on a lead. But there was no response from her. She was still frozen. In fact, everyone was frozen…except me.
Then I saw Rainbow racing towards me. But the wolves had also spotted him, and charged towards him, splitting into a three-pronged attack, covering his front and two flanks. The poor darling ran and dodged as much as he could but I was sure the wolves would get him. I crawled on the ground to pick up a big stick to try to defend him, but I could only find flimsy pathetic thin twigs and brittle branches.
Finally I saw a walking stick lying in some bushes, and scrambled for it, but how can I reach Rainbow in time. I was certain the lovely dog was doomed, even though he was racing like mad towards me. It was a desperate situation.
Then, a man who previously seemed frozen, came alive and turned into a golden dog, which valiantly charged at the wolves. At first, I thought it was Leonie, my dead Chow, but she was never so fast when alive. Then, I saw that the rescuing dog was in fact a beautiful golden wolf, reminding me of a Californian wolf I once knew, called Luna. Well, whoever this magnificent, glorious heroic wolf was, it was without doubt, Rainbow's saviour. Truly, one of the good wolves. And there are many, I'm proud to say.

December
11 Thursday

I was told I needed to die. They wanted me to commit suicide. They said it as if it were for my own good. The concept of "Assisted Suicide" had moved to "Enforced Suicide", and had become completely medicalised. So the kindly doctor (why does he remind me of the cuddly Lord Richard Attenborough?) prepares the lethal injection for me. He fills the syringe with the killing agent – MILK. Having filled it with the prescribed measure, he hands me the syringe and tells me to go into the room next door, lie on the death bed and inject myself. But I am very reluctant. First, I don't wish to kill myself. "Why should I commit suicide?" I ask. "I am not yet ready to die. Secondly, what about Geburah? How can I say goodbye to her? She will be very unhappy at my leaving her." As I say this, she appears.

The winding streets, racing with Geburah pushing me, but where are we going? I stop the wheelchair just in time. A deep step - almost a precipice at the wheels edge. We turn and there's a cheerful man who needs more gas for his cigarette lighter. He knows exactly what to do. He has a secret invention. I'm one of the first to be given a public demonstration. He takes out a glass jug, fixes a special device on the neck and onto that attaches his cigarette lighter, strikes the flint and suddenly air is being sucked in the jar as lighter fuel. He has devised a cheap and efficient way of converting the plentiful air into gas energy. He explains to me that it's simple because air is naturally changing to gas every three months, anyway. We just hadn't, until now, cottoned on to tapping this ongoing chemical process.

Later, back at my lodgings….I am being hunted by the lion and also a tiger. I try to keep the beasts out of the house but they succeed in slipping in, and they are outside the bedroom door which I forgot to close properly….It's just a matter of time before they get me.

Later still, and I am able to escape…but then I see a lioness in the kitchen. Of the seven lion cubs she gave birth to, only three survived – all female. They are killing their children.

Meanwhile I sense the aliens are up to no good. Are they still experimenting with my body? I fear they are manufacturing another Doomsday Virus.

December
12 Friday

Rainbow, the new dog, felt the urge to leave us, and ran away. This was very upsetting, and we went chasing after him. Old Jacinta Groser had come for a visit, and insisted on accompanying us. Perhaps she felt partly to blame for our doggie seemingly choosing to do a runner, though I don't see how Jacinta could have been responsible, especially as they seem to get on so well together. Anyway, she gets in the car and we drive down the road, heading out to the country. To our amazement on our left, slightly ahead of us, we see three brown bears galloping along the side of the road. Jacinta says stop the car, she wants to get out and see the bears. Before I can say I don't think it would be a good idea, the old lady of 93 has leapt out of the car, and is chasing after the bears. By the time we have caught up with the scene, the bears have turned around and attacked her, badly mauling her. They would have killed her if Rainbow hadn't suddenly appeared and scared them away. Jacinta was rushed to hospital.
By this evening, the tough old gal had fully recovered, had been discharged and sent home.

Celestial music. Fairy music. I dance and feel liberated. The urge to fly as the beautiful singing uplifts me. Soon I sense my soul beginning to leave the body and then I separate and float and waltz. I whirl around in ecstasy as the music draws and beckons me upwards.
Am I leaving my body for good? I don't mind. Maybe now is the time to die.
Suddenly, I hear a cry "No". It is Geburah. I float back into my body. She saved me from disappearing…or from being abducted by fairies or aliens.

Geburah said that I am still incapable of completing the picture puzzle of the Check-Mole, which suggests I cannot die until I find all the pieces to complete the final image of me.

December
13 Saturday

Earlier this morning, Rainbow was very disturbed. He kept climbing up things. Trying to be above ground. Trying to climb trees. Well, he did succeed in sitting on a branch, even though he is a dog. He was looking up at the sky, perhaps expecting something to appear – to fall down. Something is on its way. Something disturbing is coming.

I ring Jacinta but the phone keeps ringing. Eventually Homer Groser picks up the phone and apologizes for not picking it up sooner, but everyone was sitting on the floor playing games. I ask to speak to Jacinta, and he goes quiet. Then he tells me she died. I start to cry and there is embarrassed silence. In the end I had to hang up and ring Lydia to tell her the bad news.

How does it happen? I find myself in Vietnam. The civil war again between north and south. That's what I'm told, anyway. But you can't trust the media, especially the Western capitalist variety. Always lying about world affairs. However, what I witnessed was that the Viet-Cong had captured a troop of South Vietnamese. The hapless prisoners were naked, and tied to stakes on their backs with their legs also tied to a Y pair of stakes, spread-eagled in the air and their genitals exposed. Each prisoner has a torturer in attendance, equipped with a large knife or cleaver at the ready, to hack off their cock and balls. At the signal from the commanding officer, the P.O.Ws were instantly dismembered of their members, apart from one guy who managed to slip away from the racks. While his comrades were being slaughtered, a young V.C. girl takes pity on him, and helps him reach the outer perimeter fence without detection. At the guard post she sees an old friend on duty, and goes up to him, asking if it is true he was a journalist before the war. He replies yes. "Well," she says, "you'd better go to the barracks, and cover an incredible story. There's a riot between the guards and P.O.Ws." The former journalist is very interested and rushes to collect his notepad and camera. "Who is winning?" he asks.
"The prisoners are being massacred." She smiles. The excited ex-journalist runs to the battle, and the sole survivor escapes the camp, to vanish in the jungle.

December
14 Sunday

A woman screamed. I was still in a jungle. We were at the edge of a guerrilla war. The Viet Cong were advancing (or Chinese? Japanese? North Korean? We haven't been told who exactly we are fighting – but they are Oriental-looking). We'd had orders to evacuate the village. Everything was in a panic. We were not a combat force but some sort of support group. The British equivalent of MASH (Mobile Army Service Hospital). There were plenty of women soldiers in our squad. We were awaiting for the helicopters to pick us up but they couldn't land. The ropes were thrown down and we had to clamber up. Meanwhile, there were orders to burn the village down. It seemed like the flames and smoke spelt (smelled?) the end for most of us. Everywhere was heavy with corpses. There weren't enough helicopters and there could be no return journeys. The enemy was advancing fast. I was surprised that many of the women, some of the most beautiful women in the world, were being left behind. Clearly, so called physical attractiveness was no longer enough to save you (unless it's a movie). I have a feeling that I am going to be left behind as well. Obviously not because of my looks but because I am expendable. The remains of the retreating force from the last village arrive and confirm that the enemy is not far away. A woman screams. The Yank top brass can't win, so they plan to nuke the whole country. How bloody typical.

December
15 Monday

The imminent outbreak of nuclear war. Just before it started, we were receiving regular news bulletins concerning the effect it will have on us both physically and socially, and what the climate would be like after the multiple atomic explosions.
"London, of course," said the announcer, "will be decimated." That cheered me no end since I was staying in London. Don't ask me how I got from the jungle back to Blighty. It just happens like that. You escape one place of doom, and end up in another. The Laws of Newton don't apply.
"All along the southern part of England there will be gales," continued the radio announcer… (or did he say, "gay walls"?) "….of blinding hot heat travelling at speeds of up to 700 miles an hour." He sounded like the weatherman, "Anything in the wind's path will spontaneously ignite," he added cheerfully.
There were advertisements in the newspapers. Entrepreneurs cashing in on the imminent pending disaster.
"Whatever the post-holocaust weather, we can bring you strippers and whores, for that extra special personal service to take your mind off your lost loved ones, your collapsed world and your radiation sickness. It doesn't matter where you are, we can bring them in and out at a moment's notice. So if you've got the Nuclear Blues… wherever you are….whatever you are… man, woman or mutant… just ring us and we will send you the whore of your choice - male or female, dog or donkey, mog or monkey. And don't worry about giving them radiation, our whores already have V.D."
This Fast Fuck service will be operated through helicopters. On learning this, I vow to shoot down the choppers as they arrive. I will not allow the capitalists to profit from a war they created.
As I decide this, I hear the nuclear attack four minute warning.

December
16 Tuesday

Well, well, you see. I got home in my peppermint suit. Just in time. Or was it a peppermint flavoured sky? I just couldn't say. Not nowadays. Things are so confused.

Anyway, sirens and warnings and things were blaring away. The noise telling us to take shelter. or telling us it's too late. I hear another of those nuclear explosion things. Well, the choice has to be made.

Do I cross over on the flyover, the rippled thin ribbon of rock spanning the sky to the place of safety beyond? I am not the only one who has to make this decision, this tenuous crossing. There is a whole bunch of us. We're all tourists. I think. Or are we all going to some party? Anyway, the crowd is very friendly. Isn't there a war on? Must be that famous Dunkirk Spirit we Brits are famous for. Well, some of the Gathering are less worried about the crossing than others.

That's the trouble, the more worried you are the more dangerous it becomes. If you are too nervous, you're more likely to lose your balance and topple over and perhaps never come back.

Luckily for me, this experienced yet very-down-to-earth man decides to cross over with me. I think his wife is on the other side preparing the snacks, the welcoming home tea. She's talking nineteen to the dozen - very comforting . The Old Dear is trying to make the crossing as easy and as relaxed as possible.

"Think about what you want when you finally get over here, Luvvies." She warbled in a nice warm, Cockney accent.

The man was crossing over on a separate strip of spiralling rock which arched like a demented rainbow, oblivious to the unfathomable (unfashionable?) valley below. He just sat cross-legged and seemed to glide effortlessly like an Eastern Mystic. Whereas I had to struggle on my hands and knees, every inch of the way, slowly, painfully, gripping the hard wave-like structure. Whenever I got to the awkward bits, dips and bumps that were either too knobbly or slippery, and felt panic rising in my gorge with visions of falling in perpetuity, I turned to the man crossing on my left and plead, in a voice so meek and mild, for some gentle assistance.

"Sir, pardon me for interrupting," (for he was in deep discussion with another), "I do not mean to be a nuisance. I ask for nothing but your hand. You don't have to carry me. A hand, a comforting hand. Just a hand to stop me from being nervous. Please sir."

And he would kindly take my left hand and steady me as I slid over the worst parts.

Soon all the bad was behind . The Journey was nearly over and I could relax. And so could everyone else. The plump lady smiled and stroked my face.
"What do you want, Luvvy? Two types of cake." They looked like fairy cakes.
I made my choice. She lifted me off the bridge and plonked me into my wheelchair. I had survived the perilous crossing and as a reward she gave me three cakes for the prize of one. Making me choose was just a gentle teas.
And the nuclear war? A peace of cake.
Fairy = 5 Cakes = 3

December
17 Wednesday

Magonia. Paradise. Geburah and I, younger versions of a former selves, basking in the perfect imaginal realm of Arcadia, beautiful melodic meadows, gentle whispering woods, soft hills and majestic mountains, and a sparkling singing sunny seashore. There we are loving each other, singing a heavenly song of the Elysian Fields. I tell her I love her, and she says she loves me, and we feel blissfully happy in our oneness.

Then, a darkness sweeps upon us, and we are back at home in our bed. Geburah gets up as if we had never visited the Fortunate Isles. Rainbow, our dog, rushes over to me for a cuddle. Then he starts to make strange noises – some of which sound human – as if he were trying to say something to us, in English. Eventually after all his struggling to make us understand, I pick out a word, "Beware". We are amazed. Did the dog really say "Beware"? Then he struggles to articulate another word, which we don't' quite manage to understand, but we think we can hear a proper word amidst the grunts and groans. Finally, he pushes his whining into a word that is very clearly pronounced. He says "Murder". Geburah and I are flabbergasted. "What was that, Rainbow?" Again he tries like someone with a speech impediment to spit out the word "MURDER".

December
18 Thursday

A woman in trouble. She is being accosted by two soldiers. Is she being arrested? Kidnapped? The soldiers are trying to take her from her man, who seems to me not to be trying very hard to defend her. I decide I must help her instead. I need a weapon with which to attack the bullying squaddies. Geburah hands me a Gold Dagger. I'm a bit skeptical at first as to whether this weapon will be effective. However, we consider the possibility that it is magical or mystical, so I take it to rescue the damsel in distress.

GOLD DAGGER = 53

Later, we discover the woman turns out to be Gedulah Kether, an old school friend of Geburah. I am shocked to find she has a knife wound in her left leg. "Was it me?" I ask, worried that I had been indiscriminate with my dagger thrusts. Instead of answering me, Gedulah hands Geburah a scrapbook of pictures of road traffic victims.

GEDULAH KETHER = 53

Hauntings, poltergeist phenomena. The wardrobe is threatening to collapse on me and Geburah while lying on the bed together, but through strength of psychic will-power, I command it to stay upright. Then the top drawer comes flying out at us, but with a sweep of my left arm I deflect it to the side. However, a smaller object, also made of wood, missiles towards me. I catch it, and find it is carved into an owl shape.
"Aliens?" Geburah asks.
"Possibly," I reply, "Owls are frequently a sign of extra-terrestrial visitation or presence. On the other hand, it may be an omen of death."
"Someone we know?" Geburah anxiously asks,
"Maybe."

December
19 Friday

For the Great Cataclysmic Event I am informed I must travel to Mexico, but that is probably where the Assassin or assassins are trying to kill me.

A long time ago I met with the would be assassins in an empty warehouse one dark night when the Moon was dripping red. I had summoned them. We were plotting to kill the Antichrist…kill him before he discovered he was to be World Dictator. We agreed it was best to kill him while he was weak and unfolding…while he was still ignorant of his God Damned Destiny. My co-conspirators asked me if I knew who the Antichrist was going to be. I lied. I said I didn't know. But there was one in their number who knew I was hiding the Great Beast's true identity. The one who knew I knew was the one the Mayans called Halach Uinic – "The True Man"…and he had lived before in the 7th century and died on this day of December 19 in 694 AD at the age of 39. The Mayans built a pyramid temple for his tomb in Palanque, Yucatan in Mexico.
As he stepped forward, fixing me with a pitying stare, I saw Halach Uinic was back. He asked to be given the deadly assignment. I had no choice but to grant him his request, even though I knew I was putting my life at risk. He took the poisoned chalice from me and vanished into the deepening shadows.

Today, thinking about him, I calculate the number of his name - Halach Uinic. As I expected – 53.

The last time I had heard from Felicia was when she sent me a postcard from Australia. She was getting married. She wrote telling me not to forget her, and wanted reassurances that my bed would always be available to her should she need to escape her new husband. This evening, something told me to ring her. Her husband picked up the phone. "Who is this?" he demanded with suspicion.
"Shiram Labif," I replied. "Friend of Felicia. Is she there?"
"No, she isn't. She's dead. Hit by a train, trying to walk across a railway track. Drunken bitch. Why didn't people tell me she was an alcoholic? You could've warned me, you Pommie bastard."
"I assumed she told you."
"No she bloody didn't. And neither did her bloody mother. Stupid cow."
He hung up. I was left wondering if it wasn't an accidental death but intended. Had Felicia committed suicide?

The phone rings. I look at the time. 11.53. It is Stella Maris. "Guess who I met on the train this evening? Felicia. She was sitting opposite me in the carriage. She looked good."
"Felicia is dead," I replied. "You saw her ghost."
"That figures. She seemed at peace."

December
20 Saturday

I wake up and find we are on the edge of a forest. Snow has fallen deep, and I am being abandoned in the log cabin. Nearly everyone has gone. They just went, hoping to find a better, more secure hospitable sanctuary. The last few are about to desert me, including Dylan who I thought was one of my most loyal friends, but he turned out to be my biggest betrayer. I call out to him, not to leave me defenceless, as he trudged away into the forest, but he ignores my pleas, as do the other two (Thor and Ferdinand) disappearing from view. I am trapped, helpless, in bed, on the balcony, cruelly exposed to all the dangers the dark wood may throw at me.
Watching Dylan creep deeper into the maze of trees, I spot a bright red fox break cover and rush out to the right of the tree line. However, the animal suddenly changes its mind, and heads back the way it came. It had sensed a coming disturbance spilling over the horizon. They are returning, all my companions, charging back through the snow on skis, panic-stricken, in peril. Their mission must have failed, they've discovered there is no escape and they are fleeing back as fast as they can to the only sanctuary they know. Then I see what is pursuing them – packs of WOLVES. I watch helpless to help them, as each of my friends are picked off by the attacking lupine guardians of Fenris. I cry out "Dylan" as he is brought down by huge black wolf. I curse my friends who struggle to reach me, because they are drawing the enemy to me, and I have only a handgun with no bullets to defend myself. All I can do is bludgeon the wolves as they leap for my throat.

As I defend myself against the Wolves of Ragnarok, I am singing the song, "The Force of Mankind".

Later, I am driving the powered sleigh across the snowy wilderness. With me on board are Geburah, Ferdinand and Delilah whom I rescued. But I am dead. A Zombie, in fact, riding along the wasteland with a long trail of people walking behind me. It was as if I was some kind of Pied Piper of the Antarctic. Suddenly I wondered if I was really a Zombie or just frozen stiff.

Meanwhile thousands of miles away (another case of bilocation?), I am caressing and fondling my new cat (Geburah gave him to me) Kama Sutra. Or was my cat caressing and fondling me? Suddenly I had the feeling that he was the dominant one, taking control of our relationship. He was going to stroke me until he had had enough. I tried to stop him and move away but he held me down with his huge paws. I became terrified. He was no longer a little white and tabby pussy. Now he seemed like a full grown tiger. But his benign eyes looking straight into mine, his soft face pressing into my cheek, still looked like the eyes of my Kama Sutra.

December
21 Sunday

I find sanctuary. A hanger-fortress, reinforced to withstand and protect against all man, nature and God can throw at it. It's an empty shell. So I found it and it's mine. Cameras are placed in the outside world so I can observe all and not be touched. I can wait for the coming Catastrophe and know I will be safe. I watch the CCTV monitors and see that "It" has started. A mile high wall of flame is a rapidly approaching, eating everything in its wake. Thousands of cars are jammed on all the motorways as the population try to flee the conflagration. For some reason, I stepped outside my haven, my cavernous bunker and wander the trembling teeming city streets, people rushing indoors or hiding in corners as the air thickens with the approaching heat. What am I looking for? People to boast to? To brag that I can be safe and they cannot? Or am I looking for people to rescue, save? Am I looking for someone in particular? A loved one? My soul mate? Must I find her before she is destroyed and I am doomed to eternal loneliness? I don't know. All I know I am on the outside where it is getting more and more dangerous. People are giving me strange looks. They suspect I have a secret key to safety. I quickly move away and escape. When I reach my sanctuary, at first I panic, feeling I have accidentally locked myself out, can't find the key. When I finally rush in with relief and slam the great doors shut, I switch on the monitors and play back how the conflagration began and see with horror that… I had started it all. My reckless driving on the motorway had caused a petrol lorry to crash and explode.

December
22 Monday

The Heretic is going to be executed. I am horrified by the New Age religious fundamentalism, which is murdering people because of its irrational unproven beliefs. The real Stargate Conspiracy has begun. The man has blasphemed, and he is to be sacrificed on the Tree of Lies, growing out of the Walls of Silence. The martyr is placed facing the tree and wall, and he is ritually stabbed in the back with a Masonic sword, and sliced into pieces. His screams were heartbreaking. The bits of flesh were disposed of by packing into a suitcase. Someone informed me that the man had been sold to halal butcher shops.

Lydia asked me if Geburah and I use a condom when we make love. Before I could answer, Lydia answered her own question. "No, of course, you don't. You are trying to have children."
I replied that after children have been born, Geburah will probably insist on me wearing a Rubber Johnny. Lydia tells me she makes all the men she screws wear a sheaf, and then, if she finds the used rubber on the floor, she picks it up, and licks out all the spent semen inside, and swallows in one gulp.

A couple, a man and woman, out driving the car. They are stopped by three ominous figures, and are made to vacate the vehicle. From where I was hiding, I couldn't see whether these mysterious interlopers were military or secret police or kidnappers or gangsters (all the same thing, really). I could see, however, that one of the three was Chinese or Oriental-looking (extraterrestrial? The Greys are usually slant-eyed). The man is separated from the woman and fears the worse for her. Before he is clubbed unconscious, he hears her protests as she is about to be abused. The horrendous happens. A moment in time is frozen as I hear spine-chilling screams of fear and agony rising up from a still-frame tableaux of death, revealing the woman gang-raped, her body mutilated amidst the shattered debris of the couple's smashed car.

December
23 Tuesday

Highly complex mathematical equation, spoken in an "alien" language. As I heard it, I also saw it in some kind of weird hieroglyphic form, suspended in the air as a hologram. I wonder if it has anything to do with the Lorentz-Einstein Transformation. Anyway, I search for Geburah, who is a bit of a maths genius, to see if she can work out the equation. I find her, ask her if she can translate the hieroglyphs. Before she could answer, there is a single almighty thunderclap which shocks the inside of my head. The light bulb, suspended from the bedroom ceiling, flickers momentarily. The question is quickly forgotten.

"Look at that!! Geburah shouts, pointing to the window. There, hovering outside is an owl sitting on spinning rotor-blades. This is a typical omen for alien visitation. It is time to do a runner.

Evening.
Geburah and I are under threat. Hostiles are after us, pursuing, searching, relentlessly. We hide in a house, and retreat into the farthest most, smallest room. As we discuss what needs to be done, how to avoid capture, I look over Geburah's right shoulder at the wall behind her, and notice the wallpaper pattern becoming animated, and I begin to see a malevolent face start to emerge, glaring and smiling at the same time. I interpret this as a warning, an omen that the enemy can't be too far away. Suddenly Geburah hears a noise outside. We fall into each other's arms in anticipation of intruders bursting in on us.

Lorentz -	**Einstein**	**Transformation**
38 =11=2;	41=5;	66=12= 3

253. Curiously, looking at it as acronym, LET, we have 352, reversing the order, which gives the numerology an elegance.

December
24 Wednesday

The Star Chart for today looks incredible…the Mayans calculated that today here at the Temple of Uxmal, Yucatan, Mexico there will be a Solar Eclipse heralding the End of the Great 5000 year cycle.

We are under attack from aliens. Why do they remind me of Cybermen from the Doctor Who TV series? They are arriving from the skies in UFOs. I saw the massive build up of their spacecraft, as they took up the whole sky in huge formations of concentric ellipses

The next thing we knew, they had landed and whole armies of the ufonauts started to advance on our settlement. Needless to say we were defenseless. As they got nearer, we could hear their war cries. It was spine chilling. We knew they would be merciless.

I rushed into the house to see what weapons I could find.

And all that was available was pathetically puny. On top of which, my rising panic was making me hopelessly indecisive. I just couldn't make up my mind whether to defend myself with the African spear, which was a joke, or with this air pistol, which was a complete farce. Maybe I could fight with the ceremonial Masonic sword, but I'm sure this would be just as ridiculous.

In the end, I knew I was doomed because I didn't know what to do.

December
25 Thursday

Invasion. I saw them arriving in spacecraft, but I refused to believe my eyes.

The enemy multitude attack. At first I am all alone, vulnerable and on the run. Eventually I find sanctuary with others who are also under threat. In the house we gather and prepare for the siege. The only weapon available to me is a blunt ornamental short sword. I look with dismay at it, wondering what hope have I for properly defending myself. I crawl in the corner and wait for the horrifying inevitability.

CUT TO -

The assassins have grown in number. There are too many and I am trapped in the tower of the house, under siege. I realize now, the assassins are really aliens and we are up against supernatural forces. They are traveling in a lift to reach those of us who have attempted to hide near the top floor. Geburah has appeared and kisses me. I'm not alone any more.

CUT TO -

Our group have barricaded ourselves in, and are trying to keep a low profile, hoping that by not drawing attention to ourselves, we will be overlooked by the approaching the agents of death.

People ask me why do I continue to write in my diary when everything is collapsing around us.
I don't have an answer. Habit, probably.

Hours later, I'm realizing the aliens are shape-shifters. They have metamorphosed into wolves.
So that is the truth behind the legends of werewolves. They are extraterrestrials disguised as wolves, and having been with us for possibly thousands of years. Geburah and I prepare for the siege. All we have to defend ourselves are still my swords, most are for fencing tournaments. I have an idea for giving these puny weapons extra power. I attach an electric cable to the sword handles, which are connected to a large array of computers in front of me. I am hoping this will make the swords more effective weaponry against the E.T. attackers.

December
26 Friday

Down in the tunnels, a red wash of light with a mind of its own attracts our dog, Rainbow, and lures him away from us. He runs deeper into the caves. I call out to Rainbow to stop but he doesn't listen, and he disappears. Geburah and I left alone without our canine friend and protector.

CUT TO -

Invasion of the Aliens continues.

THEY Attack.
We, the faithful and heroic few are still under siege.

Proteus, who reminds me of one of the benign aliens, the Archangel species, was sent out on a reconnaissance mission, and carried out some independent guerrilla action of his own –
My boy has returned safely - flushed with success.
I felt a Father's pride seeing him perched, all perky-like, on a highly branched tree - chirping away his good news, and his golden wings beating out a rhythm of hope.

The Malevolent Aliens have met their match in him. Things are looking positive now. We may win after all.

December
27 Saturday

I spoke too soon. People are being infected with alien powers, and rotting into homicidal zombie creatures. I'm the only one left, running for my life, trying to escape the honeycombed labyrinthine mansion, full of cavernous rooms and entrapping twisting corridors. The escape door into a beautiful garden and freedom and safety is closing, and can only be opened from the outside - As I run for the door with the dead humans in hot pursuit, to my relief the door opens and a smiling black man comes in. I wonder if he realises the danger he is walking right into. I run faster to get to the door before he closes it behind him. I make it and slide into the garden, sunlight and fresh air.

December
28 Sunday

I woke up feeling refreshed, until…
Damn. Trapped again in another house awaiting invasion.
Alien Invasion. Again. And again.
Sinister little machines that beguile and enchant, only to explode in your face and wipe you out forever. Night has fallen. Survivors escape leaving me behind to observe. The reality is not clear. Most do not suspect the truth. We are being taken over for ultimate destruction and replacement. One old fool collaborates but is stalked, ensnared and then "taken out". I sit helplessly by, unable to prevent the carnage. My disability pins me to the floor even though I know more than most. I've seen it all before. Just as the menacing machines begin to turn their tiny but lethal attention on to me, Geburah, Inigo and Proteus arrive to the rescue.

December
29 Monday

Geburah is disappointed and angry that I am no longer able to get an erection. I have become impotent.

The last radio broadcast (it's a wind-up) tells us the Earth is completely occupied by the invading alien monsters. The last survivors are hiding out with me in an isolated farmstead. Everyone is asleep except for me and Geburah. I decide we should go on the move. The monstrous creatures are getting closer. They may be surrounding us already.

I go to the garage to check our vehicle…a coach once belonging to New Age Hippy travellers. Geburah comes with me. I get in the driver's seat. She in the passenger seat beside me. Just as I try the ignition, I jump out of my skin….an alien creature suddenly appears at my offside window, his long thin hands grabbing and clawing at me.

Next, I feel I am flying high, possibly in a hovering discoid spacecraft. Geburah is somewhere nearby. I am looking down on baby zoo animals being born in their multitudes. So many of them. Every kind of creature bouncing up and down on watery rocks. I laugh at a hippo baby with huge droopy ears like Dumbo. A future flying hippo, perhaps.

December
30 Tuesday

The coach, we the last survivors are travelling in, becomes submerged under water. I go beneath the vehicle to the bottom of the river, to see how Rainbow, our watchdog is getting on. He is encapsulated in a special structure enabling him to breath underwater while guarding us against attack from the enemy which is searching for us. I enter the doggy's bubble to give him a cuddle, when I caught sight of enemy prowler swimming alongside us. I realised that if I stopped looking at him, he may not see us, and pass us by, not thinking we were who they were hunting. I slowly turned my back to him, and pressed myself into Rainbow, covering him, hoping to keep him concealed.
It worked. We avoided detection.

CUT TO

I see the Man get out of the car. He looks vaguely familiar. As he turns to greet me, I think "Jess Clars". He smiles paternally at me, and we hug. Then I realise he can't be Jess because Jess has pure white hair, but this man still has natural black hair. Yet he still seems very familiar. As he kisses me on the lips goodbye, a kiss of honey, I realise who he is – my Father. I am overjoyed to see him, as I have not seen him since he died 53 years ago, when I was 12 years old. I tell him I will see him again very soon.

CUT TO

The Earth is knocked away from the Moon, sent in an opposite orbit around the Sun. When it returns on the other side, it will barely miss colliding with the Tenth Planet (Nibiru?) that lay hidden from our view, and will come so close that 460 people will leap onto its barren surface from the Earth.

December
31 Wednesday

I was with a group of people on an alien planet. There was in doom in the air. First I thought we were marooned but it slowly dawned on us that we were all prisoners. And somehow I was responsible for creating this dire situation. Yet, strangely, no one in the group seemed to resent or blame me. There's nothing more precious than human forgiveness.

As time dripped by, and we all grew steadily weaker, a thought occurred to me, from where I know not. There was a way out for our group. Well, at least, for most of the group.

The planet was the problem. That was my discovery. The planet had to be destroyed. This would give the trapped group their release - their freedom. Why? Because the damn planet was holding all of us against our will.

However, the planet could not be destroyed unless I... and this is the catch. Unless I chose to kill myself first. If I was prepared to sacrifice myself to the planet, it was prepared to release the others and in doing so, destroy itself.

After much heart rendering debate, the group agreed to go along with my plan. Except for one person, that is. Geburah. Who so loved me that she refused to leave without me. And if she refuses to go, then the rest of the group are not permitted to leave. Unless I accepted her.

Of course, I did. Her love for me pleased me. And my love for her, could refuse her nothing. Even though, this time she would also have to die. If I can honour myself by being a martyr, it would be hypocritical to deny her the same privilege.

Needless to say, the planet was more than happy to accept Geburah's self-sacrifice as part of the bargain. It got two for the price of one.

Minutes later, and the group have gone, leaving Geburah and I, lying in each other's arms, slowly dying.

APPENDICES

Editor's note: The following two papers were found with Shiram Labif's manuscript of this diary, so I have taken the liberty of publishing them in this edition, as they seem to be relevant.

APPENDIX I

Triadic Union
Strange Numerological Coincidences concerning
various Holy, Mystical and Mythical Trinities
which may indicate some Gnostic Truths
discovered by Nabil Shaban 1986

revised with new discoveries - January 1993

"All Things are Numbers" - Pythagoras (592 - 510 BC)

Introduction
As far as one knows, there has always been an irresistible urge to structure and order the universe and its contents in terms of numbers. Mathematics and Physics are the orthodox science disciplines in which the manipulation of Numbers is paramount. Equally, however, there has been an irresistible urge to bestow upon Numbers magical or mystical properties. The Qabbalah and Numerology are the disciplines which treat Numbers in this respect. The dividing line between science and meta-science is not always what it seems. Some Numbers are more "magical" or "scientific" than others. The number Seven, for example, is, in Western traditions, a particularly potent number: for instance;

7 days of Creation
7 archangels
7 virtues
7 deadly sins
7 Wonders of the World
7 gifts of the Holy Spirit
7 days of the week
7 Sleepers in Ephesus
7 Pillars of Wisdom
7 sacraments
7 grades of initiation
7 note musical scale
and so on....

Actually, the Book of Revelations contains no less than 54 quantity descriptions of seven...

However, not even scientists can resist tidying up their data into bundles of 7. - for example...

7 colour spectrum, the human body completes its change in cells every 7 years, the periodic table of chemical elements is divided into 7 periods, crystals fall into 7 basic shapes, sight is responsible for 70 per cent of our sensory information, we are said to be using only 70 per cent of our brain, 70% of the human body is

supposedly liquid and by a strange coincidence so is the Earth's surface.

The other Number high on the popularity stakes is Three. Scientists, artists, mystics, magicians and priests love Triads. - for example....

3 particles in an atom (electrons, protons and neutrons), and in every neutron or proton there are 3 quarks

3 Newtonian Laws of Motion

3 components of Einstein's E=mc2 (Energy, Mass and Speed of Light)

3 "families" of fundamental particles predicted by Grand Unified Theories

3 major classes of foods (Carbohydrates, Fats and Proteins)

3 bases for every codon in the genetic code

3 Freudian personality components (Id, Ego and Super-Ego)

3 Jungian personality divisions (Conscious, Sub-conscious and Collective Unconscious)

3 processes in Hegel's method of dialectics (Thesis, Antithesis and Synthesis)

And then, there are the folklore traditions, fairy tales, myths and legends which organise themes or items in terms of Threes - for example

3rd time lucky
3 Bears (Goldilocks)
3 Blind Mice
3 guesses
3 wishes
3 Graces
3 Fates
3 Furies
3 Wise Men
3 Denials
3 Temptations of Christ
3 - fold God (Holy Trinity)
3 - fold Goddess (Triple Goddess)

And it is the discovery that there seems to be a numerological significance for a variety of Triads that is the subject of this paper.

Numerology

Briefly, Numerology is a system of divination by numbers whereby the diviner "seeks to analyse the character of his subject by assigning certain numerical values to the letters of his name." The modern system is as follows:

1	**2**	**3**	**4**	**5**	**6**	**7**	**8**	**9**
A	B	C	D	E	F	G	H	I
J	K	L	M	N	O	P	Q	R
S	T	U	V	W	X	Y	Z	

The number of subject's name is obtained by adding together the appropriate numbers for each letter in the name until a single figure remains.

e.g. J O H N S M I T H
1 6 8 5 1 4 9 2 8
1+6+8+5+1+4+9+2+8 = **44**: 4+4 = **8**

The derived number, in this case 8, is supposed to indicate something of the subject's general character. however, for the purposes of this paper, it is not the respective meanings of the numbers 1 to 9 that is of interest but the simple method of reducing a name or word to a single number.

What is of interest is that this method enabled me to discover a numerical similarity between a wide variety of Triads or Holy Trinities. And that there is an uncanny numerical literalness to the notion of "the Three in One".

What you are about to read of my discovery may astound you. On the other hand, you might just consider it a series of flukes.

The Discovery

In Egyptian mythology the Great Triad consists of Osiris, Isis and Horus. Looking at them numerologically they can be written down as thus:

O S I R I S
6 + 1 + 9 + 9 + 9 + 1 = 35; 3 + 5 = **8**

I S I S
9 + 1 + 9 + 1 = 20; 2 + 0 = **2**

H O R U S
8 + 6 + 9 + 3 + 1 = 27; 2 + 7 = **9**

The numbers for Osiris, Isis and Horus are '**8**', '**2**' and '**9**' respectively, and if we add these numbers together we get '**19**' and if we add '**1**' and '**9**', we get '**10**' which is finally reduced to **1**. Thus, the Three Elements of the Egyptian Holy Trinity add up to One.

Egyptian
Osiris = 8
Isis = 2
Horus = 9
--
19 = 1

You can imagine my complete astonishment when I applied this approach to Godly Triads found in other myths and legends.

Pre- Olympian		**Greek**		**Persian**		**Roman**	
Uranus	= 4	Zeus	= 8	Mazda	= 9	Jupiter	= 9
Gaea	= 5	Maia	= 6	Ahura	= 4	Juno	= 6
Titan	= 1	Hermes	= 5	Mithra	= 6	Mercury	= 4
	--		--		--		--
	10 = 1		19 = 1		19 = 1		19 = 1

		Celtic			
Merlin	= 8	Myrddin	= 6	Arthur	= 5
Cup	= 4	Holy Grail	= 8	Morgan Le Fay	= 9
Sword	= 7	Excalibur	= 5	Mordred	= 5
	--		--		--
	19 = 1		19 = 1		19 = 1

Then I started wondering about the Biblical mythologies and the Holy Trinity in the New Testament.

		Christian			
Moses	= 8	The Father	= 1	Faith	= 9
Elijah	= 9	The Son	= 9	Hope	= 8
Jesus	= 2	The Holy Ghost	= 9	Charity	= 3
	--		--		--
	19 = 1		19 = 1		19 = 1

In the Genesis myth we have a trinity in the form of "Adam the Man", "Eve the Woman" and "Lucifer the Serpent".

Adam the Man	= 8
Eve the Woman	= 5
Lucifer the Serpent	= 6
	--
	19 = 1

In the story of the Great Flood, an archetypal fable with versions found in many diverse cultures around the world, we have the three sons of Noah, who are obviously responsible for the regeneration and renewal of the devastated human species, forming a 3 in 1 pattern.

Shem	= 9
Ham	= 4
Japhet	= 6
	--
	19 = 1

In Christian esoterica, there are Three Persons made manifest in the Devil - the Rebel, the Tempter and at times, the Collaborator with God, existing with divine consent.

Rebel = 6
Tempter = 7
Collaborator = 6
--
19 = 1

In the Book of Revelations one can discern an Unholy Trinity, which we can interpret in terms of the Father figure, the Mother figure and the Offspring figure. The Dragon and the Beast I regard as representing a single entity and so I call it the Dragon-Beast and it symbolizes the Father. The Whore is the Mother and the False Prophet is the Offspring. And so in Revelations we have, numerologically speaking, the Three in One.

Dragon-Beast = 7
Whore = 6
False Prophet = 6
--
19 = 1

The three great cities which are said to be referred to in the Book of Revelations are Babylon, Jerusalem and Rome.

Babylon = 8
Jerusalem = 5
Rome = 6
--
19 = 1

Also in Revelations there is another Trinity which consists of the 3 sources of life. They are the Tree of Life, the River of Life and the Book of Life. If we "trinumerate" Tree, River and Book, this is what we find;

Tree = 3
River = 9
Book = 7
--
19 = 1

Thinking back on the Male and Female duality, with the Product / Offspring making up the trinity, I wondered if there was a Triad consisting of the words "Mother" and "Father".

Father = 4
Mother = 7
Sons + Daughters = 8
--
19 = 1

I also thought about a planetary version of the Trinity Family, with the Sun as male, the Moon as female and the Earth as offspring.

Sun = 9
Moon = 3
Earth = 7
--
19 = 1

In the Apochraphal Books of the Bible, we have another fable as to how the world became populated with the human species. God sent down the "Sons of Heaven" to couple with the "Daughters of Earth" - a notion which seems to be confirmed by another "3 in 1" presentation.

God = 8
Sons of Heaven = 8
Daughters of Earth = 3
--
19 = 1

This apparent suggestion in the Bible of "Male Beings from the Sky" (angels?) mating with "Females of the Earth" to produce the human race, has encouraged some UFO believers to adhere to the Extra-terrestrial Hypothesis. But more of that later.

All these ideas of dualities giving birth to a third element, caused me to wonder if there was a Tri-cycle of existence in my "numero-theosophy" (sic). Would I find the "Three in One" relationship in the Birth / Death dichotomy held together by Life?

Birth = 3
Life = 5
Death = 2
--
19 = 1

One of the most ancient Trinities which describes the Life Cycle of Woman is the Triple Goddess who is represented with the three-faced persona of the Virgin, the Mother and the Old Crone (or Wise Woman, which still has the same number (5)). Again this Holy Trinity is numerologically consistent and reveals the Three in One truth.

Virgin = 7
Mother = 7
Old Crone = 5
--
19 = 1

Returning to the Book of Revelations, I found a Four in One pattern as revealed in the Four Horsemen of the Apocalypse; Famine, Plague, War and Death.

Famine	=	3
Plague	=	8
War	=	6
Death	=	2
		--
		19 = 1

If we look at the three great monotheistic religions of the Middle East, i.e. Judaism, Christianity and Islam, we find that their respective adherents form a numerological trinity. This demonstrates in an arithmetically beautiful way that the Jew, the Christian and the Muslim are three branches of the one tree;

This obvious and yet frequently tragically ignored truth is reiterated when one applies this test on the three principal heroes of the Jews, Christians and Muslims, namely Moses, Jesus and Mohammed. Simple sums prove the pointlessness of anti-Semitic pogroms, bloody crusades and other religious wars.

Jew	=	2	Moses	=	8
Christian	=	2	Jesus	=	2
Muslim	=	6	Mohammed	=	9
		--			--
		10 = 1			19 = 1

Eastern religions have their trinities confirmed by the "3 in 1" alpha-numeric calculation. For example in Hinduism we have Shiva the Creator God, and Kali the Goddess of Destruction producing Krishna the God Redeemer on Earth.

Shiva	=	5
Kali	=	6
Krishna	=	8
		--
		19 = 1

In the Chinese Daoist tradition, you have a trinity consisting of the Circle, and the Yin and the Yang contained within it.

Circle	=	5
Yin	=	3
Yang	=	2
		--
		10 = 1

In the study of the origins of human language, evidence has been found to support the view that there was once a single root language from which all languages stemmed. This proto-language has been called the "Mother of all Mother Tongues". When I learned that this "Babel" or "Baby" language only had three number words for counting - which were "One", "Two" and "Many" - I, in hopeful anticipation, performed the numerical calculation to test whether this primitive Trinity would reiterate the "Three in One" pattern. As you can see, it did!

One = 7
Two = 4
Many = 8
--
19 = 1

Today, the three most widely spoken languages are Chinese, English and Hindi.

Chinese = 9
English = 2
Hindi = 8
--
19 = 1

From a pseudo-scientific point of view, there has been a populist anthropological tradition that humanity can be divided into three basic racial types, e.g. Negroid, Aryan and Mongoloid, and it should come as no surprise to you, having now read thus far, that this "Trinity", numerologically speaking, conforms to the 3-in-1 pattern.

Negroid = 9
Aryan = 5
Mongoloid = 5
--
19 = 1

Nostradamus stated that within his hallowed prophetic space, the three aspects of time, Past, Present and Future, were clasped in one eternity. Numerology agrees!

Past = 2
Present = 7
Future = 1
---
10 = 1

If we look at the tripartite psychological structure based on the Freudian analysis, this is what we find;

Conscience = 9
Self = 6
Id = 4
---
19 = 1

When the Intellect is coupled with the Heart, then we have the Will, a packet of three that knows no bounds!

Intellect = 1
Heart = 7
Will = 2
---
10 = 1

In evolutionary biology, the human species is said to be a composite of three categories of animal, - Reptile, Mammal and Insect - bringing with them their particular defining behavioural characteristics. Our Reptile nature is epitomised by the Striving and Territorial instinct. The Mammal nature by the Nurturing and Nesting instinct. And our Insect nature is evidenced by the Communication and Networking instinct.

Insect = 7
Reptile = 4
Mammal = 8
---
19 = 1

The Human in Society progresses from the particular to the general and here we see a Trinity for the widening of responsibility from the singular to the plurality.

Individual = 6
Family = 3
Nation = 1
---
10 = 1

In my tentative search for those trinities of concepts or elements which have aided scientific
discovery, the following two derive from **Chemistry**.

Hydrogen = 6
Helium = 5
Carbon = 8
---
19 = 1

Acid = 8
Alkaline = 2
Base = 9
---
19 = 1

In **Physics** and **Maths**, we have a pair of Trinities for describing either the charge status of a particle or the direction of a number respectively. As you can see, they have near or identical values.

Positive	= 7	Plus	= 5
Neutral	= 1	Zero	= 1
Negative	= 2	Minus	= 4
	---		---
	10 = 1		10 = 1

Moving on to the realms of occult, astrological and esoteric traditions we find similar trinumerate syllogisms. For example, the 3 Spiritual Masters of the Trans-Himalayan Wisdom as accessed by such mediums and Theosophists as Blavatsky, Collins, Florence de la Rue and Alice Bailey, provide a Three in One Trinity. The names of these three Masters, Koot Hoomi, Djwhal Khul and Master Morya, when added to together, equal one.

Koot Hoomi = 4
Djwhal Khul = 2
Master Morya = 4
---
10 = 1

The lowest end of the Spiritual Spectrum in the Kabbalah, is known as Yetzirah, the World of Formation, which consists of a Duality producing a Third, thus reiterating the 3 in1 formula. In the Kabbalistic tradition, the Realm of Formation, which we might understand as the known Universe, is made up of Hod (the sphere of Imagination), Netzach (the sphere of Nature) and the product, Yesod (the sphere of Ego).

Hod = 9
Netzach = 5
Yesod = 5
---
19 = 1

Another symbolic trinumerate syllogism of "cosmos genesis" is provided by Gnostic tradition, which speaks of the Universe being created by the **Mind** evolving into **Thought** and then to the **Word**.

Mind = 4
Thought = 9
Word = 6
---
19 = 1

The Gnostics also see the Creation as having occurred because the **Logos** needed **Life** in order to Know Itself. And from this self-knowledge came **Love**, because the Divine Within had been recognised.

Logos = 5
Life = 5
Love = 9
---
19 = 1

And what of astrology? can we find "Trinumeracies" in that system? Yes. The 12 signs of the Zodiac can be categorized in three ways. They can be grouped in terms of Quadruplicities, Triplicities and Polarities. The Quadruplicities are the four elements; Fire, Earth, Air and Water. The Triplicities are the three states of motion; Cardinal, Fixed and Mutable. And the Polarity is the Male / Female duality. If you add the constituents of each of these categories and then sum the thre sub-totals, this is what you will find.

Quadruplicity		**Triplicity**		**Polarity**	
Fire	= 2	Cardinal	= 8	Female	= 6
Earth	= 7	Fixed	= 3	Male	= 4
Air	= 1	Mutable	= 2		
Water	= 4				
	---		---		---
	5 +		4 +		1 = 10 = 1

And how about Quadruplicity, Triplicity and Polarity as three words forming a Triad?

Quadruplicity = 5
Triplicity = 6
Polarity = 8
--
19 = 1

Now, within astrology I have discovered something as equally astonishing as the "Three in One". And that is a series of "Four in Ones" embedded within the Triplicities, that is, the Cardinal signs (Aries, Capricorn, Libra, Cancer), the Fixed signs (Leo, Taurus, Aquarius, Scorpio) and the Mutable signs (Sagittarius, Virgo, Gemini, Pisces).

Cardinal		**Fixed**		**Mutable**	
Aries	= 7	Leo	= 5	Sagittarius	= 9
Capricorn	= 7	Taurus	= 1	Virgo	= 8
Libra	= 6	Aquarius	= 8	Gemini	= 3
Cancer	= 8	Scorpio	= 5	Pisces	= 8
	---		---		---
	28 = 1		19 = 1		28 = 1

In alchemy, the transmutation of base metal into gold is a metaphor for the mystical procedure of transforming the imperfect human into the Perfect Spiritual Being. The three basic ingredients for achieving this fabulous event are Mercury, Sulphur and the Philosopher's Stone. (Incidentally, the Philosopher's Stone is also called the Philosopher's Egg. "Egg" and "Stone" both add up to 1). As you can see what I call the "Trinumerate Routine" confirms this alchemical tradition.

Mercury = 4
Sulphur = 7
Philosopher's Stone = 8
---
19 = 1

Striving for the apparent impossible in alchemy can be likened to the apparently impossible task of "squaring the circle" which is also a metaphor, this time for discovering the perfect dimensions needed to create that Holy Temple of the New Jerusalem in which all irreconcilable differences will undifferentiate into One. The three basic geometric shapes are the Circle, the Triangle and the Square, and according to Sacred geometry it is the combination of these three which resolves the problem of "squaring the circle".

Circle = 5
Triangle = 5
Square = 9
---
19 = 1

Still in the area of geometry, I find it fascinating that the Five basic regular solids....Cube, Tetrahedron, Icosahedron, Octahedron and Dodecahedron... all add up to One, and that the Three basic types of Triangle.... Equilateral, Isosceles and Right ad up to One.

Cube = 4
Tetrahedron = 2
Icosahedron = 3
Octahedron = 4
Dodecahedron = 6
---
19 = 1

Equilateral = 4
Isosceles = 7
Right = 8
---
19 = 1

One could suggest that the Trinity in many of the examples listed above is made up of the Male principle, the Female principle and the Product or Offspring which ensures that the cycle is renewed. The Trinity describes the fusion between the Celestial and the Terrestrial, giving birth to a new element, which is at the junction of Heaven and Earth. This spark which ensures the survival of the cycle is, in terms of myth, the Messiah.

Heaven = 1
Earth = 7
Messiah = 2
---
10 = 1

Speaking of this Saviour who was expected to usher in the Millennium (or lead the New World Order?), we find whilst in Jewish-Christian traditions he is called Messiah, in Islamic tradition the Imam Mahdi, and in Hinduism he is the Avatar. It is no longer a surprise to me to find that these three representations form a Triad that adds up to one.

Messiah = 2
Imam Mahdi = 8
Avatar = 9
---
19 = 1

What seems to be shown here are various numerological illustrations of a basic Hermetic / Gnostic idea that WoMan contains within him/her the Divine Spark which will unite that which is Above with that which is Below, that which is Within with that which is Without, that which is of the Spirit with that which is of the Matter. According to Gnostic doctrine the unification of WoMan's Divinity with the Supreme Spiritual Being can neither be achieved through **Reason** alone nor **Faith** alone but in combination with a third element; **Gnosis** - "Imaginative thinking or knowledge by the Heart". This Hermetic Doctrine can be numerologically verified thus;

Reason = 9
Faith = 8
Gnosis = 2
---
19 = 1

Just By Chance?

Critics will no doubt argue that my examples are specially selected to prove a point. What about those Triads that do not add up to 1? Such as Neutron, Electron and Positron; Thor, Odin and Frigg? My only answer is that to date whenever I have sought a "Three-in-One" solution in a given Triad, more often than not, my expectations are fulfilled. What are the odds of these expectations being fulfilled?

Test for Probability

I devised a computer program which randomly generated nonsense words of 3 to 9 letters long (the length of the words were also randomly determined) and these were randomly collected into groups of three, that is, into "Trinities". Because in the alphabet some letters are used more frequently than others, e.g. "A" and "S" are much more common than say "Z" or "K", the random letter generation was biased according to a weighting system based on their use in the dictionary.
Thus words beginning with "A" in the Chambers' Dictionary took up 91 pages, "B" took up 87, "C"; 145, "D"; 82 and so on. I also included the frequency of letters in the board game "Scrabble" and the card word game "KAN-U-GO".
The nonsense words thus generated grouped into "Trinities" were then "numerologized" and the incidence of those "Trinities" which added up to 1, 2, 3 etc. up to 9 was recorded.

The Result

With a sample of 10,000 nonsense word "Trinities" there was the following incidence of "final result numbers";

Trinities adding up to	One	= 1113
	Two	= 1057
	Three	= 1135
	Four	= 1115
	Five	= 1063
	Six	= 1114
	Seven	= 1147
	Eight	= 1170
	Nine	= 1085

Clearly what this indicates is that the probability of a Trinity adding up to One is as one would expect, namely, a 1 in 9 probability (9 divided by 10000 = 1111.11). Given this rate of probability it is surely astonishing to discover that so many Vital Trinities add up to one, thus seeming to reiterate this ancient and constantly recurring theme of "the Three-in-One".

APPENDIX II

NUMBERS OF THE BEAST.

It's crazy but true Numbers build an Ark Two by Two,
Accept Black is White, One is All, Heaven is Hell,
Nay is Yea, the Jewel is the Crown, the Square is Round,
Everything is Opposite, what you Lose can be Found,
The Ring is a Spiral, Winter is Summer, War is a Whore,
Destruction is Creation, the Assassin is Messiah,
The Apocalypse is Salvation, the Dream is a Nightmare.
The Meaning is in the Sums, Order means Nothing,
The Numbers say Ugly is Beauty, so you mustn't cry,
We should count the beasts who steal fruit from your eye.
Alien from Sirius begets its Dragon,
Satan cracked an Egg with a Stone called Adam,
The End of the Circle is both Open and Shut,
Meaning the Snake is Eve and the Lock is the Key,
The Core of the Apple makes the Pip your Home.

If the Spelling can ride High, then the Numbers don't Lie,
Seasoning of Reason creates a Style of Why,
He's a Devil of a Beast, taking Fruit from his Eye

Take Christ from Positive, be left with Negative,
Take Jesus from Love and be left with Hate,
Fluid is Solid with Energy added,
Jesus was a Comet, an Omen for Change,
Death will Light your Fire on the Cross of Time.

If the Spelling can ride High, then the Numbers don't Lie,
Seasoning of Reason creates a Style of Why,
He's a Devil of a Beast, taking Fruit from his Eye

From Nowhere the Mother is a Door to the Earth,
The Answer is a Mystery when the Question is Forgotten,
The Word is Knowledge meaning Truth Is Destiny,
Life is Good, Fear is Evil, God is Unity.

If the Spelling can ride High, then the Numbers don't Lie,
Seasoning of Reason creates a Style of Why,
He's a Devil of a Beast, taking Fruit from his Eye

Know that the Secret Chiefs are The Nine Unknown Men,
The same as the Old Ones who know your Best Friend,
Who is both Guardian and Angel from the Abyss,
The Stranger, the Outsider with the Hidden Kiss.

If the Spelling can ride High, then the Numbers don't Lie,
Seasoning of Reason creates a Style of Why,
He's a Devil of a Beast, taking Fruit from his Eye

The Sun is Red, the Moon is Blood,
Jesus is the Bride, Mary is Bread,
Christ is the Groom, the Fish is Wine,
At the Wake most Weep, some Laugh while others Smile,
Add Resurrection to Crucifixion, you have the Holy Grail.

If the Spelling can ride High, then the Numbers don't Lie,
Seasoning of Reason creates a Style of Why,
He's a Devil of a Beast, taking Fruit from his Eye

Liberty is the Sacrifice of the Spirit,
Swapping Chaos for a Body that is Prison.
If Iron that's Yellow accepts Paper that's Gold
Equality is a Legend the Will must Rule.
The Bible is Freedom but it's also a Myth,
Claiming Charity and Peace is no Illusion.
The Abacus played with Napier's Bones spat a Numeral,
My albatross strayed to salvage a home at a funeral.
The Mind thinks it's Way to the Soul through Alchemy,
From Water to Silver, Harmony shines Surreal.
The Power as Glory will Help call Omega,
To End the Fun and Virtue of all Existence.
If Desire is a Sin, then Justice is a Ghost,
Like the Trickster who plays Saviour in a Ufo.
Confucius Computes the cowardly Cipher of dry Letters,
The obtuse refutes the hourly writers of my betters.
Mass craves Anarchy which the Heart makes Possible,
Through the Crucible of Chance and Revolution.
Religion is a Game whose Goal is a Mirage,
From Womb to Grave, Faith is a Chain of Confusion.
Reality is Law but then Physics is a Fox,
Your journey to Know will Progress to Delusion.
What maketh the Words worth their Summation is the smaller Whole,
Hot acres of burnt earth scare some nation to play the cheap role.

Nabil Shaban, 6th May 1992

Nabil Shaban
Dreams My Father Sold Me
Poems and Graphic Art

With a Foreword by Lord Richard Attenborough
Introduction by Colin Baker.

Dreams My Father Sold Me is Nabil Shaban's first published anthology of his poetry spanning 20 years (1983-2003) and graphic art spanning 30 years (1975- 2005)

"This magical book is fascinating...." - Lord Richard Attenborough

"...direct and stark anthology..." - Colin Baker

"...loved the book. particularly like the art work...really gets under the skin...truly the stuff of nightmares...the poems really very moving...singular perspective...unique and utterly familiar at the same time..." – Douglas Hodge

"...an excellent production, very high quality... a book to be proud of...poems...images -- word play -- riddling speech -- which can be felt intuitively in the instant...The paintings...the emotion comes through -- strongly! I can look at them for ages...." – Cathy Lester

"...I rather rashly bought your book and instantly regretted doing so. It reminded me of all those scary stories and pictures you told me when I was a kid which gave me nightmares and got you banned from coming to see me (in the children's home)" - Jazz Shaban, the author's sister

"...I can honestly say I have never owned such a book! It's beautiful!" - Meaghan

ISBN 0954829409
£14.99

SIRIUS BOOK WORKS publishing

Nabil Shaban

The First To Go

an original theatre play
about disabled people in Nazi Germany

Everyone knows about the millions of Jews who died in the Nazi extermination camps. Countless books, plays and films have been produced to ensure that we never forget and so remain vigilant against any likely recurrence. Yet until Nabil Shaban decided to do something about it, there has never been a play or film which seeks to tell the story of Hitler's Euthanasia program for disabled people.

In fact, THE FIRST TO GO, the First Victims, in Hitler's systematic drive to purify the Aryan race were people with physical, sensory, mental and psychiatric disabilities. Gas chambers were originally created to speed up the culling of such unwanted "Useless Eaters", the term used by Hitler to describe disabled people.

Nabil Shaban's play doesn't just tell the story of Disabled Victims, it also tells of Disabled Heroes and Disabled Villains.

The Disabled Victims, **Siegfried**, **Heide** and **Helmut**....it is their destiny to be given lethal injections.

The Disabled Villain, **Dr. Josef Goebbels**, a man who so hated being crippled with a clubbed foot, he chose to hate all disabled people, he masterminded the propaganda campaign advocating Euthanasia.

The Disabled Heroes, **Claus von Stauffenberg**, the one armed, one eyed "terrorist" who attempted to blow up Hitler.

And **Brunhilde**, the German Army nurse who becomes disabled and consequently joins the ranks of the persecuted but in doing so, helps thwart Hitler's plan to rid the world of so-called "imperfect" people.

"...brilliant... moving and funny and very scary." Linda Rogers

"...this play flies very justly in the face of all the stereotypes holding every one of us hostage to this day." Jessica Sharp

"...engaging and poignant..." Robyn Hunt

ISBN 9780954829414
£7.99

SIRIUS BOOK WORKS publishing

Nabil Shaban
The Ripper Code

Max, a little disabled man in a wheelchair, seems to be a nice respectable civil servant, whose job is to help the unemployed find work.

Except, he has a problem... he is addicted to sex...and so goes out every night, curb-crawling the Red Light areas of London, to pick up a prostitute...or two, spending nearly all his wages.

Another thing about Max... he fancies himself as a detective, and believes he has discovered the Ripper Code which has lead him to the true identity of Jack the Ripper.

But now Max's addiction to prostitutes has got him into trouble, not only with the police but also with a serial sex killer of prostitutes, who turns out to be a copycat of the bygone Jack the Ripper. Max has to employ the Ripper Code to try to identify and catch the new Whitechapel murderer before he kills again...again...again.

"Could be the most notorious book of the 21st Century" – George Parrot

"...a wild mixture of good humoured banter, bloodthirsty murder, bizarre plotting and uncomfortable sex....an unusual book in that it doesn't ask itself to be taken at all seriously while doing some in-your-face things...." - Bill Hamilton, A.M. Heath, literary agents

"Shaban tempers the dark matter that pervades his tale with a lightness of touch which lends a humour, appropriately of the black variety, to proceedings. But there is a biting political wit at the heart of things, which we are left to consider at will." Jez Strickley

"…love it. Very exciting, funny, sad and more-ish…" - Tuppy Owens

ISBN 978-0-954829421
£9.99

SIRIUS BOOK WORKS publishing

Other books by Nabil Shaban soon to be published
by Sirius Book Works

Ivarr the Boneless
I am the Walrus
King of the Incurables
Fellows of the Ring: Circus Daze
No One Knows Eddie
Snicker-Snak and other Stuff

SIRIUS BOOK WORKS publishing